GOLD

HISTORICAL AND ECONOMIC ASPECTS

GOLD

HISTORICAL AND ECONOMIC ASPECTS

Advisory Editor
KENNETH CARPENTER

Gold Mining Company Prospectuses

Part I: California

Part II: Alaska, Arizona, Colorado, Idaho, Utah

ARNO PRESS

A New York Times Company
New York • 1974

Reprint Edition 1974 by Arno Press Inc.

Reprinted from copies in the Baker Library,
  Harvard University Graduate School of
  Business Administration

GOLD: Historical and Economic Aspects
ISBN for complete set: 0-405-05910-8
See last pages of this volume for titles.

Publisher's Note: The colored maps in
STATEMENT, REPORTS AND EXAMINATION OF THE
ST. LUIS PARK GRANT, IN COLORADO TERRITORY
have been reproduced in black and white.

Publisher's Note: This volume was reprinted
from the best available copies

Manufactured in the United States of America

————◆————

Library of Congress Cataloging in Publication Data
Main entry under title:

Gold mining company prospectuses.

    (Gold: historical and economic aspects)
    CONTENTS: Articles of association of the Philadelphia
and California Mining Company, together with the by-laws,
lease, map, etc. Philadelphia, 1852.--Quartz mining,
the Burns Ranche Gold Mining Company, Township No. 2,
Mariposa County in California; an account of its location, title, mineral riches, etc., with its charter and
proceedings, letters, certificates, and other matters.
New York, 1851. [etc.]
    1. Gold mines and mining--United States--History--
Sources. I. Series.
HD9536.U52G65   338.7'62'23420973   74-365
ISBN 0-405-05926-4

Contents

Part I: California

ARTICLES OF ASSOCIATION OF THE PHILADELPHIA AND
CALIFORNIA MINING COMPANY, TOGETHER WITH THE
BY-LAWS, LEASE, MAP, ETC. Philadelphia, 1852

Burns Ranche Gold Mining Co.
QUARTZ MINING. The Burns Ranche Gold Mining Company,
Township No. 2, Mariposa County in California. An Account of Its
Location, Title, Mineral Riches, Etc. With its Charter and Proceedings,
Letters, Certificates, and Other Matters to It, etc. New York, 1851

Consuelo Gold Mining Co.
STATEMENT AND REPORTS OF THE CONSUELO GOLD
MINING COMPANY OF CALIFORNIA. Incorporated in the State
of New-York. New York, 1864

Grass Valley Gold Mining Co.
CHARTER OF THE GRASS VALLEY GOLD MINING COMPANY,
ORGANIZED JULY 25, 1851, UNDER THE GENERAL
INCORPORATION ACT OF CALIFORNIA. Together with Extracts
from the Law, and Various Documents Illustrating the Business of
Quartz Mining. N. Y., 1852

Hendel, Charles W.
REPORT ON THE PLUMAS CONSOLIDATED GRAVEL MINING
COMPANY. San Francisco, 1878

The Lightfoot Gold Dredging Company
PROSPECTUS. New York, [1907]

The Prudhomme Gold Mining and Milling Co.
SOMETHING ABOUT THE PRUDHOMME GOLD MINING AND
MILLING COMPANY. Los Angeles, [1903]

Sierra Nevada Gold and Silver Quartz Mine
THE SIERRA NEVADA GOLD AND SILVER QUARTZ MINE,
WOOD-RANCH, AND WATER-POWER, LOCATED IN EL
DORADO COUNTY, CALIFORNIA. Boston, 1866

WHAT THE KLONDIKE AND BOSTON GOLD MINING &
MANUFACTURING COMPANY HAS ACCOMPLISHED IN A
FEW MONTHS. Boston, Mass., [1898]

[Ryan, M. I.]
THE CONQUEST MINE, ARIZONA. [1870]

Wetherbee, John
A LETTER ON COLORADO MATTERS TO THE STOCKHOLDERS
OF EXCELSIOR CO. AND OTHERS WHOM IT MAY CONCERN.
Boston, 1867

Shelden, Albinus Z. et al
STATEMENT, REPORTS AND EXAMINATION OF THE ST.
LUIS PARK GRANT, IN COLORADO TERRITORY: Its Title and
Resources in Gold, Silver & Other Mineral Wealth. New York, 1865

REPORT OF SUPERINTENDENT AND THE BY-LAWS OF THE
TREASURY MINING CO. OF COLORADO. Boston, 1868

THE POORMAN GOLD AND SILVER MINING CO. OF IDAHO.
New York, [1867]

DALTON AND LARK GOLD, SILVER AND LEAD MINING
MILLING CO. Salt Lake City, Utah, 1896

PART I
California

ARTICLES OF ASSOCIATION

OF

THE PHILADELPHIA AND CALIFORNIA

MINING COMPANY,

TOGETHER WITH THE

BY-LAWS, LEASE, MAP, &c.

PHILADELPHIA:

PRINTED BY JOHN C. CLARK, 68 DOCK STREET.

1852.

ARTICLES OF ASSOCIATION

OF THE

PHILADELPHIA AND CALIFORNIA

MINING COMPANY.

~~~~~~~~~~~~~~~~

The subscribers hereto, having acquired a lease of Six Hundred feet square of land, granted by John Charles Fremont, upon which there is a large quartz vein of gold, situate upon the river Mariposas, in the State of California, and which is deemed to be of great value—the title to which property the subscribers have conveyed to the Trustees of this Company, in trust for the stockholders—offer an opportunity to others to participate in the advantages and profits of said property, upon the plan of the Articles of Agreement hereunto annexed.

ARTICLES OF AGREEMENT,

Made the fourteenth day of February, A.D. 1851, between Palmer, Cook and Company, of San Francisco, California, merchants, of the one part, and those who shall become purchasers or holders of shares in the Philadelphia and California Mining Company, of the other part.

ARTICLE I.

This Association shall be called The Philadelphia and California Mining Company.

ARTICLE II.

The property of this Association shall be divided into Twenty-five Thousand shares of Twenty Dollars, each of which shall entitle the proprietor to the one undivided one twenty-five thousandth part of all the property which has been or may be hereafter acquired by the Association, or which may hereafter be held by the Trustees hereinafter named, their successors or assigns, for the use or benefit of said Association.

ARTICLE III.

No stockholder shall be bound or held liable to pay any debt or obligation contracted by the Company or its agents, with any person or persons other than himself.

ARTICLE IV.

The lease of land on the river Mariposa, and all other real estate that has been or shall be acquired for this Company, shall be conveyed to and vested in two Trustees, as joint tenants, according to the provisions of these articles, and no person shall be a Trustee who is not a stockholder.

ARTICLE V.

The affairs of said Company shall be managed by seven Directors, to be elected as hereinafter stated.

The Directors shall elect one of their number President. They shall choose a Secretary and Treasurer (who may be one and the same person), and may require him or them to give bonds in such sums, and with such sureties, as they shall deem adequate for the faithful performance of the duties of his or their trust.

They shall have power to appoint all other officers and agents of the Company, and to fix the compensation and define the duties of all their officers and agents.

Stated meetings of the Board of Directors shall be held at the

Company's office in the city of Philadelphia, on the first Thursday of every month. Special meetings may be called at any time by the President or Secretary.

At all meetings of the Board of Directors, four members shall form a quorum.

If a quorum is not present at any stated or special meeting, two Directors may transact the business, and their acts shall be valid, if approved at the next meeting when a quorum is present. They shall have power to fill all vacancies in the Board occurring by death, resignation, or otherwise, and generally to do all acts not inconsistent with these articles, which they shall deem will best promote the interests of the stockholders.

They shall, from time to time, declare and pay dividends of profits to the stockholders as they shall deem advisable.

They shall render a full report of the affairs of the Company at every annual meeting, and also at every special meeting, whenever required by a majority in interest of the stockholders.

ARTICLE VI.

Charles Schaffer and John M. Lisle shall be the first Trustees of the Company, and shall continue in office until others are elected according to the provisions of these articles.

George W. Wright, Charles Schaffer, Francis N. Buck, Solomon Alter, Hiram Walbridge, John M. Lisle, and John L. Newbold, shall be the first Directors of the Company, and shall continue until others shall be elected according to the provisions of these articles.

ARTICLE VII.

The first annual meeting of the stockholders shall be held on the first Monday of December, 1851, in the city of Philadelphia, and annually thereafter, on the first Monday of December, at such place as the Directors shall designate, of which, public notice shall be given by the Secretary. Special meetings may be held at any time, by order of the Directors or by the holders of two thousand shares of stock, of which a reasonable public notice shall be given.

At all meetings of the stockholders, each share of stock shall entitle the holder thereof to one vote, and absent stockholders shall be entitled to appoint proxies.

ARTICLE VIII.

The stockholders, at any general or special meeting, shall have power to elect a new Trustee or Trustees whenever occasion may require; and said new Trustee or Trustees shall succeed to all the rights and powers of the former Trustee or Trustees.

ARTICLE IX.

The stock of the Company shall be transferred by the holder, in person or by attorney, on the books of the Company, upon the surrender of the old certificate.

ARTICLE X.

Certificates of stock shall be issued in the following form:—

THE

PHILADELPHIA AND CALIFORNIA MINING COMPANY.

No.   VIGNETTE.   *Shares.*

This is to certify, That   proprietor of   shares in The Philadelphia and California Mining Company. Transferable only on the books of the Company, in person or by attorney, upon surrender of this certificate.

In witness whereof, the President and Secretary have hereunto set their hands, this   day of   18

Secretary.   *President.*

25,000 Shares—$20 each.

Capital Stock, $500,000.

Article XI.

The provisions of these articles may be amended or altered at any annual or special meeting of the stockholders, by a vote of a majority in interest of the stockholders.

Article XII.

The twenty-five thousand shares of capital stock, shall be issued as follows:—

Five thousand shares shall be retained by the Company, until disposed of by order of the Board of Directors for the use and benefit of the Company.

Nine thousand shares shall be issued to the subscribers for the same, and the remaining eleven thousand shares to Palmer, Cook & Co., or such persons as they may direct.

Article XIII.

Whereas, it is intended to obtain from the State of California, as soon as practicable, a charter for this Company, it is agreed that the Board of Directors shall have power to procure said charter, and when obtained shall submit the same to a meeting of the stockholders; and if a majority of all the stockholders at such meeting agree to accept the same, the requisite steps shall be thereupon taken to merge this association in said chartered Company.

Article XIV.

The said Trustees and their successors shall, whenever required by a resolution of the stockholders, certified from the minutes, by the President and Secretary of any annual or special meeting of the stockholders, grant, bargain, sell, lease, or otherwise dispose of any of the leases, lands or property, of this Company, to any person or persons as may be directed by such resolution, and make and execute deed or deeds, in fee simple or for any lesser estate, to the purchaser or purchasers.

Given under our hands at the City of Philadelphia, the fourteenth day of February, A.D. 1851.

(Signed)   PALMER, COOK & CO.

Witnesses,

(Signed)   H. WALBRIDGE,

JNO. L. NEWBOLD.

Amendments to the Articles of Association adopted at a Meeting of the Stockholders, held January 27, 1852.

ARTICLE XV.

The capital stock of the Company shall hereafter consist of four hundred thousand shares, of five dollars each, making the whole capital stock two millions of dollars, of which forty thousand shares, of the par value of two hundred thousand dollars, shall be issued to John C. Fremont, in payment of the lease granted by him to Solomon Alter, John L. Newbold, John M. Lisle, Charles Schaffer, and Francis N. Buck, dated Nov. 10th, 1851; eighty thousand shares shall be retained until disposed of for the use and benefit of the Company, and the remaining two hundred and eighty thousand shares shall be issued to the present stockholders, pro-rata, at the rate of fourteen shares of new stock for every share of old stock, upon the surrender of the old certificates, and that new certificates shall be issued in the following form:—

THE

PHILADELPHIA AND CALIFORNIA MINING COMPANY.

No.   VIGNETTE.   *Shares.*

This is to certify, that   proprietor of   shares of the capital stock of The Philadelphia and California Mining Company.

Transferable only on the books of the Company, in person or by attorney, upon the surrender of this certificate.

In witness whereof, the President and Secretary have hereunto set their hands, this   day of   185   at the city of Philadelphia.

Secretary.   *President.*

(Margin left: 400,000 Shares—$5 each.   Margin right: Capital Stock, $2,000,000.)

To amend the 5th article of the Constitution, by increasing the number of Directors to nine, and that the two additional new Directors be the Hon. Wm. M. Gwinn and the Hon. Col. John Charles Fremont, and that the present Directors have power to fill vacancies until the next annual meeting.

Amendment to the Articles of Association, adopted at a Meeting of the Stockholders, held August 27, 1852.

ARTICLE XVI.

The Board of Directors shall have full power and authority, either by themselves or their agents, to make contracts or agreements for the lease, sale, or other disposition of any part of the veins, lands, rights, mining privileges, and property belonging to the Company, in such manner and upon such terms as they shall judge best for the interest of the Company. And the Trustees, for the time being, shall, upon receiving a request in writing signed by the President and a majority of the Board of Directors, attested by the Secretary, execute a deed or deeds to the lessee or lessees, purchaser or purchasers, for any part of said veins, lands, rights, mining privileges and property, which may have been leased, sold or disposed of, by the Board of Directors or their agents.

BY-LAWS

Of the Philadelphia and California Mining Company, adopted at a Special Meeting of the Stockholders, held the 27th day of August, 1852.

I.

The principal business office of the Company shall be in the city of Philadelphia, and the Directors shall have power to establish other offices in California and elsewhere, as they shall deem expedient.

II.

The President shall preside at the meeting of the Board of Directors, sign certificates of stock, and perform such other duties as are incident to the office of President. In his absence the Board may appoint a President pro tempore, who shall discharge all the duties of the President.

III.

The Secretary and Treasurer shall hold their offices during the pleasure of the Board of Directors. The Secretary shall keep proper books of account, a stock ledger, minute book, and such other books as are necessary, and perform such other duties as shall be required by the Board.

The Treasurer shall deposit all moneys received by him for the Company, in such bank as shall be designated by the Board of Directors, and shall disburse the same under the direction of the Board.

IV.

Transfers of stock shall be made on the books of the Company, in presence of the President or Secretary, either in person or by attorney, upon the surrender of the old certificate.

V.

The Directors shall declare dividends of the profits of the Company, whenever they shall deem it expedient, giving due notice in one or more newspapers published in the city of Philadelphia, of the time and place of payment of such dividends. The transfer books of the stock shall be closed for ten days immediately after the declaration of any dividend.

VI.

The Directors may pass any by-laws not inconsistent with the Articles of Association and these By-laws, which they shall think proper.

VII.

The foregoing By-laws, and any by-laws passed by the Directors, may be amended, altered or repealed, by the stockholders, at any annual or special meeting.

VIII.

The Directors shall have power to establish agencies for the transfer of the stock of the Company, in London and elsewhere, if they shall deem the same advisable, under such rules and regulations as they shall judge safe and proper.

LEASE FROM COL. FREMONT.

These Articles of Agreement, made and concluded this tenth day of November, in the year of our Lord one thousand eight hundred and fifty-one, between John Charles Fremont, of the City of San Francisco, and State of California, of the first part, and Solomon Alter, John L. Newbold, John M. Lisle, Charles Schaffer, and Francis N. Buck, of the City of Philadelphia, and State of Pennsylvania, of the second part, witnesseth: That the said John Charles Fremont, for and in consideration of the sum of Two Hundred and Fifty Thousand dollars, to him in hand paid by the parties of the second part, the receipt whereof is hereby acknowledged, and in the further consideration of the covenants, provisions and agreements hereinafter contained, and which on the part of the said parties of the second part, their heirs, executors, administrators and assigns, are to be fulfilled, executed and performed, he, the said John Charles Fremont, hath demised, leased and let, and by these presents, doth demise, lease and let, to the said parties of the second part, their heirs, executors, administrators and assigns, two certain lots, parcels or measurement of mineral land, bounded and described as follows, to wit: The first lot, known as the " Heap and Sargent location," to commence at the north-westerly edge of the vein, at a point where it intersects the centre of the Mariposa river, the point being indicated by letter A. upon the map hereunto attached; thence following up the middle of said river, one hundred feet, to a point indicated by the letter B. upon the map hereunto attached; thence parallel to the vein, nearly east, eleven degrees fifteen minutes south, to the middle of the river Ave Maria, the point being indicated by letter C. upon the map hereunto attached; thence following down the middle of said river, to a point intersected by a line drawn parallel to and distant six hundred feet from the northern boundary, the point being indicated by letter D. upon the map hereunto attached; thence north-westerly to the centre of the river Mariposas, the point being indicated by letter E. upon the map hereunto attached; thence and following up said river to place of beginning. The second lot, known as the "New Britain location," to commence at the north-westerly edge of the vein, at the point where it intersects the centre of the Mariposas river, the point being indicated by letter F. upon the map hereunto attached; thence following up the middle of said river, one hundred feet, to a point indicated by letter G. upon the map hereunto attached; thence parallel with the vein, nearly east, eleven degrees fifteen minutes south, to the middle of the river Ave Maria, the point being indicated by letter H. upon the map hereunto attached; thence following down the middle of said river to a point intersected by a line drawn parallel to and distant six hundred feet from the northern boundary, the point being indicated by letter I. upon the map hereunto attached; thence northwardly to the centre of the Mariposas river, the point being indicated by letter J. upon the map hereunto attached; thence following up said river to point of beginning: with all and singular the mines, ores and minerals, on, in or under the same: together with the appurtenances to the said lots or parcels of land belonging, or in any wise appertaining; the said lots or parcels being a part of a certain tract of land called the Mariposas, and owned and possessed by the said John Charles Fremont, by virtue of a purchase from Don Juan B. Alvarado, ex-governor of California, situate on, in and near the Mariposas river, and its branches, in the County of Mariposas, and State of California, agreeable to the plat hereunto annexed: To have and to hold the said lots or parcels of mineral lands above described, to them, the said parties of the second part, their heirs, executors, administrators and assigns, for and during the term of ten years from the date hereof. And the said John Charles Fremont, in consideration of the payments, covenants, provisions and agreements herein contained, doth further agree to extend, at the option, will and demand, of the parties of the second part, their heirs, executors, administrators or assigns, the time of this lease for a like term of ten years, from and after the expiration of this lease, to the parties of the second part, their heirs, executors, administrators and assigns. And the said John Charles Fremont, in consideration of the payments, covenants, provisions and agreements herein contained, doth still further agree to demise, lease and let, to the said parties of the second part, a quantity of land, equal both in length and breadth to either of the lots or parcels above described, the same to be selected at any time during the continuance of this lease, by the parties of the second part, from any part, point or portion of the whole Mariposas district, owned and held by the said John Charles Fremont, and not otherwise disposed of previous to such selection : but no such lease shall be made to extend beyond the eighth day of November, in the year one thousand eight hundred and seventy-one. And in consideration of the premises, the said Solomon Alter, John L. Newbold, John M. Lisle, Charles Schaffer, and Francis N. Buck, their heirs, executors, administrators and assigns, do covenant to and with the said John Charles Fremont, his heirs, executors, administrators and assigns, that they will peaceably yield up each and all of the said lots or parcels of land, and all the privileges thereunto belonging, at the expiration of the term of this lease, or at the expiration of the time of the renewed lease, as contemplated and provided for by this testament; together with all and singular the improvements (machinery alone excepted) which shall have been made on or within said lots or parcels of land, the same becoming the property of the said John Charles Fremont.

In witness whereof, the said parties have hereunto set their hands, and affixed their seals, the day and year before mentioned.

JOHN CHARLES FREMONT. [L. S.]

Signed, Sealed and Delivered }
    in presence of   }

G. W. WRIGHT,

Witness to the signature of John Charles Fremont.

SOLOMON ALTER,   [L. S.]

JOHN L. NEWBOLD,   [L. S.]

JOHN M. LISLE,   [L. S.]

CHARLES SCHAFFER, [L. S.]

F. N. BUCK,   [L. S.]

THOMAS HALE,

Witness to the signatures of the parties of the second part.

Letter from the Hon. Col. John Charles Fremont to the Company, dated

San Francisco, Nov. 10th, 1851.

GENTLEMEN—The object of this note is to inform you, that I have become interested in the mining operations which you propose to carry on at Mariposas, and have consequently this day executed to you, a lease of mining land, of unusual extent and privileges. In doing this I have acted principally on the representations of the Hon. Mr. Wright, who informs me that your Company, has at command large capital, which they design to employ in working the mines faithfully and giving them their full development for the benefit of all who may be concerned.

Believing that mining operations so conducted would be eminently successful, and having at my command a large extent of mineral ground, I have associated myself with your enterprise, and have accordingly assigned to the Company, locations which, as you will see in the lease, are very large and which comprise the best situations and the most valuable veins at this time known to be on the place.

I am desirous to aid the operations of the Company by giving them all the advantages in my power, and to this end have granted them the right to occupy and work any more valuable vein which may hereafter be discovered, and will be glad, in other ways which may offer in the progress of the work, to contribute to their success, and in the meantime, I am very respectfully,

Your obedient servant,

JOHN CHARLES FREMONT.

Messrs. Solomon Alter, John L. Newbold, and others,

Philadelphia.

———

Report on Condition, Prospects, &c., of Company.

The Philadelphia and California Mining Company, was organized in the early part of 1851, by a number of energetic, practical business men of Philadelphia, in conjunction with others of like character in California, for the purchase of a lease which has been granted by Col. Fremont, for the term of seven years, of six hundred feet square, on a vein known as the Heap vein, on his Mariposa Estate in California.

This lease like all others granted by Col. Fremont, was subject to the payment of one-sixth of all the gold collected under it, as a royalty or rental to Col Fremont.

Subsequently in Nov. 1851, by special arrangement with Col. Fremont, the Company obtained from him a new lease with vastly increased privileges, extending its term to twenty years, embracing the Heap vein for the extent of about three quarters of a mile,—and the New Britain vein, nearly three miles in length, each stretching from the Mariposa to the Ave Maria rivers, with the including strip of land, six hundred feet wide. In addition, the

lease grants to the Company, the privilege of occupying any un-
leased vein or veins that may be discovered in any part of the Mariposa Estate, to an extent equal to their range on the New Britain
vein, making the total of their range on the veins, near seven miles.

This liberal grant is subject to no royalty or rental, but in lieu
thereof Col. Fremont receives one-tenth of the shares of the capital
stock, the whole number of which is four hundred thousand. Of
these eighty thousand are reserved for the general use and benefit
of the Company—forty thousand belong to Col. Fremont—and the
remaining two hundred and eighty thousand are distributed among
the stockholders.

The primary object and design of the Company, is to erect proper effective machinery for crushing or stamping the quartz rock,
and extracting the gold contained; but as this object may be accomplished upon the largest scale known in the annals of mining,
by the occupation of a limited portion of their vast range on the
viens, it is obvious they will have a large surplus of mining ground,
which it is proposed to make early available by sales or sub-leases
to individuals or to other companies, who may desire to embark in
like enterprises. It is well known that the gold region of California is principally upon the public domain.

The Mariposas Estate claimed by Col. Fremont under a grant
from Mexico made in 1844, prior to the cession of California to the
United States, is believed to be the only mineral land in California,
which is not owned by the government. The confirmation of this
grant by the United States commissioners, now in session in California, it is expected will soon be obtained.

But to prevent all cavil about title the Company have taken the
necessary steps to enter the lands leased to them, in the office of the
Recorder of Mariposas County, in accordance with the mining regulations of the County, so as to avoid all difficulty either as to title
or possession.

By adopting this course, the Company will in any event be on
as favourable a footing as any other occupants of the public domain,

c

and if Col. Fremont's title is confirmed, whatever policy may be hereafter adopted by the government, they cannot be affected by it, holding a lease from the owner of the fee simple.

It has been ascertained by numerous careful experiments upon the out-cropping rock of the New Britain vein, that the auriferous portion will yield on an average at least two cents per lb. of rock, without counting upon rich pockets or seams, which are so characteristic of the auriferous veins of California.

Mr. H. S. Parke, who has visited and examined the veins in question, as well as most of the theatres of active operations in California, and who is justly regarded as reliable authority, after a careful inspection and numerous experiments upon the out-cropping quartz, states in his report to the Company, his confident opinion, that a single steam engine of 45 horse power, with suitable stamps, would yield an average of at least $1500 per twenty-four hours of net profits, from the rock of the New Britain vein. He estimates the yield per lb. of rock at the rate of two cents, which he deems to be moderate and safe, as there are many veins which yield on an average five cents per lb. This gentleman possesses so largely the confidence of the business community of Philadelphia, his native city, that he has recently raised among them a large capital for the business of quartz mining in California, to be conducted under his supervision.

The New Britain vein varies in width at the out-crop from six inches, to ten feet: with a regular course as regards the main lode, but having many branches or intersecting veins; at the intersections, as is usually the case in metalliferous veins, there is evident enrichment, as shown in the out-crop, but in no case has a shaft been opened to develop the treasure that may reasonably be expected to lie beneath. The vein runs longitudinally in a lofty hill, dips at an angle of about 43° to the south-west, and is favourably circumstanced for advantageous mining. The Heap vein is unsurpassed by any in that region in point of advantageous position. Its out-crop in the bed and on the bank of the Mariposa river, is five feet in width, and on the summit of the hill which it traverses, about eight feet wide.

Wood is abundant in the region, but at the dry season, there is insufficient water to justify reliance upon that as a driving power; hence steam engines are indispensable, and for these nature has provided ample stores of fuel, as well as excellent timber for building. The Company have reliable information of the existence of other veins, which give greater promise in their out-crops than even the above named, and which by the terms of their lease, are subject to their right to occupy to the same extent as is embraced on the New Britain vein. This privilege is deemed of greater value even than their rights on the two named veins, as some of these unoccupied veins are apparently highly auriferous. There are a great number of veins on the Mariposa estate, presenting often the appearance of a net work, from the numerous branches and intersections; some of these are of a highly ferruginous quartz, partially decomposed, which in auriferous regions, indicates ordinarily, rich veins, and from their friable character they are worked with great facility. But so little development has been made, that little more is known of their character than what may be inferred from their out-crops, which in numerous instances are very promising. And it must be observed, that the present out-crops do not offer a just and sufficient standard whereby to estimate the veins, inasmuch as the richer rocks have been carried away by the numerous explorers, who have been prospecting throughout the country. The steam engine and stamps, which were sent last year to California by the Company, to be erected on one of their veins, were thought to be of insufficient weight and power for effective operations, and were therefore temporarily stored at Stockton. They can be advantageously sold, and their place will in due time be supplied by machinery of greater power, and better adapted to the character of the work to be done.

From the foregoing plain unembellished statement, it may be reasonably asserted, that the Philadelphia and California Mining Company possess the requisite elements for a great and prosperous enterprise. The extraordinary privileges of their lease, the vast extent and ascertained value of some of their veins, and the hopeful promise of others, present an array of advantages placing them incomparably in advance of any similar enterprise in California, or elsewhere.

They have a sufficient extent of valuable veins for the supply of a great many sub-companies, each on the most liberal scale known in California, with an ample residue for their own peculiar operations, and under the privilege before named of occupying any discovered vein, they may reasonably expect that in a region hitherto but superficially explored, yet known to be among the richest in the land, opportunity for exercising their privilege in future valuable discoveries will not be wanting.

QUARTZ MINING.

THE

Burns Ranche Gold Mining Company,

TOWNSHIP NO. 2, MARIPOSA COUNTY

IN

CALIFORNIA.

AN

ACCOUNT OF ITS LOCATION, TITLE, MINERAL RICHES, ETC., WITH ITS
CHARTER AND PROCEEDINGS, LETTERS, CERTIFICATES,
AND OTHER MATTERS RELATING TO IT, ETC.

DECEMBER, 1851.

NEW-YORK:

OFFICE OF THE BURNS RANCHE GOLD MINING COMPANY,
NO. 45 MERCHANTS' EXCHANGE.

1851.

Burns Ranche Gold Mining Company.

Capital $1,000,000.

LOCATION,

Burns Ranche Township, No. 2—Mariposa County, California.

OFFICERS.

SIMEON DRAPER, *President.*
JAMES HALL, *Vice-President.*
ALFRED D. SELLECK, *Secretary.*
GILDEMEESTER, DE FREMERY & CO., SAN FRANCISCO, CALIFORNIA, *Treasurers.*

BOARD OF DIRECTORS.

SIMEON DRAPER, NEW-YORK.
JOHN HORSEPOOL, NEW-YORK.
HENRY ERBEN, "
GEORGE NICHOLS, BRIDGEPORT, CONN.
ASA C. SWIFT, BURNS RANCHE, CALIFORNIA.
EGBERT G. BARTON, " "
ALFRED CLAPP, SAN FRANCISCO, CALIFORNIA.
ROBERT S. RANDALL, " "
KINGSBURY ROOT, " "

Office of the Company in New-York, 45 Merchants' Exchange.

JOHN F. TROW, PRINTER,
49 Ann-street.

QUARTZ MINING.

———————•◆•———————

THE BURNS RANCHE GOLD MINING COMPANY.

IT appears to be the destiny of America to carry on the greatness of the future, and that Providence—which shapes the ends of nations as well as of persons, at a time when it was most needful for the prosecution of her mission, when war and the expedients of political strategy are out of vogue, and the people is most powerful of which the individual civilization, energy, ambition and resources are greatest—that Providence, at this crisis, has opened the veins of the Continent, slumbering so many thousand years, in order that we might derive from them all that remained necessary for investing the United States with the leadership of the world.

The first intelligence of the discovery of gold in California fell upon the general mind like news of a great and peculiar revolution. It was at once—even before the statements on the subject assumed a definite or certain form—it was at once felt that a new hour was signalled on the dial-plate of history. Immediately, those immense fortunes which were acquired by the Portugese and Spaniards nearly four centuries ago—fortunes which, in the decline of nations, have still remained in families as the sign and substance of the only nobility and power which mankind at large acknowledge—those astonishing fortunes which raised the enterprising poor man to the dignity ánd happiness of the most elevated classes in society, were recalled, and made suggestive of like successes to new and more hardy adventurers. The reports came with increased volume; every ship confirmed the rumors brought by its predecessor, and new intelligence, that, in its turn, tasked the popular credulity; and it came soon to be understood that we had found a land literally flowing with gold and silver, as that promised to the earlier favorites of Heaven did with milk and honey. As many as were free from controlling engagements, and had means to do so, started for our El Dorado, making haste, in fear that the wealth of the country would quickly be exhausted—not dreaming, even yet, that there was any thing to be acquired but flakes and scales and scattered masses of ore, which would be exhausted by the first hunters who should scour the rivers and turn the surface soil.

But at length the geologists began to apprehend, what experience soon confirmed, that, extraordinary as were the amounts of gold found in drifts of gravel and deposits that had been left in the beds of streams, these were merely the signs of far greater riches—merely indexes of the presence of rocks and hills, and underlayers of plains, impregnated with gold, in quantities that the processes of nature could never disclose, and that would reward only the scientific efforts of miners having all the mechanical appliances which the laborious experiments of other nations had invented. The fact of the existence of veins of gold in vast quartz formations, and ribs of gold in hills, was as startling almost as the first news of the presence of the precious metal in the country. This at once changed the prospect, and from a game of chance, elevated the pursuit of gold in California to a grand industrial purpose, requiring an energy and sagacity that invest it with the highest dignity, and to such energy and sagacity promising, with absolute certainty, rewards that make it worthy of the greatest ambition.

Now, men of character and capital—the class of men whose speculating spirit is held in subjection by the most exact reason—began to turn to the subject their investigations, and to connect with it their plans. This will account for the fact that has so much astonished the world, which had supposed our Pacific Colony to be composed of the reckless, profligate and desperate only—the fact that when California made her constitution of government, it shot at once in unquestionable wisdom directly and far in advance of all the States on the Atlantic, presenting to mankind the very highest type of a free government that had ever been conceived. The demonstration that California was a *mine*, like other mines in all but its surpassing richness, elevated it from a scene of gambling to one for the orderly pursuit of riches, and by the splendor of its promises, drew to it the most sagacious and most heroical intelligences of the time.

Astonishing as are the present and prospective results of the discovery in California, however, we are not to suppose that there is any possibility of a decline in the value of the precious metals. In absolute material civilization, the world in the last three quarters of a century has advanced more than it had in any previous three full centuries : and the supply of gold, for currency and the thousand other objects for which it was demanded, was becoming alarmingly insufficient, so that the addition of more than 30 per cent. to the total annual product of the world, which we are led by the officially-stated results thus far to expect from California, will merely preserve the historical and necessary proportion and standard value.

It was when it became known that the new State was largely underlaid with an auriferous formation, that the projectors of the BURNS RANCHE GOLD MINING

COMPANY determined on the course they have pursued. They employed the very best scientific talent that was attainable to enter upon surveys, and finally located at a point which is conceded to be immeasurably, in the opinion of geologists of high character, the *richest on the globe.*

In a Report on the Gold Mines of California by Dr. CHARLES H. SPIEKER, that accomplished geologist remarks :

" At Mariposa, Agua Frio, Bear Valley, *Burns Ranche,* and Carson's Creek, are some of the most noted localities, known for rich quartz. Two monster veins, which caused the former report of an auriferous quartz *mountain* in California, are found running in southeast to northwest directions from Mariposa, through Bear Valley to the Senora gulch and Carson's Creek, a distance of nearly forty miles. In some parts of this region, as at *Burns Ranche,* a space of six or seven miles long, and four to five broad, appears to be covered as with a web of quartz veins, running in all directions of the compass."

Extract from a Report made by Dr. J. A. Raymond, a distinguished geologist, now in California.

" After having visited the Northern Mining District of California, and closely examined its features, my attention was next directed to the gold-bearing quartz mines of Southern California, particularly those lying to the south and southeast of Stockton. I have spent many months in travelling through those regions in which there is so much to gratify the taste of the geologist. I have thoroughly examined the quartz veins in many places, and am fully convinced that they are of unexampled richness, and that, worked with ordinary skill, they must yield an ample return to the miner.

" I consider that the world has had only a foretaste of California gold, and that for years to come, she will pour forth her wealth from her quartz mines in untold millions. It cannot be otherwise. No geologist can look upon those quartz veins, and not feel the greatest certainty, that in them is to be found gold sufficiently abundant to satisfy the most craving appetite. With regard to the veins on BURNS RANCHE, I can speak in the most unqualified terms, as I have examined them in the most careful manner, taking specimens from many portions of the mines, and testing them with the utmost particularity. The yield was about 34 cents to the pound from ordinary pieces, while from many specimens $6 00 and $8 00 to the pound was readily obtained. From every geological indication about the Ranche, I am fully convinced that the veins are of UNEXAMPLED RICHNESS, and if properly worked will pay an hundred-fold all capital invested. Indeed, all that region of country gives abundant evidence that the *quartz mines* alone, of California, will yield, when in successful operation, from one to two hundred millions annually.

" J. A. RAYMOND."

Mr. WATKINS, of San Francisco, in a letter published in the New-York Tribune of the 15th September, says:

SAN FRANCISCO, Friday, Aug. 1, 1851.

" As the attention of the public is much directed at present to the quartz mines of California, and as I have visited all those lying in Mariposa county, I feel confident, from my own observation, that that attention is not misdirected. I have been on Burns Ranche, and all the places in its vicinity, and am convinced that there are localities on and near that Ranche, from which immense supplies of gold can be obtained. I have no doubt that in an area of eight acres in one locality on that Ranche, there is now more gold than the Bank of England ever had on deposit at any one time. For the next twenty years the mines in that section will yield an amount that will astonish the world. In fact, the most skeptical and unbelieving in regard to the yield of gold from California, would be forced to change their opinion, could they see the mines that I have visited. For my part, all that I should desire would be sufficient means to set good machinery in motion at one of these mines, as I am confident that the result would be an immense fortune."

EXTRACTS FROM LETTERS RECEIVED BY ONE OF THE DIRECTORS.

1. From Mr. A. C. Swift, dated Burns Ranche, Sept. 20.

" The men are doing as well as can be expected. The ditch is progressing finely. We shall soon have it arranged for machinery. We have about 500 cords of wood cut, and about 300 feet of the vein exposed, to the depth of 15 feet, and it proves to be very rich. Many tons of specimens are already thrown out. Timbers for the rail-track are mostly got out. I am much pleased to learn that you are getting the right kind of machinery for crushing the quartz. I do not hesitate to say, that within three months from the time we get the machinery in operation, we will get out gold enough for us all. I do not think it advisable to accept Brennan's offer of $15,000, for the 15 acres. (The 15 acres here alluded to are wanted for building purposes, but not supposed to be valuable for mining.) There are now ten quartz mills about going into operation, in the neighborhood of our ranche.—Those springs are invaluable; I have had many offers for them," &c.

2. Extract of letter from Mr. Robert S. Randall, dated San Francisco, Sept. 30, 1851.

" I learn with pleasure that you are getting the machinery ready to commence the operations at Burns Ranche, and hope you will expedite it, as much as possible, for it has become a settled fact that, with good powerful machinery for working, the quartz rock is the surest way of making a fortune in California. Every day gives new proofs of the richness of the veins which you selected. There is one vein near yours which Johnson's company is working with great success. The blasts of late are so astounding, that a person unacquainted with what lies hidden in California would not credit it. The quartz mining far outstrips the surface mining. The largest shipment of gold that ever has been made by one steamer, will be made to morrow—a very large proportion of which has been derived from the quartz rock. I hope you will be favored with one of those beautiful clipper ships to bring out your machinery—for time here is emphatically money. As you anticipated, the produce that has been raised on the Ranche, has not only paid for the labor of raising, but, has also paid for getting out a large quantity of excellent ore; all things considered, I am convinced that the veins and the locality you have selected, are the best in the country. For that reason I would advise you not to part with any more stock than is absolutely necessary," &c., &c.

3. *Extract of a Letter from Mr. K. Root, dated San Francisco, October* 1, 1851.

" I am glad to see that you are urging forward our machinery, and sparing no pains to get the best kind. Mr. Shelton, who has been lecturing here recently upon the resources of our State, says our location is the best in the State for quartz mining, and he is as well posted up as any other man. The specimens he collected there take the lead decidedly; but these things do not of course affect our opinions of the richness and extent of our mines, and I only mention them to show that our neighbors are not getting ahead of us. The Mercede Company have had a portion of their machinery—six stampers—running about a week, though to much disadvantage, as is apt to be the case in starting new machinery; and it has produced an average of over $800 a day ; but that is nothing to what they will do when in full operation," &c., &c.

4. *Extract of a letter from George W. Gibbs, Esq., dated San Francisco, Oct.* 1, 1851.

" There is little news here. The public attention is much engrossed at present with the results of quartz mining—veins of which are now being worked with great success. I believe as soon as proper machinery can be brought here from the States, that those engaged in quartz-mining operations will make large fortunes. I have seen several fine specimens lately brought from Burns Ranche by Prof. Shelton, which were very rich—one piece of which, weighing eighteen pounds, was estimated to contain $900 worth of gold. It requires heavy machinery to break the rock, and without that I don't think much can be done to advantage. Some of our large bankers have been engaged extensively in this quartz-mining business, and are now making large fortunes out of it."

The history of Mining presents many interesting facts, perhaps not fully understood or appreciated by the public at large, and we are fully aware that no pursuit of industry presents more temptations, and consequently has been pursued with so little judgment and discretion, as that of mining for the precious metals.

All ages, and almost every neighborhood, have had their gold hunters and their mineral seers, stimulated by desire, but guided by no light save their own wild imaginations. It cannot therefore be regarded strange, that the result, in most cases, should be a waste of time, money, and energy. Hence the impression, that gold and silver mining has cost more than has been realized. A closer investigation, however, of the subject, will show that this general impression is not more correct in relation to the subject of mining than to most other branches of human industry, provided all the *follies* of men are chargeable to the account of the cost of production. We do not deem it necessary, nor will we attempt to enter into lengthy details of facts to prove our position; still it may not be inappropriate to present some statistics, derived from authentic sources, of long experience, and directed by the aid of science, which seem to demonstrate that fair remunerating profits have been obtained from sources of far less promise than that which this company propose to occupy and work.

We find by consulting a table of celebrated mines in Europe and America, these facts:—In Mexico, the richest silver mine at the present time is the Vetegrand, near Zacatecas. It yields only about three and a half ounces metal to the quintal of ore, (equal to about three cents to the pound.) It is worked by a shaft eleven hundred feet deep. Costs 20,000*l*. per annum, for draining alone; employs nine hundred hands at from eight to nine shillings English per day, yet pays over seventy-five per cent. per annum, clear profits over and above expenses, and interest on the original capital.

The Valencia mine, the richest in Mexico, in 1800, had a shaft of eighteen hundred and sixty feet, and cost 40,000*l*. annually for draining; employed three thousand one hundred hands at from four to five shillings per day; yielded only four ounces silver to the quintal, and paid one hundred per cent. per annum, profit.

The Hamelsford mine in Saxony, the richest in Europe, in 1800, had a shaft one thousand and eighty feet deep, and discharged fifty gallons water per minute by steam power, yielded from six to seven ounces to the quintal, although comparatively but little ore was produced (only about one hundredth part as much as the Valencia mine), still paid over twenty-five per cent.

The consolidated and united mines of Cornwall, England, producing chiefly copper, with a little tin, have shafts from two hundred and forty-eight to two hundred and seventy-five fathoms, or sixteen hundred feet; discharge from two to three thousand gallons water per minute; employing nine huge steam engines, and a water-wheel forty-eight feet in diameter. Annual expense 12,000*l*. sterling. The ore yields only nine and a quarter per cent. of copper, or about two cents per pound. The gross receipts on an average of ten years was 119,800*l*. sterling, and expenses 93,500*l*. showing a clear profit of 26,300*l*. per annum.

In the States of Virginia and Georgia, where the expense of procuring the ore is much less, yet generally taken from shafts, it is regarded as a fair and very safe business at a yield of fifty cents to the bushel, or half a cent per pound of quartz, and that too where steam is wholly relied upon for the operating power.

More recent experiments have shown that the Zinc Mines of New-Jersey, and the Copper Mines of Connecticut, may be made to pay better than most other branches of business pursued in the same vicinage.

The official reports from Mexico, for the last eighteen months, also show that since the treaty of peace with the United States, the business of mining has been as productive as at any former period. Hence may we not expect from such sources as are found in California, with machinery sufficient, and directed by energy and skill, returns corresponding at least in magnitude with the difference in advantages and richness there presented? When we take therefore, our calculations of twenty cents to the pound, we are enabled to state that every recent discovery, both in the Southern and Northern mines, more than sustains us, and it is with increased confidence that we anticipate that result.

An inspection of the machinery now nearly completed, by competent judges, confirms the opinion that we shall be enabled to crush at least forty tons per day. The conclusion seems therefore almost irresistible, that our anticipations will be fully realized,—viz: forty tons would be 80,000 pounds, at twenty cents, produces $16,000 per day, or $4,800,000 per annum: allowing $800,000 for costs and charges, and we have 400 per cent. to divide among the stockholders. Yet, should our estimate be reduced even to one quarter of that amount (a result which we by no means suppose probable), the profits would far exceed any other enterprise in which capital could be invested with an equal degree of security.

Having taken this general survey of gold mining, the Directors of the Burns Ranche Gold Mining Company, in the fullest confidence of the substantial accuracy thereof, would respectfully present to the stockholders the following account of the

OPERATIONS OF THE COMPANY.

The Directors of the Burns Ranche Gold Mining Company, in view of the formation of an association for the object of gold mining, had for several months employed the most experienced and scientific geologists to locate for them a quartz mine, which they would certify to be of a richness equal, if not superior to any mine in California. After patient and continued research and investigation, a tract of land embracing 1,000 acres, and extending nearly two miles in length, was pointed out as answering entirely the required object. This tract was known as the Burns Ranche, and had been in the possession of John and Robert Burns and Amos and Resin Widener, hardy New-England pioneers, since the year 1847, and their title was confirmed absolutely in them by the laws of California after it became a State. Negotiations were entered into, and the Ranche finally purchased, and on the fourteenth of February, 1850, the said John and Robert Burns and Amos and Resin Widener executed a conveyance of the entire tract to A. C. Swift, E. G. Barton and William T. Henderson, who, to carry out the proposed arrangement, conveyed the same premises to Alfred Clapp, on the 12th February, 1851. On the 6th of March, 1851, a company was formed at San Francisco; on the 29th of March following, it was duly incorporated according to law, under the name of the Burns Ranche Gold Mining Company; and on the 31st of March, Alfred Clapp conveyed the premises to the Company, which at once set on foot a plan of operations. Men were immediately employed to open a trench, who are now busily at work under the superintendence of two of the Directors of the Company.

As the Company are not influenced by any prospect of

speculative action, and as it is not intended by the stock-holders to dispose of any of the shares except for the purpose of erecting and putting in operation the most approved machinery for working the mine, the capital stock of the Company is fixed at one million of dollars, represented by shares of one hundred dollars each—one thousand of which are the exclusive property of the Company, constituting a working capital; which are, for the present, to be got at the office of the Company, 45 Merchants' Exchange, by paying one hundred dollars in cash for each share. The value of these shares it is impossible to estimate. In the opinion of the Directors, they will be worth, the moment the machinery arrives at the mine, at least one thousand dollars to the share. This would seem to be an exaggeration, unless the very low estimate on page 12 be considered; and when an estimate be made at sixty tons per day, which is the amount those who know the capacity of the machinery confidently say will be crushed daily, stockholders can form their own conclusions. Indeed, the prospect of increase in the riches of the quartz defies any estimate in the premises.

CHARTER.

1. To Incorporate the Burns Ranche Gold Mining Company. Be it enacted by the Senate and Assembly of the State of California, and by the authority of the same, provided as follows:

2. That the persons whose names are hereinafter mentioned, to wit; A. C. Swift, Alfred Clapp, Samuel B. Tucker, E. C. Zollicoffer, and such other persons as shall be associated therewith, as hereinafter provided, and their successors, be, and the same are hereby incorporated and constituted a body politic and corporate in the name of the "Burns Ranche Gold Mining Company," to continue and have succession for the term of Forty Years from and after the twenty-ninth day of March one thousand eight hundred and fifty-one, to sue and be sued, to make and use a common seal; and the same to break, alter, and amend at pleasure.

3. The said Corporation shall have power, and is hereby incorporated for the purpose of engaging in gold mining, raising and working gold ore, extracting gold and other metals, and precious stones, from quartz and other minerals and substances, by means of machinery and otherwise; and selling and exporting gold ore in the crude state.

4. And it is hereby declared, that the mining operations of said company may be carried on in the County of Mariposa, in and upon the whole course of the veins of gold ore and auriferous quartz by the said incorporators therein held, located, and claimed, between the waters of the Merced and Mariposa rivers; and also in all other mines or veins within this State, which the said company shall hereafter by discovery, grant, purchase, or otherwise acquire the right to use or work; and may also carry on their business in the County and City of San Francisco, and establish their offices for the business of the company in the City and County of

New-York, and in such cities in the United Kingdom of Great Britain as shall be required by the stockholders and directors of the company.

5. And by their corporate name, the said company shall be capable in law of purchasing, holding, and conveying any real as well as personal estate whatever, which may be necessary to enable said company to carry on their operations, mentioned in the section next preceding.

6. The capital of said Corporation shall be one million dollars, and shall be divided into ten thousand shares of one hundred dollars each, and the stock thereof shall be deemed personal property.

7. When certificates of the shares of the capital stock of the company are issued, such shares may be transferred by the proprietor or his attorney or legal representative; but such transfer shall not be valid, except between the parties thereto, until the same shall have been so entered on the books of the Corporation as to show the names of the parties by and to whom transferred, the number and designation of the shares, and the date of the transfer.

8. There shall be a President of the Corporation, who shall be designated from the number of the Directors. There shall also be such subordinate officers of the company, who may be elected or appointed by the stockholders of the company, and required to give such security for the faithful performance of the duties of their office as the company may require.

9. The property and concerns of the Corporation shall be managed by not less than three nor more than nine Directors, who shall, except the first year, be annually elected by the stockholders, at such time and place as shall be designated; public notice whereof shall be published in one or more of the daily papers in the cities of New-York and San Francisco, not less than thirty days previous thereto. And the election shall be made by such of the stockholders as shall attend for that purpose, either in person or by proxy. And during the first year, or until their successors are chosen, the three incorporators first above mentioned shall be the directors of the company.

10. Elections shall be held by ballot; and each stockholder

shall be entitled to as many votes as he holds shares of stock in the company ; and the persons receiving the greatest number of votes shall be Directors.

11. When any vacancy shall happen among the Directors, by death, resignation, or otherwise, it shall be filled for the remainder of the year by the remaining Directors.

12. The Directors shall have power to make such prudential by-laws as they shall deem proper for the management and disposition of the stock belonging to the company, for working capital, and for the business affairs of the company, and prescribing the duties of officers, artificers, and servants that may be appointed or employed ; for the appointing of all officers, and for carrying on all kinds of business within the object and purpose of the company.

13. The by-laws of the Corporation shall determine the time and manner of calling and conducting meetings, the mode of selling shares belonging to the company, and the tenure of the office of the several officers ; and may prescribe suitable penalties for the violation of the by-laws, not exceeding in any case one hundred dollars for any offence.

14. It shall be the duty of the Directors of the said Corporation to make dividends of the net productions in specie, semi annually, or as much oftener as in the opinion of said Directors it may be for the interest of the stockholders.

15. All transfers of any stock in the said Corporation shall be entered in a book to be kept for that purpose by said Directors; and all books containing a record or statement of the affairs of the said Corporation shall always be open to the inspection of any stockholder.

16. This Corporation may sue or be sued by its corporate name.

17. Stockholders shall not be liable for any more than the amount of stock subscribed.

A. C. SWIFT,
ALFRED CLAPP,
SAMUEL B. TUCKER,
E. C. ZOLLICOFFER.

San Francisco, 29th March, 1851

State of California. }
County of Santa Clara. }

On this 29th day of March, A. D. 1851, personally appeared before me, a Notary Public, in and for said county, Samuel B. Tucker, who being duly sworn, made oath that he saw each one of the subscribers, to the within and foregoing Instrument, sign their names to the same, and heard them, and each one of them, acknowledge the same as and for their act and deed, for the purposes therein expressed.

In testimony whereof I have hereunto affixed my official seal, at San Jose, on the day and year above written.

[SEAL.]   WILLIAM L. SMITH,
Notary Public.

State of California—Executive Department.
SAN JOSE, March 29, A. D. 1851.

I, John McDougal, Governor of the State of California, do hereby certify that William L. Smith, whose name appears subscribed to the foregoing instrument of writing, is, and was at the date of signing the same, a duly commissioned and acting Notary Public in and for the county of Santa Clara and State aforesaid, and that all his official acts as such are entitled to full faith and credit.

In Testimony whereof I have caused the great seal
[SEAL.]   of the State to be hereunto affixed, at the city of San Jose. Done this 29ht day of March, A. D. 1851.

(Signed,)   JOHN McDOUGAL.

Attest—W. VAN VOORHIES, Secretary of State.

Office of Secretary of State, San Jose, }
California, March 29, *A. D.* 1851. }

I, W. Van Voorhies, Secretary of the State of California, hereby certify that the foregoing is a true copy of an original this day filed in this office.

(Signed,)   W. VAN VOORHIES,
Sec'y of State.

GENERAL REMARKS.

Product of Quartz Mines.

The value of investments in vein mining, as a permanent business, necessarily depends upon two circumstances, both of which must be established by unimpeachable testimony. These are—the quantity, or extent of the gold-bearing quartz, and whether its average richness is sufficient to pay a profit under the heavy expenses of labor which now prevail, and are likely to prevail for many years to come. Both points have been so far established by geological and mineralogical explorations by scientific men, and by the results of machinery employed in crushing and amalgamating the ore during the past summer, that they may be considered no longer a matter of dispute.

In making estimates of probable profits to be derived by quartz mining, we have based our calculations upon an average product of 20 cents per pound of rock. Such estimates are calculated to astonish, although it is an undeniable fact that there are numerous veins already opened where this sum, or even a much higher average, is obtained, and where the profits will be absolutely startling. Let us look at the figures, based upon the operations of machinery, such as is now making, capable of crushing 100 tons per each twenty-four hours, founded on this estimate:

One hundred tons at 20 cents per lb. is $40,000.

Cost of quarrying, say at $10 per ton,					.		$1000 00
2 Engineers, at $10 each per day,							20 00
2 Firemen,	5	"			.	.	10 00
16 Feeders,	5	"		.	.	.	80 00
5 Mill hands,	5	"		.	.	.	25 00
1 Superintendent,		.	.	.	.	.	20 00
1 Amalgamator,		.	.	.	.	.	10 00
1 Millwright,	.	.	.	.	.	.	10 00
1 Blacksmith, .		.	.	.	.	.	10 00
8 Cords wood, at $5,	.	.		.	.	.	40 00
Iron. oils, nails, for repairs, &c.,			.	.	.		10 00

Total expenses, ... $1,235 00

Which shows a profit of $38,765 per day, and for 250 working days per annum will give the enormous profit of $9,691,250, or over 950 per cent. on capital invested. We do not say that stockholders of the Burns Ranche Gold Mining Company will, for a year or two, realize so large a profit as above stated ; but we can confidently state, that if machinery can be erected capable of crushing 100 tons of rock per day, we have abundance of the gold-bearing quartz on our property which will yield 20 cents per pound.

It is the intention of the Directors to prosecute this work with vigor, and in order to complete the sale of the remaining stock appropriated for working capital, we, for the present, offer shares for sale at the office of the Company, 45 Merchants' Exchange.

Persons at a distance wishing stock may address the Secretary of the Company, Alfred D. Selleck, and inclose the necessary amount of funds to cover their order. Certificates of stock will be forwarded to subscribers, by return mail.

Specimens of the quartz and maps of the property may be seen at the office of the Company, 45 Merchants' Exchange, where all who feel an interest in quartz mining are invited to call.

    SIMEON DRAPER, *President.*
    JAMES HALL, *Vice-President.*
    ALFRED D. SELLECK, *Secretary.*

New-York, Dec., 1851.

STATEMENT AND REPORTS

OF THE

Consuelo Gold Mining Company

OF

CALIFORNIA.

INCORPORATED IN THE STATE OF NEW-YORK.

OFFICE:

No. 31 PINE ST., NEW-YORK.

NEW-YORK:

J. O. SEYMOUR & CO.,

Nos. 9 AND 11 NASSAU STREET.

Consuelo Gold Mining Company

OF CALIFORNIA.

INCORPORATED IN THE STATE OF NEW-YORK.

——— • • • ———

TRUSTEES.

JOHN B. SPAULDING, Esq., New-York.
CHARLES A. GREELEY, Esq., New-York.
JOSEPH CUSHMAN, Esq., New-York.
S. L. GARDINER, Esq., Sag Harbor, L. I.
Dr. JOHN L. HALL, Geologist, N. Y.

PRESIDENT.

JOHN B. SPAULDING, Esq.

TREASURER.

CHARLES A. GREELEY, Esq.

SUPERINTENDENT AT MINE.

E. L. H. GARDINER, Esq.

SECRETARY.

JOSEPH CUSHMAN, Esq.

OFFICE, NO. 31 PINE STREET, N. Y.

CAPITAL STOCK, $2,000,000.

NUMBER OF SHARES, 40,000.

PAR VALUE, $50 PER SHARE.

NECESSARY WORKING CAPITAL RESERVED.

STOCK UNASSESSABLE.

CONSUELO GOLD MINING COMPANY.

———————•••———————

STATEMENT

AND

REPORTS.

THE following statement and reports of the "Consuelo Gold Mining Company" are submitted for the most critical examination of its merits, that rigid investigation may demand. Evidence the most positive and abundant, of the facts stated, is produced, and courts the power of the most sceptical business mind, to disprove the conclusions, sound and practical, to which those facts lead. All connection with fanciful speculation is disclaimed. Patient industry, acting in subservience to capital, both coöperating and guided by competent management and skill, are alone designed as the basis of a business at once practical, permanent, and largely remunerative to the capitalist, without the hazard of a failure or the loss of the investment.

The comprehensive mind will readily grasp the whole subject from the general facts. Without further preface, the sober attention of honest men is solicited to the information developed in the few following pages, and their coöperation in the enterprise to such an extent, as their judgment may approve, is respectfully but confidently invited.

DESCRIPTION.

The "Consuelo" Lode or Mine is situated in the State of California.

The range of mountains in which the "Consuelo Lode" is situated, runs through the counties of Calaveras, Sierra, Stanislaus, Tuolumne, Nevada, and Eldorado.

The Consuelo Lode, or vein, is from one to six feet thick in its whole extent. The entire length of the claim is *eighteen hundred* (1800) feet, and has every evidence of being a true vein, averaging over five feet in thickness at the outcrop, and remarkably regular in its formation. It possesses, in a striking degree, that uniformity which constitutes an essential element in the value of all mines.

The course of the vein is N. N. West, and S. S. East, dipping *into the body* of the mountain at an angle of about 45 degrees. The vein is well and clearly defined by smooth and regular hanging and foot-walls. A shaft has been sunk in the centre of the Lode to the depth of eighty feet. The mine is four hundred yards above the river. The quartz itself is friable, porous, and brittle. It yields with the greatest ease to the operations of reducing and to the labor of the miner. At the croppings, a smart stroke will drive the pick plumb to the eye. The gold is free and in the metallic state, and not, as found in Colorado, in the condition of sulphurets. The quartz is free from *base* metals, and is very rich in *free gold*. The far greater portion of the gold now produced in California is the product of quartz veins, and in a short time all the supply must come entirely from that source. All surface mining is but the collec-

tion of the gold liberated through disintegration and abrasion from these quartz veins. It
would seem that for centuries or ages the
quartz, by natural causes, had been under-
going the process of decomposition or purifi-
cation, rendering its reduction easy, and the
separation of the precious metal thorough.

Specimens of the quartz from the "Consuelo Mine" can be seen at the Company's
office; also an assay or working test by *crushing* and washing—not a *fire assay*—showing
a yield of $95.62 to the ton of two thousand
pounds. This test is duly verified beyond
a suspicion. The report of those eminent
engineers, Professors Snell and Clayton, annexed hereto, are full in their details, and are
on file in the Company's office. From these
reports the following extract is made:

Says Professor Snell: "The 'Consuelo Lode'
in many places is exceedingly rich in *free gold.*
I had many pieces prospected, that is, crushed
in a mortar and washed, taken from different
places in the vein, which, in richness, far
exceeded my most sanguine expectations. I

have visited nearly all the mines in California, and to the full discharge of my duty, I am gratified to report that the ' Consuelo Vein,' so far as I have examined it, exceeds in richness and extent, and is as free from breaks, dykes, etc., as any which I have been called upon to examine and report. And in concluding this Report, I would say that the Mine is easy of access, and, in fact, presents almost unparalleled inducements for the investment of capital."

These Reports are unimpeachable for their truth.

In working mines a rule, which seems to be very uniform, and which commands general confidence among miners, is this, *that the deeper the mine is penetrated, the richer the ore becomes.* It is regarded as an entirely safe calculation to expect large profits from a mine which barely pays expenses at or near the croppings; and this mine has proved no exception, but has confirmed this rule. Had a company the privilege to select a position and location expressly adapted to this enterprise, they could not, under any circumstances, improve upon that of the Consuelo.

In quartz-mining, a vein of rock can be reduced to possession, and all the gold extracted from it be secured to the rightful owner.

The employment of labor and capital is uniform and regular, and can be carried to any extent. Quartz-mining is attractive to both the labor of miners and capital. But the *power* by which the results are to be obtained is an essential element in the calculation.

POWER TO BE USED IN THE OPERATIONS.

The power to develop this Mine is provided by nature, and is inexhaustible. The Tuolumne River at the foot of the mountain, and but twelve hundred feet distant from the main trunk vein, the " Consuelo," affords a constant and unfailing water-power through the *whole year*. The water-course lies well up to the foot of the mountain, and the supply *is free*. A mill site is already secured, and also the exclusive right to the water of the stream for three quarters of a mile in distance, along and on the river. By running a flume nine hundred feet, a waterfall of forty-seven and a half feet can be obtained.

A better combination of all the facilities for opening this Mine, and delivering and reducing the ore than is here presented, could not be found. The river lies close at the foot or very base of the Mine, as it descends from the out-croppings, at an eminence of twelve hundred feet on the face of the mountain to the water's edge. The successive steps by which the mountain falls off from its greatest eminence to the level of the river, for a distance of more than a mile, present innumerable points on the line of the river from which tunnels could be driven to great advantage, opening the Mine to any desired depth. Such tunnels would establish the certain and enduring value of the Mine many years in advance. They would, besides, by allowing of a drainage at that depth, furnish advantages for mining that are seldom if ever equalled.

1*

The elevation of the " Consuelo Mine " gives it immense superiority over mines situated in a more level country, as it can be worked at a high elevation, and will drain itself. The expense of pumping and hoisting, and other expenses incident to working mines in lower levels are saved. Comparing water-power with steam-power in mining operations, the preference may be given the former, for the reasons following: Water-power is much more economical than steam. It is better. By simply raising the break, the wheel carrying the machinery is set in motion, and will continue to run till the break shall be lowered. No firemen or engineers are needed; there is no wear and tear of the engine or machinery. There are no explosions or destructions of boilers or buildings; no expense of fuel, or its transportation. In short, none of those numerous and unavoidable expenses of running a steam-engine.

The water-power is always on the spot, and never wears out.

It is not out of place here to state that

in the same range with the "Consuelo,"
and only one and a half miles north-west,
is the famous "Eureka" mine, owned by D.
Davidson, Esq., of England. On the Eureka
mine or lode, a shaft has been sunk to the
depth of five hundred and twenty-six feet, at
which point of depth the vein is twenty-eight
feet thick, and pays from the foot to the hanging walls. Within Tuolumne county there are
about ten gold mines, all of which are owned
by private partnership companies, and all of
which are worked, and yield large and remunerative returns to the proprietors. Keeping in
view constantly the necessity of absolute facts,
as the only reliable basis for estimating the
advantages of, or objections to a proposed business negotiation, we will advert to the cost of
the proposed works, and the results of actual
operations, consequent upon their establishment. In estimating cost and receipts, it must
be remembered that *gold*, and not greenbacks,
is used as the standard of value. Gold, and
not paper, is produced by our machinery. *The
true secret* of success in mining operations con-

sists almost wholly *in the perfect adaptation of means to the ends sought to be accomplished.* It is not so much in the extent or abundance of those means as in the *economy* of their *application*, and the method of combination, by which their greatest productive power is developed.

Economy in *the productive elements* is superior in importance to mere economy in the expenditure of money. For this reason a twenty-stamp mill is deemed sufficient power for the operations of this enterprise. A larger power would require larger expense, while one of the proposed power will yield ample returns at small expense, if *made available to its maximum capacity.* If dead capital is to exist, it is much *better to have it in the work done in advance on the mine, and the ores accumulated* in advance of the daily requirements of the reducing power, than to have it in an *excess* of that power itself. In one case the loss is temporary. In case of *excess* of power, it is final and irreparable. The production of the mine in remunerative ores should be equal to the capacity for producing them. And a twenty-stamp mill reducing the supply produced from day to day, at the estimated yield, would be amply sufficient to maintain the value of the property, and give enormous dividends.

The work should be equal, constant, and regular, from month to month, up to the actual maximum capacity of the mill. When a reasonable reserved stock has been secured, it is easy to reduce the mining labor.

A twenty-stamp mill, crushing thirty tons a day, at $95 per ton, will produce.......................... $2,850 00
Cost of quarrying and extracting gold, at seven dollars per ton, *a large estimate*,.................. 210 00

Net profit per day,.........................	$2,640	00
" " month,.........................	79,200	00
" " year,.........................	950,400	00
Net profit a year, at $80, is,...................$864,000		00
" " 70, ... 756,000		00
" " 60, ... 648,000		00
" " 50, ... 540,000		00
" " 40, ... 432,000		00
" " 30, ... 324,000		00

From this it will appear that at the *minimum* yield of thirty dollars per ton, an annual interest of more than fifteen per cent in gold is given on a capital of two million of dollars. The quartz *can be quarried*, and delivered at the mill, and the gold extracted at a cost of not exceeding *five* (5) *dollars per ton.* The actual results of a few months' operations will demonstrate beyond question the great intrinsic value of the property.

The mountains on either side, as well as the intervening valleys, are well covered with a growth of heavy oak and pine timber ; an abundant supply for many years to come is near at hand for all required purposes of mining.

GENERAL REMARKS.

Portions or sections of the "Consuelo Vein or Lode" are fabulously rich, paying many hundred dollars to the ton. The rich portions of the vein have been left undisturbed through the long months of labor which have been employed in developing its value. These rich sections of the vein will be worked out only as the quartz is taken in regular order. Had our estimate of the value of the mine been based upon the result of the working of these rich deposits, it would have far exceeded in value or richness any mine on the Pacific coast. But we have chosen rather to base our estimate on the *general average* working of the ore, thereby showing the least possible value of the mine, and which value may certainly and confidently be relied upon.

The richness of the gold-bearing veins has been fully tested and proved. At the present day, the cost of setting up these establishments for the extraction of gold can be accurately estimated. Capital is ever wary of new enterprises, and hesitates to engage in them without thorough investigation of present condition and future prospects. This investigation is courted for *this* mine. Failure can result only from inadequate skill and capital. The great difficulty of saving gold formerly made mining unproductive. Gold existing only in a metallic state, though often in a state of almost atomic subdivisions, the necessity of liberating it, and the danger of doing so, presented once such difficulties that it seemed impossible to accomplish the one, and at the same time avoid the other. But the methods of separating the gold are now almost perfect. It cannot elude the method of catching when the rock has been reduced to impalpable condition. Human ingenuity has resorted to many devices, and such improvements have been made that success is now made certain, where heretofore failure was inevitable.

It is hardly necessary to refer to the many valuable mines in California. The Gould and Curry, and Ophir, have been noted mines ; other mines, like the Potosi, Savage, and Gold Hill, are all remunerative and valuable. The Chollon is worth $750. The Potosi, $730. The Savage, $1425, per share, and constantly advancing. Other claims, not heard of in the market, are paying largely. It is confidently believed that the " Consuelo " will equal any of these lodes in richness, and afford dividends regularly of a large amount.

But to accomplish this, it is of paramount importance to have upon the property a resident agent and superintendent of administrative ability, and of a *practical* knowledge of mining operations. Such a one we have secured. It will be his pleasure as well as duty to supervise and inaugurate a system of management which shall combine to the best advantage the various elements and resources by which such results can alone be obtained. We repeat, good management is essential to an efficient administration of the estate. The " Consuelo " property has been purchased by this Company, after the most careful investigations; having satisfied themselves beyond a shadow of a doubt in regard to its value. A working capital has been subscribed, and *paid* into the treasury ; and our agent and superintendent is now *en route* for California, for the purpose of erecting a mill with the capacity of crushing twenty-four tons of quartz in twenty-four hours ; and opening and developing the mine; all of which will be fully completed and in running order within one hundred and eighty (180) days after commencing the works in California.

REPORT OF PROFESSOR SNELL.

SONORA, TUOLUMNE CO., CALIFORNIA,
June 30, 1864.

To MESSRS. GARDINER, WARFIELD, AND OTHERS,
LOCATORS AND OWNERS OF THE CONSUELO
QUARTZ VEIN OR LODE:

GENTLEMEN: In accordance with your request I did, on the 27th and 28th inst., visit the " Consuelo " Quartz Vein or Lode, and would respectfully submit the following report as the result of my investigations :

LOCATION.

The " Consuelo " Quartz Vein or Lode is situated on the east side of the north fork of the Tuolumne River, Tuolumne County, State of California, distance about fourteen miles from the city of Sonora, and about one mile south of the Eureka and Grizzly Mills.

The course of the vein is N. N. W. and
S. S. E. It appears from the notice containing the names of the locators, that the
claim contains eighteen hundred feet; said
notice is posted by the shaft which is the
centre of the claim, and running each way
nine hundred (900) feet from said shaft.
In ascending the hill from the river, the
trail intersects the vein near the southern
boundary. At this point a cut (No. 1) has
been made, which discovers the lode to be
at this point some two and a half feet
thick, and well defined. Following the
course of the lead or vein in a northerly
direction, I find a large open cut (No. 2)
about forty (40) feet long and twenty (20)
feet deep, and the quartz taken out. At
this point, which is about four hundred
feet north from the southern boundary, the
vein is from five to seven feet thick, well
defined by smooth, regular hanging and
foot-walls.

I had quartz broken from different places
on the vein in this cut, and prospected,

and am satisfied that the rock will yield
from forty (40) dollars to sixty (60) dollars per ton.

One hundred lineal feet on this vein,
that is, fifty feet either way from the centre
of the cut, will keep a twenty-stamp mill
running many years. The vein dips eastward and into the body of the mountain
at an angle of about fifty degrees. Following on in a northerly direction, I find the
vein cropped out and exposed in a gulch
or ravine, about midway between the shaft
and open cut No. 2.

One hundred feet further north, I come
to another open cut, (No. 3,) where the
lead is about five or six feet thick, and
well cased, as in cuts Nos. 1 and 2. The
next point in a northerly direction, is the

SHAFT,

Which is eighty (80) feet deep. In this
shaft I also gave the vein a minute and
careful examination. The dip is the same
as in the open cuts 1, 2, 3, till we reach

the depth of about seventy (70) feet, when the angle of the vein seems to become steeper. The vein in the shaft is about one foot thick on the surface, or at the mouth of the shaft, and gradually increases with the depth of the shaft. At the bottom of the shaft it is upward of four (4) feet thick.

The foot and hanging walls are regular and smooth, as in the open cuts 1, 2, and 3, and well and clearly defined from top to bottom of the shaft. The rock in many places is exceedingly rich, and will yield largely in free gold. I had many pieces prospected, taken from various parts of the lead, from top to bottom, and which, in richness, far exceeded my most sanguine expectations. The vein from top to bottom of the shaft is rich in free gold.

Leaving the shaft, I followed the course of the vein in a northerly direction to its boundary, finding it at different points where it had been opened.

ADVANTAGES FOR WORKING.

The location and surroundings of the lode or vein add materially to its value. At the foot of the hill, on the western slope, runs the *river*, which affords a never-failing supply of water for a twenty (20) or more stamp-mill.

A dam can be built on the river at the point located by you, the span not exceeding twenty feet, and fifteen feet high, and a flume to your mill site, giving a fall of forty-seven feet — flume nine hundred feet long.

The mountains are covered with a large growth of pine and oak-timber, free to those who desire to cut and use it. Rock can be quarried and delivered at the mill, and crushed at a cost not exceeding five (5) dollars per ton.

I have visited nearly all the mines of any note in California, and to the full discharge of my duty, I am gratified to report, that the " Consuelo " Vein, so far as

I have examined, exceeds in richness and extent, and is as free from breaks, dikes, etc., as any which I have been called upon to examine and report. And in concluding this report, I would say that the vein is easy of access, only thirty hours' ride from San Francisco; and, in fact, it presents almost unparalleled inducements for the investment of capital.

PEREZ SNELL,

Mining Engineer and Professor of

Geology, Mineralogy, Etc.

STATE OF CALIFORNIA, ⎱
⎰ ss.
TUOLUMNE COUNTY, ⎰

On this thirtieth day of June, one thousand eight hundred and sixty-four, before me, J. D. Redmond, a Notary Public in and for said county, personally appeared the above-named Perez Snell, to me personally known to be the individual whose signature is affixed. to the above report on the

"Consuelo" Quartz Lode or vein, and he acknowledged to me that he made and signed said report freely and voluntarily.

In witness whereof, I have hereunto set my hand and affixed my offi-
[L.S.] cial seal the day and year first in this certificate written.

J. D. REDMOND,
Notary Public.

STATE OF CALIFORNIA, ⎫
   TUOLUMNE COUNTY, ⎬ ss.

I, R. E. Gardiner, County Clerk in and for said county, State aforesaid, and Clerk of the County Court of said county, do hereby certify that J. D. Redmond, who took the within acknowledgment of Perez Snell, was, at the time of signing the same, a Notary Public in and for said county, duly commissioned and sworn, and duly authorized by law, to take such acknowledgments. I further certify that I am well ac-

quainted with the handwriting of the said
J. D. Redmond, and verily believe that his
signature to the above acknowledgment is
genuine.

Witness my hand and the seal of
the County Court of said county,
[L.S.] affixed at Sonora this thirtieth day
of June, A.D. 1864.

ROBT. E. GARDINER,
Clerk.

2

REPORT OF PROFESSOR CLAYTON.

Messrs. Warfield and Gardiner:

Gents: In pursuance of your instructions, I have examined the Consuelo Lode or vein, situated on the east side of the north fork of the Tuolumne River, in Tuolumne county, and about fourteen miles east of the town of Sonora, and about one mile south-easterly from the Grizzly Mill and Mine.

The vein has been cut at two points. One place, called the "Open Cut," on the map herewith submitted, has an opening to the depth of about twenty feet below the cropping, and has been opened for a distance along the river of some thirty feet, and most of the quartz removed. The vein at this point is from four to six feet thick, and is well defined with smooth, regular walls, both on the foot and hanging walls of the vein. The vein dips towards the east and into the body of the mountain at an angle of about fifty degrees, but becomes steeper at a greater depth. The course of the vein is S. S. east and N. N. west. The geological structure is principally composed of metamorphic slate, with numerous dikes of eruptive rocks, such as granite, diorite, or greenstone. The eruptive rocks have produced disturbances in the strata of the country rock that have most likely caused "faults" in the veins for short distances; but a little careful observation will point out the breaks, and readily set the miner right. The general course of the vein, however, is well defined for a distance of three miles, including in its course the famous Grizzly claim, the Summers and McGee claim, and the celebrated Blakely claim, now owned by Donald Davidson, Esq., of England, now resident in San Francisco.

The second opening on the vein is at a point about five hundred feet north of the "*open cut*," and marked on the map as the

"*Shaft.*" Here the vein was followed down from the surface to the depth of eighty feet. The vein at this point is from one to four feet thick, being *thinnest* at the surface and *thickest* at the bottom of the shaft. The vein is very rich in free gold, and will yield from forty to sixty dollars per ton. The ore at the open cut is not so rich as that in the shaft, but will yield from twenty (20) to thirty dollars per ton, if properly reduced.

Extraction of ore or mining in the vein will be quite easy and cheap, for the reason that most of the quartz is decomposed, and the selvage or lining on the walls is soft, and yields readily to the pick.

The other facilities are good. Timber and water abundant and convenient.

The water at the foot of the mine is permanent, and sufficient to drive a twenty-stamp mill.

Lumber will cost, *delivered* at the mill-site, twenty-five dollars per thousand feet.

Freights from San Francisco about one and three quarters to two cents per pound.

The cost of erecting a first-class stamp-mill will be about one thousand dollars per stamp, *including* the dam and flume.

Cost of extracting and delivery of ore, per ton,....................	$4 00
Cost of reduction by water-power, per ton,.....................	2 00
Cost of superintendence and incidentals, per ton,..............	1 00
Total cost,...............	$7 00

It will thus be seen that the location of the mine is exceedingly favorable, and if properly worked, must yield great profit to the owners. Very respectfully, etc.,

J. E. CLAYTON,
Mining Engineer.

SAN FRANCISCO, June 1, 1864.

CHARACTER OF PROFESSOR CLAYTON.

PROFESSOR SILLIMAN, in his report on the Sheba, without flattering, has pronounced a generally favorable opinion on the mines in this neighborhood; a view that is confirmed to some extent by the equally valuable judgment of his assistant, J. E. Clayton, now here prosecuting a geological examination of the country. As a field geologist and mining expert, Mr. Clayton has no superior on this coast, and it would probably have been worth something to this region if the mines here had been sufficiently opened to warrant him in expressing a more unreserved opinion of their merits. As it is, he pronounces several of the ledges here to be regular fissure veins, carrying heavy masses of the most valuable ores, and as bearing the indications of permanency. Upon these he thinks money might be spent to advantage; though there are hundreds of others that he would advise no one to touch—an opinion that very many miners here seem disposed to concur in. — *Humboldt N. T. Correspondence.*

LETTER FROM PROFESSOR SILLIMAN.

VIRGINIA CITY, Nov. 4, 1864.

DEAR SIR: Mr. J. E. Clayton has shown me his sections, specimens, and notes on the Tuolumne gold mine, to which you refer in your note of second instant, and I can say with pleasure that I have confidence in the accuracy of his observations and conclusions respecting this property.

Mr. Clayton has been in my employment this year in many important investigations, and I have had good occasion to put confidence in his skill and sagacity as an observer in geological and mining subjects, and as a mining engineer.

Yours truly,

B. SILLIMAN, Jr.

ALEX. WARFIELD, San Francisco.

CHARTER

OF THE

GRASS VALLEY GOLD MINING COMPANY,

ORGANIZED JULY 25, 1851,

UNDER THE

GENERAL INCORPORATION ACT OF CALIFORNIA.

TOGETHER WITH EXTRACTS FROM THE LAW, AND VARIOUS
DOCUMENTS ILLUSTRATING THE

BUSINESS OF QUARTZ MINING.

NEW YORK:

PRINTING OFFICE 107 FULTON STREET.

1852.

GRASS VALLEY GOLD MINING COMPANY.

INCREASED CAPITAL, **$250,000.**

LOCATED AT GRASS VALLEY, NEVADA CO., CALIFORNIA.

Officers Elected August, 1852.
J. WINCHESTER, *President.*
R. J. RICHARDS, *Secretary.*
D. NORCROSS, *Assistant Secretary.*

Board of Trustees.
J. WINCHESTER, Grass Valley.
S. C. RICHARDSON, do.
LEWIS W. SLOAT, San Francisco.
HENRY P. ROBERTS, Middletown, N. Y.
RICHARD J. RICHARDS, New York.

Bankers.
PAGE, BACON & CO., San Francisco.

New York Agency.
R. J. RICHARDS, Secretary and Transfer Agent,
107 Fulton Street.

☞ Dividends payable quarterly, at the Agency and Transfer Office, New York, on the 1st of March, June, September, and December. Shares transferable by endorsement. Subscriptions to the stock may be made at the Agency Office, payable *in cash* at the time of subscribing. Letters by mail must be prepaid.

CHARTER.

THIS IS TO CERTIFY, that the subscribers hereto have this twen
fifth day of July, in the year of our Lord one thousand eight hundre
and fifty-one, under and pursuant to the Act of the Legislature of the
State of California, entitled, "An Act concerning Corporations,"
passed April 22d, 1850, associated themselves for the purpose of carrying on the business of *Mining*, to be known as a Company, as follows, to wit:

First. The name and style of the Company shall be,
" *The Grass Valley Gold Mining Company*," and the concerns
of the Company shall be carried on in the township of Grass Valley,
in the county of Nevada.

Second. The Capital Stock of said Company shall be *One Hundred Thousand Dollars,* divided into five hundred shares, of two
hundred dollars each, with the privilege of increasing the said Capital
to *Two Hundred and Fifty Thousand Dollars,* and the number of
shares to twelve hundred and fifty.*

Third. The duration of said Company shall be *Fifty Years,* from
the day and date hereof.

Fourth. The concerns of the Company shall be managed by a
board of Five Trustees or Directors, and the said Trustees or Directors for the first year, and until their successors shall be legally chosen,
shall be, *William G. Wood, Jonas Winchester, Elisha Cook, Heman Winchester, and Lewis W. Sloat.*

JONAS WINCHESTER,
HEMAN WINCHESTER,
(Signed,)   WM. G. WOOD,
L. W. SLOAT,
ELISHA COOK.

---

* An adjourned meeting of the stockholders of the Grass Valley Gold Mining Company was
held on Tuesday, August 10th, 1852, at the office of the Company. The president in the chair.
A proposition was made that the capital stock be increased to Two Hundred and Fifty
Thousand Dollars, as provided in the Certificate of Incorporation; on which the vote was
taken, and three hundred and seventy-nine shares voted in the affirmative. Two-thirds of the
shares being in favor, the proposition was declared to be carried

STATE OF CALIFORNIA, } ss.
COUNTY OF SAN FRANCISCO, }

On this twenty-eighth day of July, A.D. 1851, before me came Jonas Winchester, Heman Winchester, William G. Wood, Lewis W. Sloat, and Elisha Cook, to me known to be the individuals described in, and who executed, the within instrument, and acknowledged that they executed the same freely and voluntarily for the uses and purposes therein mentioned.

In witness whereof, I have hereunto set my hand, and affixed my [L.s.] official seal, in the City of San Francisco, County aforesaid, the day and year first above written.

WARD McALLISTER,
Notary Public.

STATE OF CALIFORNIA.

OFFICE OF SECRETARY OF STATE,

City of Vallejo, July 29th, 1851.

I, W. Van Voorhies, Secretary of State of the State of California, certify, that the foregoing is a correct copy of the Certificate of Incorporation of the "Grass Valley Gold Mining Company," now on file in this office.

In testimony whereof, I have hereunto set my hand, and affixed [L.s.] the Great Seal of the said State, the date above written

W. VAN VOORHIES,
Secretary of State.

At a meeting of the Stockholders of the Grass Valley Gold Mining Company, held at San Francisco, August 14, 1851, present Wm. G. Wood, J. Winchester, L. W. Sloat, and Elisha Cook, the certificate of charter was read, and the Board organized by the election of J. WINCHESTER, as President, and L. W. SLOAT, Secretary *pro tem.*

The following resolutions were offered and adopted :

Resolved, That the President be, and he is hereby authorized to cause certificates of capital stock to be issued, and proceed to New York, and offer for sale so much thereof, as he may deem necessary to procure suitable machinery for Quartz Mining, and for putting the same in operation at Grass Valley.

Resolved, That until the further action of the Board of Trustees, the entire management of the concerns of the Company be placed in the hands of the President, with power to appoint such subordinate officers, and employ such servants, in any department, as he may judge for the advancement of the interest of the Company.

On motion, adjourned, to meet at the call of the President.

L. W. SLOAT, Secretary *pro tem.*

"ACT CONCERNING CORPORATIONS,"

Passed April 22d, 1850.

CHAPTER V.

Companies for Manufacturing, Mining, Mechanical, or Chemical Purposes.

§ 122. At any time hereafter, any three or more persons who may desire to form a company for the purpose of carrying on any kind of manufacturing, mining, mechanical, or chemical business, may make, sign, and acknowledge, before some officer competent to take the acknowledgment of deeds, and file in the office of the Clerk of the County in which the business of the company shall be carried on, and a duplicate thereof in the office of the Secretary of State, a certificate in writing, in which shall be stated the corporate name of said company, and the objects for which the company shall be formed, the amount of the capital stock of said company, the time of its existence, not to exceed fifty years, the number of shares of which the said stock shall consist, the number of trustees and their names, who shall manage the concerns of said company for the first year, and the names of the town and county in which the operations of the said company are to be carried on.

§ 123. When the certificate shall have been filed as aforesaid, the persons who shall have signed and acknowledged the same, and their successors, shall be a body politic and corporate, in fact and in name, by the name stated in such certificate, and they shall, by their corporate name, be capable, in law, of purchasing, holding, and conveying any real and personal estate whatever, which may be necessary to enable the said company to carry on the operations named in such certificate, but shall not mortgage the same, nor give any lien thereon.

§ 124. The stock, property, and concerns of such company shall be managed by not less than three nor more than nine trustees, who shall, respectively, be stockholders in such company, and citizens of the United States, and a majority of whom shall be citizens of this State, who shall, except the first year, be annually elected by the stockholders, at such time and place as shall be directed by the laws of the company; and public notice of the time and place of holding such election shall be published, not less than ten days previous thereto, in the newspaper printed nearest to the place where the operations of said company shall be carried on; and the election shall be made by such of the stockholders as shall attend for that purpose, either in person or by proxy. All elections shall be by ballot, and each stockholder shall be entitled to as many votes as he owns shares of stock in the said company, and the persons receiving the greatest number of votes shall be trustees; and when any vacancy shall happen among the trustees, by death, resignation, or otherwise, it shall be filled, for the remainder of the year, in such manner as may be provided for by the by-laws of the said company.

§ 125. In case it shall happen, at any time, that an election of trustees shall not be made on the day designated by the by-laws of said company, when it ought to have been made, the company, for that reason, shall not be dissolved; but it shall be lawful, on any other day, to hold an election for trustees, in such manner as shall be provided for by the said by-laws, and all acts of trustees shall be valid and binding against such company, until their successors shall be elected.

§ 126. There shall be a President of the company, who shall be designated from the number of the trustees, and also such subordinate officers as the company, by its by-laws, may designate, who may be elected or appointed, and required to give such security for the faithful performance of the duties of their office, as the company, by its by-laws, may require.

§ 128. The trustees of such company shall have power to make such prudential by-laws as they shall deem proper for the management and disposition of the stock and business affairs of such company, not inconsistent with the laws of this state, and prescribing the duties of officers, artificers, and servants that may be employed; for the appointment of all officers, and for carrying on all kinds of business within the objects and purposes of such company.

§ 129. The stock of such company shall be deemed personal estate, and shall be transferable in such manner as shall be prescribed by the by-laws of the company; but no shares shall be transferable until all previous calls thereon shall have been fully paid in, or shall have been declared forfeited for the non-payment of the calls thereon; and it shall not be lawful for such company to use any of their funds in the purchase of any stock in any other corporation.

§ 134. Nothing but money shall be considered as payment of any part of the capital stock, and no loan of money shall be made by any such company to any stockholder therein; and if any such loan shall be made to a stockholder, the officers who shall make, or who shall assent thereto, shall be jointly and severally liable to the extent of such loan, and interest, for all the debts of the company contracted before the repayment of the sum so loaned.

§ 140. Whenever any company shall desire to call a meeting of the stockholders, for increasing or diminishing the amount of capital stock, or for extending or changing its business, it shall be the duty of the trustees to publish a notice, signed by at least a majority of them, in a newspaper in the county, if any shall be published therein, at least three successive weeks, and to deposit a written or printed copy thereof in the post-office, addressed to each stockholder, at his usual place of residence at least three weeks previous to the day fixed upon for holding such meeting, specifying the object of the meeting, the time and place when and where such meeting shall be held, and the amount to which it shall be proposed to increase or diminish the capital, and the business to which the company would be extended or changed; and a vote of at least two-thirds of all the shares of stock shall be necessary to an increase or diminution of its capital stock, or the extension or change in its business as aforesaid.

GENERAL PROVISIONS.

CHAPTER I.

§ 1. Every corporation, as such, has power: 1. To have succession by its corporate name, for the period limited, and when no period is limited, perpetually. 2. To sue and be sued in any court. 3. To make and use a common seal, and alter the same at pleasure. 4. To hold, purchase, and convey such real and personal estate as the purposes of the corporation shall require, not exceeding the amount limited by law. 5. To appoint such subordinate officers and agents as the business of the corporation shall require, and to allow them a suitable compensation. 6. To make by-laws, not inconsistent with any existing law, for the management of its property, the regulation of its affairs, and for the transfer of its stock.

§ 2. In addition to the powers enumerated in the preceding section, and to those expressly given in the chapter of this Act under which it shall be incorporated, no corporation shall possess or exercise any corporate powers, except such as shall be necessary to the exercise of the powers so enumerated and given.

§ 3. No corporation created, or to be created, shall, by any implication or construction, be deemed to possess the power or discounting bills, notes, or other evidences of debt, of receiving deposits, of buying gold or silver, bullion or foreign coin; of buying and selling bills of exchange, or of issuing bills, notes, or other evidences of debt, upon loans, or for circulation as money.

§ 7. All corporations may, by their by-laws, where no other provision is specially made, determine the manner of calling and conducting their meetings, the number of members that shall constitute a quorum, the number of shares that shall entitle the members respectively to one or more votes, the mode of voting by proxy, the mode of selling shares for the non-payment of assessments, and the tenure of office of the several officers; and they may prescribe suitable penalties for the violation of their by-laws, not exceeding, in any case, one hundred dollars for any one offence.

§ 12. Whenever the capital stock of any corporation is divided into shares, and certificates thereof are issued, such shares may be transferred by endorsement and delivery of the tickets thereof, such endorsement being by the signature of the proprietor or his attorney, or legal representative; but such transfer shall not be valid, except between the parties thereto, until the same shall have been so entered on the books of the corporation as to show the names of the parties by and to whom transferred, the number and designation of the shares, and the date of the transfer.

GENERAL REMARKS

THE foregoing documents will exhibit to the public the fundamental basis of the "GRASS VALLEY GOLD MINING COMPANY." The principal "claims" of the Company are upon Virginia Ledge, Virginia Hill, Bryan Ledge, Union Hill, Jefferson Hill, Empire Hill, St. Charles Hill, Weehawken Hill, Caledonia Hill, Smith Hill, Grass Valley Slide, Daisy Hill, and Ophir Hill, consisting of more than four hundred lots.

It will be seen that the stock of this company has been fixed at an amount deemed *sufficient* for the accomplishment of the best results, with an honest and economical administration of affairs, and in no degree partaking of a *speculative* character. The public are apt to look with distrust upon those enterprises which, while holding out extraordinary incentives to investment, in the promise of large dividends, create a *nominal* Stock of half a million or a million of dollars, really with a view to the personal aggrandizement of the projectors. Such distrust is both natural and proper. While we do not deny that even in many such cases a *fair dividend* may be earned and paid, no judicious man of moderate means can fail to see that he has not an equal chance for profitable returns upon his Stock, when the portion he holds forms so small a fraction of the aggregate amount.

The Directors of the Grass Valley Company are not entirely unknown to the public, and they can fearlessly challenge any scrutiny touching integrity and character. Col. WILLIAM G. WOOD was a former resident of the city of New York; is a lawyer of excellent standing as well on the Pacific side as on this, and is connected with a family long esteemed and eminent in the legal profession. Mr. L. W. SLOAT is a son of Com. Sloat, of the U. S. Navy, who commanded the squadron in the Pacific during the war with Mexico. He is, more than this, a gentleman of unimpeachable honor and high standing in California. He is at this time editor of the oldest Prices Current publication, to which the merchants of the Atlantic cities are accustomed to look for reliable and authentic intelligence. Mr. COOK is well known as a former (and for many years) resident of the city of Buffalo, and as a gentleman having few equals for industry and talent in the legal profession of San Francisco. Of the other Directors, we can not properly speak here; for one of them, at least, the public know by reputation as a publisher. Mr. R. J. RICHARDS, Secretary pro tem., and New York agent, is well and honorably known in the city, where he has been for nearly twenty-five years a resident. His character for honorable, upright dealing, and his enlarged business experience and capacity, admirably fit him to represent the interests of Atlantic Stockholders. The gentlemen connected with the Company cannot afford to jeopard their reputation, honorably earned during the major part of a life-time, by giving their sanction to a scheme not founded upon the most reasonable and substantial basis. The confidence of the public is asked for and expected only so far as the characters of the Officers and Directors of the Grass Valley Gold

Mining Company are a sufficient guarantee for fidelity and integrity in the management of its concerns.

The operations in Quartz Mining by this Company will be carried on near the village of Centreville, situated upon Wolf Creek (a small stream rising in the dividing ridge bordering Deer Creek) which falls into Bear River, after a course through the foot hills of some fifteen or twenty miles. The village already (1851) contains an active population of about 2000 souls, among whom are many families. It possesses excellent hotels, meat and vegetable markets, bakeries, stores for all kinds of groceries and supplies for mining, and dwellings of size and comfort, neatly enclosed with palings. The hills surrounding are covered with a heavy growth of pine, redwood and oak, giving abundant material for lumber for general building purposes, and for fuel for the steam-power. There are now ten Quartz Mills in constant motion, and seven or eight others in process of erection. *All the mills at work are paying good, and some of them very large dividends*, with machinery mostly of California manufacture, and with methods of saving the gold comparatively rude and imperfect. Reference is made to the Appendix for more detailed information on many of these points.

It is designed to connect with the business of quartz crushing, a saw-mill; the whole to be moved by steam-power. The facilities for getting out lumber, and the ready sale for all that can be manufactured, for building there and in the surrounding mineral district, will render this not only a great convenience, but an additional source of profit. Sawed boards sell for from $50 to $70 per 1000 feet.

TITLE TO QUARTZ VEINS.

The *title* by which the quartz mines are held by individuals and companies, is equal to a FEE SIMPLE. The whole question of title to claims has been settled by regulations made by the miners themselves; and, so well defined and understood are these "laws," that it is exceedingly rare that a case of difficulty arises under them. Probably not a hundred instances have occurred, since the discovery of gold in California, of suits growing out of adverse "claims." These "regulations" are different in different sections of the mineral district, being always adapted to the peculiar circumstances of the locality. At the last session of the State Legislature, the "regulations" of the miners, in regard to claims, were *legalized;* so that, in all cases of trespass, suit may be brought before any justice of the peace, who is bound to give a decision in accordance with the regulations or customs of the *particular locality*, though within a hundred yards entirely different rules may obtain. There can be no doubt but that the system, which has grown up under a free occupancy of the gold mines, will be undisturbed for a long period, and probably become the settled policy of the country. President FILLMORE, in his Message to Congress, Dec. 1, 1851, says:

"The proper disposal of the mineral lands of California, is a subject surrounded by great difficulties. In my last annual message I recommended the survey and sale of them in small parcels, under such restrictions as would effectually guard against monopoly and speculation. But upon further information, and in deference to the opinions of persons familiar with the subject, I am inclined to change that recommendation, and *to advise that they be permitted to remain, as at present, a common field, open to the enterprise and industry of all our citizens,* until further experience shall have developed the best policy to be ultimately adopted in regard to them. It is safer to suffer the inconveniences that now exist, for a short period, than by premature legislation, to fasten on the country a system founded in error, which may place the whole subject beyond the future control of Congress."

The following "laws," passed by a Convention of Miners in Placer County, held at Auburn, on the 2d of August, 1851, will suffice to show the nature of the "right and title" to quartz veins, though, as we have observed, each township or locality possesses the power to make its own regulations:

"1st. All diggings shall be designated by some particular name, and claims registered accordingly.

2d. All claims taken up, shall be registered by the county recorder, with their number, date, and names of the owners.

3d. One hundred and fifty feet in running measure, with the dips and angles, shall constitute a claim.

4th. To designate a claim, one stake shall be driven at each end of said claim, and each claim shall be numbered.

5th. When a claim is properly staked, numbered and registered, the owner can hold the same until the 1st day of January, 1852, having expended the sum of $100 or more in work thereon.

6th. In all disputes or disagreements arising from title, boundaries, or otherwise connected with said work, each of the contending parties shall choose an arbiter from among those interested, and the Recorder shall act as the third; nevertheless, recourse may be had to law.

7th. Any person may hold one claim on said quartz diggings by location, and any number by purchase.

8th. Any person throwing dirt or rock on the claim of another, and refusing to remove the same when notified, shall forfeit his interest in said quartz work.

9th. Any person convicted of taking the tools of another, without leave, shall forfeit his interest in said diggings.

10th. The register shall be entitled to one dollar for registering, and fifty cents for transfering a claim."

PRODUCT OF QUARTZ MINES.

The value of investments in vein mining, as a permanent business, necessarily depends upon two circumstances, both of which must be established by unimpeachable testimony. These are—the quantity or extent of the gold-bearing quartz, and whether its average richness is sufficient to pay a profit under the heavy expenses of labor which now prevail, and are likely to prevail for many years to come. Both points have been so far established by geological and mineralogical explorations by scientific men, and by the results of machinery employed in crushing and amalgamating the ore during the past summer, that they may be considered no longer a matter of dispute.

In making estimates of probable profits to be derived by companies in quartz mining, many have based their calculations upon an average product of 20 cents and upwards per pound of rock. Such estimates are calculated to deceive, although it is an undeniable fact that there are numnrous veins already opened where this sum, or even a much higher average, is obtained. Were *all* the gold-bearing quartz of such rich quality, which, however, is not the fact, the profits would be absolutely startling. Let us look at the figures, based upon the operations of machinery, such as is now making in this city, capable of crushing 100 tons per each twenty-four hours, founded on this high estimate:

EXPENSES.

One hundred tons at 20 cents per lb. is $40,000.

Cost of quarrying, say at $10 per ton,	-		-	-	-	$1,000 00
2 Engineers, at $10 each per day,			-	-	-	20 00
2 Firemen,	5	"		-	-	-	10 00
16 Feeders,	5	"		-	-	-	80 00
5 Mill hands,	5	"		-	-	-	25 00
1 Superintendent,	-	-	-	-	-	20 00
1 Amalgamator,	-	-	-	-	-	10 00
1 Millright,	-	-	-	-	-	-	10 00
1 Blacksmith,	-	-	-	-	-	-	10 00
8 Cords wood, at $5,	-	-	-	-	-	40 00
Iron, oil, nails, for repairs, &c.,	-	-	-	-	10 00
Total expenses,	-	-	-	-	-	$1,235 00

Which shows the enormous profit of $38,765 per day!

The above estimate we desire no man to credit, for it is not necessary that it should be true, in order to prove the business profitable. Let it be admitted that the ore yields but *one cent per lb.*, which is the *lowest* product of the *poorest* rock crushed by any of the mills at Grass Valley, and a profit of $765 per day is shown, for each 100 tons, which gives, for 250 working days per annum, a yearly profit of $191,250, or nearly *two hundred per cent.* upon a capital of one hundred thousand dollars. This estimate shows conclusively that a *satisfactory* profit can be made by the use of powerful machinery, working upon the poorest ores.

By a reference to the documents in the appendix of this pamphlet, it will be seen that the Grass Valley quartz is estimated by the most impartial and intelligent men—those who are either engaged in the business, or have closely investigated the subject—at fully *five cents per lb.* This product would give, from a hundred tons of ore per day, a daily profit of $8,765, and a yearly aggregate of (for 250 working days) $2,191,250. THERE IS NO REASON WHATEVER TO DOUBT THAT SUCH A RESULT IS OBTAINABLE, with improvements that may be made in the process of amalgamation. It is the opinion of John A. Collins, Esq., founded upon the working of his own mill, that not more than one-fourth to one-third of the gold contained in the rock is taken out by the present process of amalgamation. He says, writing from Grass Valley, under the date of Sept. 28, 1851:

"The quartz of this section is generally more or less auriferous, yielding by a fire, or chemical test, from three to twenty-five cents per lb. Some is much richer, and some ledges or veins somewhat poorer. Our present mode of operating is very rapid, but the process of saving the gold very imperfect, not saving from ordinary rock more than one-fourth or one-third of the gold which the quartz rock contains. *This defect, however, produces but little embarrassment, inasmuch as fortunes can be easily acquired by the present method.* I think it would [not] be a large estimate to average the product of quartz rock at two cents per lb. or $40 per ton. We have crushed rock that yielded $20, $30, $40, $60, and even $100 and upwards, to the ton, and are crushing some at this time that yields more than $100 a ton. This rock is from Daisy Hill, a little to the south and east from Union Quartz Mountain.

"The auriferous quartz is very abundant, and I think there is enough of the rock within the radii of thirty miles from this place, to employ hundreds of mills, much more extensive than those now in use, for one generation, at least. The expense of getting out the quartz rock will range from $2 to $20 per ton, depending altogether upon the location and thickness of the vein or ledge."

The average, according to the above statement of Mr. Collins, is found to be $50 per ton; and this is the *actual fact* of the operations in that locality up to the present time. As but one-third, at most, of the gold is extracted, it shows that the amount that would be obtained *by assay*, is $7\frac{1}{2}$ cents per lb. A skillful metallurgist assures us that he can, by the quicksilver process of amalgamation, save at least *six cents per lb.* from rock of this character, which, of course, more than establishes the aggregate of over $2,000,000 per annum, from the operation of machinery, calculated to reduce a hundred tons of rock daily.

We need not go further into these calculations to show the profits, *on different estimates of averages* per lb. of ore. Enough that the fact stands out boldly, that at least two hundred per cent. per annum dividend can be made from the poorest rock, with heavy machinery. All that can be accomplished more than this, may be considered as clear gain. Every man can judge for himself, on the testimony we present, whether a higher profit is likely to be made. That the business, as now carried on with light and comparatively inefficient machinery, pays a very satisfactory remuneration, is beyond a cavil true. That the yield of gold will be largely increased, as capital, science, and experience are brought to bear upon quartz mining, no intelligent man can for a moment entertain a doubt.

These remarks could be extended, and numerous facts and illustrations given to prove that quartz mining is destined to be a lucrative and permanent business, for a long series of years; but the limits to which this pamphlet must necessarily be restricted, forbid a further argument. The intelligent reader will be enabled to judge by an examination of the evidences we present, whether an investment in the Stock of this Company will be *safe*, and the dividends FAIR. It is designed to treat the matter as upon which opinions will be formed and action based, by those who desire to find for their capital a more remunerative employment, according as the facts are presented in a clear manner, and sustained by adequate proof. The Act of the Legislature, under which the Company is organized, exhibits fully the powers, duties and responsibilities of Officers, Directors and Stockholders, and gives all the guarantees, and imposes all the restrictions deemed necessary for the protection of parties.

NEW YORK AND ATLANTIC AGENCY OFFICE.

The New York, and principal Atlantic Agency of the "GRASS VALLEY GOLD MINING COMPANY," is at 107 Fulton Street, at the office of the New York Cast Steel Works. R. J. RICHARDS, Esq., has accepted the appointment of Transfer Agent, by whom all dividends will be paid, as declared by the Directors, quarterly, on the first days of December, March, June, and September.

☞ Cash for Stock can be sent by mail in bank notes or drafts, addressed R. J. RICHARDS. Certificates will be forwarded to subscribers by the first return mail.

APPENDIX.

WE propose to give, in this Appendix, a brief account of the Geological formation and character of the Gold Regions of California, theories in regard to the primary cause of Gold in quartz, its diffusion in the veins, and such other evidences, in letters and extracts from the papers, as shall furnish to the general reader a comprehensive view of this great California interest. It is hoped that the nature of this absorbing subject will compensate any one, not already well-informed, for the time spent in a perusal of the documents below :

GEOLOGICAL CHARACTER OF THE GOLD REGION.

The California Gold Mining Region proper, that is to say, where active operations are being carried on, extends at present from the Mariposa river in the south, to the Klamath River, the boundary line of Oregon on the north, running in a southeast and northwest course, a distance of nearly five hundred miles, and consists of the spurs and foot range of mountains of the Sierra Nevada. The igneous rocks belonging principally to the formation of the Greenstone Trap, are, and have been the great depository from whence golden treasures which have astonished the world have emanated ; constituting a belt, along the nucleus of the Sierra Nevada, they appear in the conical hills and peculiarly shaped ridges, with steep and almost perpendicular sides of that formation- forming thus the gulches, canions, and ravines of the different localities. Although the geological character of this formation is given to it, by the Greenstone and sienitical traprock, still other igneous rocks, such as Granite, Sienite, Feldstone-porphyry, and particularly Greenstone-porphyry, appear to a considerable extent; while on the other hand the Greenstone or Diorit, by having taken up a predominating quantity of Talc or Mica, passes into Diorit slate, Talcose slate, and Magnesia rock. The relative position of these different rocks to each other is not always constant; it is generally found that granite takes the lowest point, and is the underlying rock; taking a section of the mining region, viz. that of the American River as an example of the whole—it appears at the very entrance of the foot range of the mining region, for instance at Mormon Island, in large masses, and ridges, and at the bottom of the deep ravines and river courses, extending towards the Sierra Nevada.

Sienitical Trap and Greenstone Trap frequently form dykes, in granite, of immense extent and size. Going towards the higher ranges of the Sierra Nevada, granite in large masses or hills disappears, and we now see the great Trap formation, sometimes alternating for a great distance with Magnesia rock, while still nearer to the central range, the Diorit slate, and the Talcose slate form high and extensive plateaus; also, however, frequently alternating with Greenstone Trap ridges, with almost perpendicular sides and conical hills. The transition, however, of one rock into the other, is so gradually and so frequently occurring, that it leads the geologist to entertain the idea that Greenstone slate and Talcose slate are merely Trap rock, modified by the metamorphic action of the igneous rocks underneath, during several succeeding up-heaving periods.—[*Prof. C. F. Spieker.*

Dr. F. P. WIERZBICKER, of San Francisco, in a small work, published two years ago, as a "Guide to the Gold Region," gives the following theory as to the orginal formation of gold:

"At some remote period in the history of the globe, the same internal convulsions that heaved up the Sierra Nevada, have also up-heaved the auriferous hills, which at first presented a naked surface to the atmospheric changes, by the influences of which the quartz constantly breaking up, left free the precious metal on its surface. In the progress of time, the same atmospheric influences caused to accumulate on these hills, soil, which grew deeper with every decay of vegetation, till it grew strong enough to support the majestic oak. The freed particles of gold thus became covered by the soil, and mixed up with it, and the process of the separation of the metal from the stone was arrested. How gold was injected into the veins of quartz is more than we can say, but the fact that it was so in a liquid state, is beyond question, as we see it adapt itself to the sides of the stone in all imaginable forms, from the finest filament to the largest lump ever found, with a most varied indented surface, filling up the crack of the stone, always tending to a rounded, tear-like appearance, as is the case with all melting substances. When freed, external friction of course modifies its appearance more or less; hence we find it in rivers particularly, in fine flakes, but when it is in larger bulk, it puts on a plate-like appearance, as if it were hammered out by the hands of an artizan, as really it is, by the frequently enormous weight of stone, under which it is deposited. Water, that universal carrier, washing the sides of the hills, brought the gold from their surface into the ravines and rivers, to which its own weight facilitated the progress.

"According to the strength of the current of waters, the weight of the particles of gold, and the obstacles in the way, it is deposited in one or another spot, the lighter particles of course floating away the farthest from the original bed. As this process of gold deposition has taken place in some period of the earth's existence, hence we find all these deposits, generally speaking, covered with greater or smaller depth of soil, sand, gravel, and stones. Strictly speaking, gold does not belong to the rivers, it was washed into them from the hills; hence it is useless to look for gold at the head of these streams, when the neighboring hills are not of the auriferous nature; and we find the fact corroborated by our personal examination of the heads of the streams of the gold region. The same rule holds good, for the same reasons, in regard to the lower portion of a gold-carrying stream, except that it is limited by the fact that light particles of gold may be deposited a considerable distance below their original source."

A writer in the *Alta California*, of an October date, remarking upon the above theory of Dr. Wierzbicker, in which we generally concur, says :

"It strikes us that this is the only theory that we have ever met in our reading that is simple, intelligible, versimilar, and meriting consideration. It can be amplified for those who are not in the habit of investigating similar subjects, but it cannot be improved, as we are convinced from our own personal application of it to the facts observed in the gold regions for these two years.

"Primitive rocks are the *matrix* of all metals; and quartz, one of them, is the *matrix* of *native gold*, as is seen in our mines. By *native gold*, of course, we mean the gold visible to the eye, as there is another form of it when it is in combination with other substances, and is perceived only in the assay. There is no gold without iron, as there is no *native gold* without quartz; iron is a sort of medium to keep quartz and gold in solid compact, or in other words, in chemical affinity. Iron, however, being extremely oxidizible, is easily acted upon by the atmospheric changes—therefore crumbles, to use a plain term, and separates from its chemical friends, and thus loosens the gold from its *matrix*, the quartz. Then comes water in its streams, carrying them both away, and scattering them according to the surface it runs upon or impediments in its way. Thus it fills ravines with native gold, and scatters through or mixes up minute particles of iron with the soil of the neighboring hills, giving them a rusty appearance."

Professor James Blake, of Sacramento City, who made extensive explorations and examinations in both the southern and northern mineral districts of California, says:

"The fact that the quartz is the matrix in which the gold now scattered over the face of the country, has been thrown up, is an opinion that, I believe, admits of but little doubt. At present it is the only rock in which the gold has been found *in situ ;* or, at least, if found in other rock, it is only in the immediate vicinity of a vein of quartz. The deposits found so extensively in the 'Coyote diggings,' undoubtedly had their origin from this source, and the same remark will apply to the gold found in the rivers and ' bars.'

"The quartz rock, as originally ejected from the bowels of the earth, must have come through in a molten state, bringing the gold with it. These veins of gold-bearing quartz were thrown up through cracks and fissures in the various stratified and crystalline rocks; and from their regularity, and the absence of any considerable faults or displacements, and also from their direction, it is probable that they were formed subsequently to the great convulsions that had up-heaved the originally horizontal stratum of stratified rocks. This opinion is also supported by the appearance of quartz veins in the trap and other trachystic rocks."

The opinions of Professor Blake, as a man of science, and thoroughly acquainted with the subject, possess a high value. We continue the quotation from that gentleman's writings:

"The richest veins of quartz that have yet been worked to any extent, are those of Carson Creek and Grass Valley, near Nevada. At the former of these places the gold has been found not only generally disseminated through the rock, but also in large masses, some of which have weighed as much as eighteen pounds. From the most reliable information I could collect on the spot, I believe as much as $300,000 have been taken out of one hole of fifteen feet on the vein, and which has not been sunk lower than twelve or fifteen feet. * * At Grass Valley, very rich quartz has been found. In many specimens that I have seen, the quartz might have been said to have been literally imbedded in the gold, rather than the gold in the quartz. * * * As regards the more limited distribution of gold in the vein, there appears to be considerable difference. In some veins the gold is found in very thin laminæ, which are spread out almost as finely as gold leaf; in other places, between the layers of quartz, it is generally distributed through the vein in the form of small particles, which are dispersed throughout the quartz without any apparent arrangement—while it is sometimes found aggregated together, in larger or smaller masses, either mixed with portions of quartz, or in solid masses of the pure metal. The gold occasionally presents the appearance of a spongy mass, from the decomposition of the sulphuret of iron, and the removal of the resulting oxide. There can be no doubt, also, that quartz, in which no gold is visible to the naked eye, often contains a considerable portion. I have analyzed rock in which a careful examination could not detect a particle of gold but which has yielded as high as twelve cents to the pound."

AVERAGE AMOUNT OF GOLD IN THE QUARTZ.

In reference to the degree of richness of the auriferous quartz, the general average cannot be stated with any degree of accuracy, for the reason that but in few places have operations been carried on a sufficient period to furnish a basis. All the veins and ledges of quartz in the Sierra Nevada mountains are not gold-bearing; and of those that are so, some are too poor to be profitably worked, except by the use of the most powerful machinery. Results already attained, however, have shown that veins sufficiently auriferous to pay well, *even at the present high rate of wages,* are inexhaustible for a long period to come. These veins have shown, by actual *assay,* that gold is found in them from one cent to eighty dollars per pound. We have seen rock of these various degrees of richness.

SIR HENRY VERE HUNTLEY, R. N., an English gentleman whose opinions will be respected wherever he is known, in both hemispheres, and who has devoted many months during the years 1850 and 1851, to an examination of the Gold Regions of California, previous to engaging in the business of Mining, writes as follows:

"*San Francisco, Aag.* 4, 1851.

"*My dear Sir :* The severe attack of fever with which I have been lately contending, has prevented my giving your request, relating to my opinions upon the general character of the quartz found in this State, that ready attention, which otherwise I beg to assure you, it would have received.

"1st. I shall state that I have tried quartz from a variety of these veins, and but *in two instances, only,* found no gold.

"2d. In quartz that to outward appearance, and which was carefully examined with a strong magnifying power, no gold whatever could be detected, but through which a stratum of iron pyrites ran, varying in breadth from a hair to the eighth of an inch, the stone highly crystallized, I found in five pounds, six grains and two-thirds of a grain of gold.

"3d. In two pounds of stone of an opaque yellowish color, I got more than *five dollars;* and from *five ounces* of stone, much decomposed, coated and impregnated with oxide of iron, I got something more than one dollar and a half.

"4th. All this was from quartz veins opened near Nevada and Grass Valley.

"Generally speaking, I think, among the veins of quartz, it will be found that, although some may be found exhibiting extraordinary richness, yet *the average product will range from three to seven cents per pound of ore.*

"* * * I have thus given you some of my views and observations upon the quartz mining here. If I appear to have overstated anything, I shall be quite ready to re-examine it, and am

"Your very obedient servant,

"To J. Winchester, Esq.　　　　　H. V. Huntly."

The following letter was written by Hon. James Walsh, Senator in the Legislature of California, himself for two years a resident in Grass Valley, and now the proprietor of one of the largest mills in operation at that place :

"Grass Valley, Nevada Co., Cal., ¿
　　　　　July 18, 1851.　　　　₎

"Gen. J. Winchester—

"Dear Sir :　*　*　*　The quartz in this vicinity—that is, in this township, (being an extent of country four and a half miles square), has been found extensively, and so far as trials have been made, it has been found in nine cases out of ten, to yield gold. Large quantities of quartz have been and are being discovered in the ading township of Nevada, and it will require more work to be done before it can be ascertained which region is the best. In this township about thirty-two hills have been examined, some of them but partially and some very effectually. The first hill on which much work was done, was Gold Mountain, and the rock on that hill, after taking out specimens enough to pay for working the hill and excavating the rock, will, beyond a doubt, pay by assay an average of *five cents per pound.*

"The machinery now crushing the rock from that hill, is saving an average of three cents per pound. The quantity of gold-bearing quartz in this (Grass Valley) district, it is impossible for any one to estimate. To quarry and grind the rock from the thirty-two hills already known, would be the work of years for any reasonable amount of labor. * * * The business of quartz mining is done at present, under many disadvantages. The machinery has cost, and is costing too much labor, at an average of six dollars per day is too high; yet, even with high labor, imperfect modes of quarrying, and very inefficient machinery, *the mills are making money.*

"* * * Here we have the advantages of plenty of timber (pine and oak), and plenty of water—a climate far beyond any I have ever seen for health, and I cannot but believe that this region is destined to be populous and prosperous for a long time to come. The rate of wages for common laborers is five dollars, and for mechanics, seven dollars per day—they finding themselves.

" I settled here in the fall of 1849, erected a saw-mill, and am now engaged in sawing lumber, and am erecting machinery to crush quartz, being satisfied now that the business will be a permanent and good one. I am selling lumber at eighty-five dollars per thousand feet. The population of this township, at present, is four to five thousand, and is increasing.

"Very Respectfully, Yours,

"JAMES WALSH."

N. B.—I neglected to state as to the advantages of heavy machinery. There is not a doubt in my mind but the profits would be greatly increased, it being an axiom that if a machine crushing five tons per day can make money, one crushing fifty tons can make more in proportion.

Mr. JAMES HOUGH, resident at Grass Valley, and engaged extensively in quarrying the quartz rock, during the past twelve months, says:

GRASS VALLEY, July 25th, 1851.

"* * * I commenced operations in quartz some time during last November. Up to the present time I have quarried some *fourteen hundred tons* of rock—have had in my employ from eight to twelve men, daily, and have more than paid my entire expenses by crushing with a hand mortar the richest portions of the rock, paying wages at the rate of four dollars per day with board. By this hand operation I have crushed quartz yielding as high as *eighty-six dollars to the pound,* and little, if any, less than three dollars.

"After these 'specimens' have been carefully culled from the whole mass of the rock by breaking it up into small pieces, the *smallest yield of the remainder,* when crushed and amalgamated at the mill, has been $30 per ton, and the largest that has come under my observation as high as $140. In my opinion $70 would be a fair average of each ton of rock. But it should not be forgotten that the business is yet in its infancy among us—that the machinery is very imperfect, and that with such improvements as daily experience is suggesting, these figures would be materially improved.

" Grass Valley is widely known in this State for its hills of gold-bearing quartz; and I am free to say that, after a pretty thorough examination of this township and county, and the immediate surrounding vicinity, the ore is inexhaustible—at least by the present generation.

"In carrying on the business of quartz mining a great desideratum, and indeed an indispensable one, is wood and water, and at convenient distances. Of these there is no lack generally. Here, about Grass Valley, they are found in the greatest abundance. As fine pine timber grows all over the hills about as can be found in any part of the world, interspersed with oak, cedar, &c."

A correspondent of the *Alta California* newspaper, published at San Francisco, writing upon the subject of quartz mining, and the expense of running a mill, gives the following estimate :—

"Suppose an establishment working an engine of forty-horse power, and driving thirty stampers, will cost $70,000, an exaggerated value. Suppose the thirty stampers crushed, in 24 hours, 12 tons, an amount much underrated. The number of hands necessary for the above work is 20, at $5 per day without board,

above work is 20, at $5 per day without board,			-	-	-	$100
One engineer, at	-	-	-	-	-	10
One assistant engineer	-	-	-	-	-	8
One blacksmith	-	-	-	-	-	5
One carpenter	-	-	-	-	-	5
Six laborers for various work, at $4 per day,				-	-	24
Director	-	-	-	-	-	16
His assistant	-	-	-	-	-	10
Total expenses per diem	-		-	-	-	$178

Suppose the ore yields only two cents to the pound, or $40 per ton ; fifteen tons will give $600. At this rate, the product per month, (twenty-six working days,) would give $15,600
Expenses for labor per month (thirty days) - - 5,340

Balance in favor of the mine - - $10,260

Being abundantly sufficient to allow for wear and tear, particularly when we consider that an engine, properly managed, may last six years, and the stampers six months.

"Now let us see the figures when the mine yields five cents to the pound; a yield which can be with justice considered an average product of the California mines.

"Without changing the amount of expenses above presented, we will have, as a result of the same mining operations (at the rate of $100 per ton), or five cents per pound, per diem $1,500, or per month, $39,000. The original monthly expenses, as above shown, $5,340, leave us a net balance of $33,660.

"*The above facts are based upon the labors of a company now in operation, can be relied upon, and proven if necessary.*

"We may here add, that a forty-horse power engine can drive thirty-six stampers of 400 pounds each; twelve stampers of the same size can crush a ton per hour, or the thirty-six will crush three tons per hour, or the engine, running night and day, will give 72 tons as the result; equal (at five cents per pound of the ore) to $7,200 per diem, and $187,200 per month; an amount sufficiently large to cover four times the expenses above estimated, and leave a handsome balance in the hands of the miners."

A writer in the *California Courier*, in speaking of the mode of working quartz rocks, and the machinery employed, says :—

"This leads me to the point I had in mind, when I spoke of the

probable failure to succeed, of many companies, which, without experience or knowledge of quartz, or of the mode of operation, have
rushed blindly into the business; and that is, that the failure of such
companies to succeed, would be no evidence of the impracticability of
quartz mining. Extensive veins of auriferous quartz, accessible to
water, and easily quarried, with machinery like that of Mr. Walsh,
or of Collins & Co., adequate to the crushing of 100 tons in 24
hours, would be one of the best investments of money that could be
made. I will here introduce some figures, and such as any man at
all acquainted with the business, will admit to be an approximation
to correctness, as the probable expense of raising and crushing 100
tons in 24 hours. This would require a force of—

150 miners, at $5 a day, - - -	$750
16 teams and drivers, at $10, - - -	100
2 engineers, at $10, - - - -	20
2 firemen, at $5, - - - -	10
16 feeders, at $5, - - - -	80
5 choppers, at $6, - - - -	30
1 blacksmith and machinist, - - -	10
1 millwright, - - - -	10
5 men about the mill, at $5, - - -	25
1 amalgamator, - - - -	10
1 sub-superintendent, - - -	10
1 superintendent, - - - -	20
Nails, iron, lumber, &c., - - - -	10
incidentals, - - - - -	15
Making a total of - -	$1100
Now, 100 tons of quartz, at $20 a ton, one cent a pound,	
amounts to - - - - -	2000
Expenses, - - - - -	1100
	$900

" This leaves a profit of $900. If there be an error in the allow-
ance for expenses, it is very probably an over estimate. The mills
now receive from $20 to $30 a ton for crushing. Hence, quartz
that will but pay from $36 to $40 a ton, is considered only as paying
a fair profit upon labor invested. It will be thus seen that poorer
veins cannot be profitably worked."

The statement may be regarded as exempt from extravagance, and
yet the results for one year, upon this estimate, are enormously large.
The estimated cost of quarrying and reducing the rock was based on
the old clumsy method of mining, and is above what the present high
wages even will justify, by some $200 a day. This estimate, at one
cent per pound, or $20 per ton, it should be kept in mind, is vastly
below the general average obtained by different quartz miners. Every
addition of one mill per pound increases the profits $200 a day, and
should the yield be 2 cents per pound, the additional nett profits by
this estimate, will be $2000 per day, or $600,000 per year of 300
days. But it is useless to pursue these speculations farther than to
remark, that, by the improvement in machinery, and the employment
of labor-saving forces, the ore can now be quarried and reduced fifty
per cent. less than eight months since.

On the same subject, (the cost of running a mill,) Judge WALSH,
of Grass Valley, gives the following opinion, drawn from his own experience :—

" To run a mill capable of crushing 40 tons of quartz per day (of 24 hours) would require eight men ; and if you excavate that quantity of quartz daily, it would take thirty hands more, probably. The men at the mill cost now an average of $7 per day—labor in mining $5 per day, they finding themselves. Fuel costs now $4,50 per cord at the mill. The only material wear and tear of machinery is the pestles, which would require to be put in new probably four times in a year.

" The rock, (from which all the richest portions have been culled) has paid as low as $20 per ton, and as high as $120 per ton. *The quartz is paying better now than at first.* The mode of saving gold has been improved, and there is yet room for improvement. I think the average of the quartz in this vicinity will be found to be about $40 per ton."

Professor Blake, in a letter to the Sacramento *Union*, says :—

" There can be no doubt but that the quartz veins of California are capable of furnishing a supply of gold, which it will probably take centuries to exhaust, and the amount of which is far beyond the limits of calculation, at least with our present data. Scattered over a belt of land, ten miles broad, and running the whole length of the country, north and south, these veins are evidently deposits of immense riches. Setting aside the extraordinary yields, where some hundreds of thousands of dollars have been obtained from holes of a few feet square, we still have hundreds of miles of veins from which ore can be obtained, yielding from two to six cents to the pound, and from which a powerful machine can extract one or two thousand dollars a day. When these veins are exhausted, there will remain many others, which will be profitably worked when labor shall be cheaper. *There can be no doubt but that quartz mining is destined to be the most permanent source of gold in this country ;* and it will not be many years before it will attract that attention which as an investment for capital it evidently deserves. For the meanwhile, many of those now engaged in it will probably be losers. The working of a quartz vein is an operation on which simple manual labor cannot be employed with any fair prospect of success. It requires capital for its development, and scientific knowledge for the direction of that capital. Already large sums of money have been invested in it, which will never produce any adequate return to those engaged in the enterprise, simply because the undertaking has been entered upon in a blind, empirical spirit, and without a careful consideration of the difficulties to be met with, and the obstacles to be overcome in extracting the gold from the rock."

[The following letter is from the pen of Rev. R. TOWNSEND HUDDART, an Episcopal clergyman, who spent two years in California, returning to New York, his former residence, in a late steamer. It is copied from the San Francisco *Herald*, of July 25, 1851.]

QUARTZ MINING.

GRASS VALLEY, Nevada Co., July 16, 1851.

EDITOR HERALD—*Dear Sir :* Having a few hours to spare, and a quiet room to myself—no trifling luxury in a mining district—I sit down to write you a long rambling letter on the subject of the auriferous quartz in this portion of the State, where I have passed nearly three months, examining the several ledges and veins in the surrounding hills; taking nothing for granted, but endeavoring to satisfy my own mind by investigation, as to the quantity and quality of the rock, avoiding the extremes of extravagant and wild calculations on the one hand, or of incredulity on the other. Should you consider this communication of sufficient importance to give it a place in the columns of your paper, it may assist in spreading information of an interesting and useful nature. My remarks for the present will be confined to this neighborhood and Nevada City, embracing a circuit of about fifteen miles. After a residence of more than a year in San Francisco, where my professional duties detained me, I determined to visit the mines, more particularly the quartz hills, of which I had heard various reports, and imagined that I knew a great deal; it has been my custom to converse with every intelligent miner I came across, and from all the information I could collect from them, as well as from reading different newspaper articles, I felt tolerably confident that I was well posted up, as we say, on this subject. But I confess that after a short residence here, and after comparing my previous opinions with those formed from personal examination, I arrived at the conclusion that I ought to be ranked among a very numerous class of my fellow-men, who assume to know much with but slight foundation for their knowledge:—in fact, that I had been a most erudite "ignoramus." Before proceeding further, let me give a piece of passing advice to all letter writers, and to all intending to return to the States, that they will not undertake to speak of the mineral resources of California, from mere reports; but if they wish to do justice to themselves or to others, let their opinions be given after a careful investigation and actual inspection of these quartz regions; for I have no hesitation in saying that those who have never visited them, and whose information is acquired by a residence in San Francisco or Sacramento, are as little acquainted with the real state of things, as persons in the States or Europe are about our commercial wants, our social condition, our geographical advantages, our noble bays, our stately forests, our rich productive land, or our healthy and invigorating climate.

I will attempt no lengthened description of the scenery and beauty of this immediate section of country in which I am at present residing; let it suffice to say that there are some as picturesque and lovely valleys lying embosomed among these gold-bearing hills as the most fastidious admirer of nature's charms could desire. The whole region abounds in auriferous quartz ; some richer in quality than others, *but all sufficiently so to pay an ample remuneration for the erection of machinery.* Your readers would at once set me down as some crazy-pated enthusiast were I to state the amount of gold which may be calculated as the product of Nevada county alone; and no doubt the opinion I am about to advance will be received with astonishment and unbelief by some, and regarded by others as chimerical and visionary—still, that does not prevent me from giving as the candid and deliberate conviction of my mind, that the quartz of this one section is amply sufficient to supply gold enough for the circulation of the whole United States during the next fifty years! Be it recollected that this is but from a single county in the State; what then must be the aggregate from other parts of California, equally rich in these wonderful depositories of the precious metal?

I will not bewilder you or your readers with a formidable array of figures and calculations based upon evidence of facts, but will simply state that a mill with proper machinery, capable of crushing twenty tons of auriferous quartz per day, yielding on an average only three cents to the pound, will produce a profit of at least one hundred per cent., upon a capital of two hundred thousand dollars, and greater in proportion to the limited amount of the stock; this, too, after allowing a liberal outlay for all necessary expenditures, and appropriating a contingent fund, to provide for all risks of explosions, breakage, or other accidents—wear and tear of machinery, &c.

It is generally supposed by miners and by scientific men who have made various assays of the different kinds of quartz, that the average value may be estimated at from six to eight cents per pound, instead of the amount already named. Nay more, there are companies who calculate upon fifteen to twenty cents, and there is one in Nevada, whose lead or vein is so exceeding rich that they expect a yield of fifty cents to the pound; but when you bear in mind that the addition of a single cent will increase the product of gold twenty fold, it would swell the amount on these two last calculations to such a degree that no credence would be given to the statement. My own impression is, that about eight cents might be a fair estimate, and that, with the best machinery, and most approved process of amalgamating and saving the very fine gold. I have therefore spoken of a *minimum*, rather than a *maximum* rate: if these data be correct, the profits from a mill of the power mentioned will be immense.

I may also remark that several of the companies at present putting up large mills at Grass Valley, calculate to crush from thirty-five to forty tons of quartz per day; while others, having less capability, intend to run their engines night and day. Now, it is by no means an overstretch of the imagination to suppose that within the next three years—particularly when confidence and conviction have taken the place of present doubt and mistrust, there will be capital enough invested to have not less than two hundred mills erected throughout the different parts of the State, each capable of crushing on an average twenty-five tons per day; yielding from $60 to $160 for the 20 cwt., according as the richness of the quartz may vary from three to eight cents per pound. Now, then, let your matter-of-fact man of figures amuse himself for an hour in making these difficult calculations. I think the result will somewhat astonish him, at least *on paper*—time alone must prove the truth of the problem.

In alluding to the vast profits to be derived by companies from this source, I wish to be understood as premising that suitable machinery, favorable location of the mine, skilful engineers, sensible directors, and honest management, will be required to make investments pay a large dividend; with these advantages combined, *the most sanguine expectations may be realized;* without them, the results will be more or less doubtful.

The drawback now upon quartz operations is the want of capital, compared with the unlimited opportunities and inducements for investing. This arises most probably from a suspicion in the minds of moneyed men, that these matters have fallen into the hands of speculators, and consequently that the investment is not a safe one; but surely the abuse of anything does not prove it to be worthless. How many banking institutions, insurance companies, railroad companies, mining associations, *et id genus omne,* have had their day of ill accounts in the older States, and by inefficient or desperately dishonest management on the part of those chiefly instrumental in getting them up, have brought ruin upon many a family, and discredit upon similar enterprises? With all this, capitalists have not been deterred from again and again subscribing to such undertakings. Why should we expect in California to escape the consequences of that greedy thirst for sudden gain which, like a raging fever, has preyed upon the moral vitals of thousands who have come among us, inducing them to adopt every conceivable mode of obtaining wealth without regard to the means used? How could it be otherwise than that hundreds of the motley crowd of needy adventurers who have flocked to the land of promise, would eagerly seize upon just such a tempting bait to entice their victims as dazzling specimens of auriferous quartz? It seems as if men were attacked with a golden mania which deprives them of the ordinary powers of prudence, reflection, and caution, leading them into the wildest speculations, set on foot by unprincipled, cunning knaves, the result of which is the certain loss of money invested, and denunciations, loud and deep, against the originators of these schemes. It is well known that several mining bubble operations have burst up in various parts of the State during the past year, and so notorious has been the conduct of the principal actors, that it has not only thrown a damper over quartz mining, but when men of undoubted veracity and honor have attempted to get up a company, they have been met on the very threshold with the taunt of some delinquent who had lately duped others. This state of things, however, cannot last; the evil will work its own cure; gradually confidence will be restored, capitalists will associate themselves together and take into their employ none but *tried and honest individuals* to manage the concerns of any crushing mill which may be erected by them; and with the requisite machinery, as well as steady perseverance, there cannot exist a doubt of larger fortunes being gained by investments in quartz mining than by any other means in California. We must be prepared to hear the doleful cry of a few croakers, of whom a number will be found in this country as in every community, but that should not deter men of sense from investigating this subject with calm and prudent determination. They will be better satisfied after such examination, and better able to judge of the boundless wealth which exists in California.

Like all other great and novel enterprises, that of extracting gold from quartz presents at first many difficulties to be overcome by the pioneers in the work; the whole thing is new to us, and must naturally be attended with obstacles and imperfections at the outset; as a matter of course various experiments will be tried; much expense and sometimes loss be incurred in them. Each succeeding mill, with its machinery, will be constructed with the latest improvements, and so the operations will progress, until a similar degree of excellence is attained in this novel branch of industry and mechanical skill as has been reached in the construction of steamships, locomotives, cotton mills, printing presses, or in the architecture of the present day, compared with that of fifty years back. We are now but in our infancy as regards mining; indeed, it may rather be said that mining is only about being commenced in California—whatever amount of gold has been obtained hitherto, being literally no more than the scratching of the earth's surface, when compared with the treasures which are yet to be discovered.

I write to you, my dear sir, as to an old friend, and one who, I would hope, has full confidence in the sincerity of my expressed opinion, and a personal knowledge of my character as a man of calm, prudent judgment and common sense, who would not advance any statement that he did not honestly believe to be reliable and worthy of consideration among his fellow-citizens. I do not profess to be either a geologist or a scientific man, but have looked into this matter with the same degree of careful attention as a merchant would use in his business transactions, or a lawyer in his profession. The result of that investigation I send you, and if deemed worth a place in your columns, it will give me sincere pleasure to be thus instrumental in spreading some information before the public on a subject about which there is very little known or understood, and one having so important a bearing upon the future interest, prosperity and welfare of our adopted State.

Very truly, your friend,   R. T. H.

CALIFORNIA.—MINING.

From the New York Daily Tribune of Oct. 22d, 1851.

The letter of J. Winchester, which we publish this morning, will be read with attention by all interested in California and her future productiveness and prosperity. Mr. Winchester is widely known as an energetic though finally unsuccessful publisher in this city, whence he migrated early in 1849 to California, where he has spent more than two years, returning on a visit a few days since. During those two years, so eventful for California, he has been a digger and worker, an Editor and Publisher, for one year State printer, and for some time a prospecter for quartz veins, &c. &c.—so that, being an intelligent and most industrious observer, he *ought* to know what there is in California as well as another man, and we believe he does. We are promised further contributions from his pen in fuller elucidation of the actual state of the country.

THE GOLD MINES OF CALIFORNIA—PLACER DIGGINGS—OPERATIONS IN QUARTZ AT GRASS VALLEY—SPLENDID RESULTS—MILLS IN OPERATION, &c.

Correspondence of the New York Tribune.

NEW YORK, 107 Fulton Street, Oct. 20, 1851.

MY DEAR GREELY :—I promised you, on my first arrival in this city from a residence on the Pacific side, of nearly three years, to write you something of what I know and have seen in my explorations in the Sierra Nevadas.

In regard to our mineral resources, and especially those enterprises that require for their successful development a concentration of capital and skill, I regret to find so much distrust as appears to exist in the financial circles of this city, and generally, on this side. The fact that, in the excitement pervading the whole people, consequent upon the discovery of gold in California, hundreds upon hundreds of vessels and cargoes have been sent to San Francisco, and proved ruinous to the shippers, ought not to weigh as a feather against the inexhaustible sources of wealth which that remarkable country presents to Industry and Capital. A population, including Oregon, at no time reaching three hundred thousand souls, could not have consumed the goods of every kind that have been poured into the Bay of San Francisco in one overwhelming stream for the past two and a half years, in a score of years. How unreasonable, then, to abuse California, and charge upon her an enormous balance over and above all the product of her mines, because the people could not purchase all the stuff that has been shipped, and pay therefor a profit of three hundred per cent!

So long as the drain upon the precious metals, to meet European liabilities, continues at the present high figure, the question as to the continued supply of gold from Califotnia assumes no trifling importance. It is a matter of grave doubt to all thinking men, whether, were the semi-monthly supplies of two millions or more of dust to be withheld for a single month, a shock would not be given to the banking and credit systems, and to business generally, sufficiently powerful to produce a revulsion equal to that of 1836-7. Indeed, in my humble judgment, abused and misunderstood California has for three years sustained the whole weight of the financial system of the Union by her large and increasing annual product of gold. Were our resources, both mineral and agricultural, better understood, and more generally sustained by the surplus capital lying idle in the Atlantic cities, the sensitiveness that now is seen and felt in the financial circles would pass away, and well-founded confidence give stability to every legitimate enterprise. Though producing by millions the *raw material* of wealth—nay, capital itself—yet with a population heretofore almost exclusively made up of "adventurers," mere "birds of passage," little of it remains to aid in developing the permanent interests of California. For this reason she must look abroad for means to properly develop her inexhaustible veins of gold ore, and other equally remunerative sources of wealth.

It is now a historical fact, that our *placeres*, or surface mines, covering an extent of territory over six hundred miles in length by probably eighty in breadth, and extending either way beyond the limits of the State, have been worked with a constantly increasing product in each succeeding year. There is no doubt on my mind that the amount of gold gathered this year will come fully up to *one hundred millions of dollars !* Great as is the yeld, I venture to affirm, that for a long period to come, the yield from this source will not be diminished. In comparison with the already "prospected" extent of the gold-producing region, the portion but partially dug over is not equal to a square rod in a mile. It is evident, then, that looking to this source alone for a continuous and regular supply of gold, there is the most ample ground for confidence in the ability of California to furnish all the specie basis necessary to sustain the commercial and monetary transactions of the Union for an indefinite period.

But California possesses surer and more lasting claims to confidence than are to be found in her *golden placeres.* Should these fail to yield a return to labor, in her extensive fields and ledges of GOLD-BEARING QUARTZ, *underlying the gold-region in the whole length and breadth of the Sierra Nevadas,* California possesses an element of wealth which no stretch of imagination can over-estimate, nor the wildest dreams of the visionary equal. Every day develops fresh evidences of the immense wealth contained in these gold-bearing veins, which have, as yet, been pierced only at intervals, and the *depth* of which centuries may be required to determine.

My principal object in this article was simply to give you some of the testimonies in regard to the productiveness of the quartz veins, *as at present worked,* though with imperfect machinery, inexperience, and a lack of knowledge as to the best methods of separating the gold from the rock.

The first operations in this article were begun a little more than a a year ago, in Mariposa. An injudicious location, and light machinery, rendered this first experiment in extracting gold, comparatively, a failure. The works were discontinued early in the past Summer. I visited this mine in June last, and was astonished to see that so much had been done, with such inefficient machinery. The Mariposa Company is the first, *and only one,* within my knowledge, that has not been eminently successful.

The present great centre of quartz mining is Grass Valley, in Nevada County. This town is distant north-easterly from Sacramento City about 70 miles, over a good road, on which a daily line of four-horse post-coaches runs—meeting at the same point another daily line from Sacramento, via Marysville, and both continuing to Nevada City, 5 miles further into the mountains. The first quartz discoveries at this locality, (which had proved exceedingly rich in the gulches,) were made about the month of November last ; but no machinery was erected until the latter part of the Winter. So rich did the veins on "Gold Hill" prove, even by the slow process of crushing in hand mortars and washing in water only, that shafts were sunk on almost every hill for several miles around, in nearly every instance striking rich veins. At this time there are between 30 and 40 hills opened in the single township of Grass Valley, (four and a half miles square,) and exhibiting incontestable evidence that extensive veins of gold-bearing quartz underlie them all.

In April last, two small mills only were ready to commence operations, with a capacity for crushing no more than six or eight tons in each twenty-four hours. At the same time several others were begun, two of which were to have engines of twenty-five and sixty-horse power respectively. The first of these was completed and commenced operations on the 21st of July. I was then residing at the Valley, and witnessed the admirable movement of its eighteen heavy stamp-heads, striking forty-eight blows each per minute, and its numerous amalgamating tables. On the second day, Hon. WM. M. GWIN, our Senator, in Congress, and a party from San Francisco, visited the mill, and saw its beautiful operation. The product for ten hours' work, as stated by Mr. Rust, one of the editors of *The Pacific Star*, who was present, was *six pounds and seven-eighths of a pound* of pure gold taken from the amalgamating tables—it being estimated that the iron trough or battery in which the stamp-heads play, (which was not cleared out,) would have yielded about *three pounds more.* The product was thus nearly TEN POUNDS, in as many hours ; the ore crushed and washed being 19½ tons, giving over one hundred dollars per ton, or five cents per pound. Let me here add that samples of pulverized and washed rock, from which all the gold had been taken that could be extracted by the present machinery, has since been tried by fire in San Francisco, and found to yield at the rate of *ninety dollars per ton additional.* The mill of which I speak was erected by Capt. Peck, of San Francisco, under the superintendence of W. R. KING, Esq., for a long time engaged in the Virginia Mines—I believe those of Com. Stockton. It is owned by the " Gold Hill Quartz Mining Company," of which Capt. Bissell, late or now of the Pacific Mail Steamship Company, is President. Stock in this Company is unobtainable at any price.

In my private correspondence from California by the mail which arrived on Saturday, I am put in possession of additional facts touching the enormous product of Captain Peck's mill, up to near the middle of September. I quote as follows, from a letter dated the 15th of September, at San Francisco :

" I have been to Nevada, and have just returned. The quartz mining is attracting general attention among our capitalists. Captain Peck's mill gives him a *net profit* of one hundred dollars per hour. His receipts in one day, while I was there, were THREE HUNDRED AND SEVENTY-TWO OUNCES ! *I saw it weighed.* It made those who had no interest in quartz mining crazy to buy into some good company."

Let me inquire of capitalists in New York, whether they consider an investment in a quartz mill that produces from *twelve* to *thirty pounds of gold* in each twenty-four hours, from forty tons of ore, is any better than bond and mortgage at seven per cent. per annum, or shaving notes at two per cent. a month ? And yet the above magnificent results of the first introduction of heavy machinery, in the very infancy of the business, attest its capacity to pay a good round profit. When some scientific man has discovered a process by which *all* the gold known to be contained in the ore can be gathered, (less than half is now obtained in most cases,) think of the high figure that must be reached in vein mining!

Does the reader ask if the gold-bearing quartz is sufficiently abundant and rich to continue this product for any considerable period of time? I venture the opinion, founded on a long residence and extensive travels in the mineral districts, that a thousand mills, in this century, cannot exhaust the supply of ore.

There are now about eight mills in successful operation in and near the village of Centreville, in Grass Valley township. Many others are in process of erection at the same locality, and still others in various parts of Nevada County. Centreville is already a thriving village of 1,500 to 2,000 inhabitants, with some good dwellings, hotels, stores, markets, &c., and a saw-mill in active operation, turning out 6,000 feet of lumber per day, which finds ready sale at $85 per thousand. J. WINCHESTER.

Mr. WINCHESTER's letter on Quartz Mines and Mining in California in to-day's paper will attract and reward attention. We regret that he should have deemed necessary any explanation of our remark that he was "finally unsuccessful" as a publisher in this City. We certainly did not intend to imply that he had not *deserved* success, nor that he was not qualified to command it. *We know that his enterprise, energy, temperance and assiduity are unsurpassed, and that whatever he undertakes he does it with all his might.* THE GOOD FAITH OF HIS STATEMENTS MAY BE IMPLICITLY RELIED ON.

[*Tribune*, Nov. 18, 1851.

From the San Francisco Morning Post of Oct. 1, 1851.

GRASS VALLEY.—We are permitted to make the following extract from a letter, under date of September 28th, addressed to a gentleman of this city, by one who has great geological knowledge, and in whose statements implicit confidence may be placed.

" All the mills now in operation, are doing an extraordinary business. Messrs. Collins & Co.'s mill is averaging one thousand dollars per day from ten stamps, and is now working rock of inferior quality. Capt. Peck's mill is doing still better, while Judge Walsh, with his powerful engine of sixty-horse power, is doing wonders.

" Capitalists are much in error with regard to the advantages of investing in this business. Had I fifty thousand dollars in hand to-day, I would invest the entire amount, without a moment's hesitation, satisfied, as I am, from observation, that no business in California will pay as well, by fifty per cent., as quartz mining."

During the past week, from the crushing mill of Collins & Co., after eighteen hours' operation, eight pounds of carefully strained amalgam were taken out. The following day, after twenty-four hours' work, *twelve pounds* were taken out. The mill had but five stamps running to produce the above results.—*Ib.*

EXTRACTS FROM FIRST ANNUAL REPORT

OF THE

GRASS VALLEY GOLD MINING COMPANY,

MADE TO THE STOCKHOLDERS, AUGUST 5, 1852,

TOGETHER WITH THE PROCEEDINGS OF THE TRUSTEES, AND OTHER DOCUMENTS.

TO STOCKHOLDERS AND OTHERS.

GRASS VALLEY, Aug. 12, 1852.

THE first Annual Report of the "GRASS VALLEY GOLD MINING COMPANY," is herewith presented to the stockholders and the public. The severely laborious duties imposed upon and performed by the undersigned, with a view to economy in the management of the affairs of the Company, till such time as the machinery could be put into profitable operation, has prevented him from bestowing that care upon the Report which the importance of the interests involved seemed to render necessary. It is believed, however, that the stockholders will be able to understand what has been done, and the true position of the concerns of the Company as regards the future.

In my opinion, the prospects for ample returns in Quartz Mining have greatly increased within the year since which this Company was organized, and it is in Grass Valley that success will be first assured, and the richest rewards obtained. The developments of the past year prove this to be the region of the richest Quartz Veins in California; and in this, also, the best informed agree. I have made assays showing a yield as high as Six Hundred Dollars per ton of *ordinary ore of the vein.* From the same vein the pyrites, gathered from the workings and assayed, yielded at the rate of Eight Hundred Dollars per ton. One mill of eight stamps, working on the vein alluded to, has taken regularly from Five Hundred to Twelve Hundred Dollars per day. A large number of new "leads" of Quartz have been opened this summer, and found to equal, if not exceed in richness, those heretofore discovered and profitably worked.

So well established and certain has the business of Quartz Mining become in this locality, that no property is held so firmly, or deemed so valuable as a ledge of gold-bearing quartz. There are geological facts connected with the distribution of the veins of quartz through this region, that render success in working them certain, where the same methods would measureably or totally fail elsewhere; and the most important of them is, that the gold is more equally diffused in the rock, *and is invariably found in granular form*, sometimes quite coarse. The consequence is that its form in rounded particles, or grains, gives the gold the necessary specific gravity to ensure its collection to a greater extent than in rock equally rich, but containing the gold in thin scales, or *laminæ.*

The belt of gold-bearing quartz, upon which Grass Valley is located, is between two and three miles in width, and within that belt may be expected the richest discoveries—indeed, such has already been the case. The facilities for wood and water, in addition, will always give this region the pre-eminence over others in this business.

The capital stock of this Company has been increased to Two Hundred and Fifty Thousand Dollars. The necessity for this was partly foreseen and provided for, by the original holders. But none of them foresaw a year since, that such strides would have been made, and opportunities presented, for profitable investment, as the history of a year has shown. With the means which the present capital of the Grass Valley Gold Mining Company will place at its disposal, it can cover a ground, command advantages, and secure an amount of the most valuable leads, that will enable it to work at a profit almost surpassing belief. I will give a single instance in illustration.

In April last, the vein on Lafayette Hill, consisting of eleven original shares or claims, was offered for sale to the extent of six-elevenths, or a controlling interest. The vein had been opened, but none of the rock crushed; yet, as gold was plainly visible to the eye, the quality of the ore was undoubted. The shares offered were held at Twenty-eight Thousand Dollars, and Messrs. Baxter, Hollis, and Bacon made the purchase. Up to this time the vein has yielded very nearly, or quite, One Hundred Thousand Dollars in the working— the product being over Eighty Dollars per ton average. The value of the vein has been increased from Six Thousand Two Hundred and Fifty Dollars per share, to Fifteen Thousand Dollars per share. Suppose Bacon & Co. had possessed a mill equal to the Grass Valley Gold Mining Co.'s machinery, and instead of working ten to fifteen tons per day, as has been the case, or at most, twenty-five tons, (when other mills were employed to assist in crushing), the number of tons crushed had been eighty. This would have given a daily product of Six Thousand Four Hundred Dollars, *of which Five Thousand Dollars would be net profit.* Here, then, may be seen, FROM ACTUAL DATA, what is to be done by command of ample ready capital. The above, as those may see who will make the figures, gives the enormous yield of Nine Millions Dollars per annum—which only the exhaustion of the vein could prevent being realized. More than this: with the process of amalgamation possessed by us, we confidently believe the ore of Lafayette Hill would yield at least Two Hundred Dollars per ton!—giving Twenty Million Dollars per annum!

Let no one be startled at these figures. The facts are simply as stated, for this very rock gives a product, to a close assay, of Three

Hundred to Six Hundred and Fifty Dollars, and in many portions to many times these amounts. We have made repeated tests, and speak from the book.

It is not to be supposed that the Lafayette vein is the only vein of the like richness in Grass Valley. All acknowledge as yet the ground is comparatively untouched. With capital to engage in putting tunnels through hills believed to possess immensely valuable ledges of quartz, judging from the richness of the surface digging, and specimens of quartz found in the adjacent ravines, the most astonishing results might be confidently looked for. In no case, could such works fail to find *paying veins*, for not a single hill in this region but contains such.

The greater number of failures that have taken place, have resulted, partly, if not in many instances wholly, from inadequate capital: and losses have thus occurred to stockholders, that, had the capital been doubled, would have converted a bad into a paying stock.

The buildings, machinery, power and capacity of the " Grass Valley Gold Mining Company," are all upon a scale of magnitude such as were never before attempted in the history of mining. In all these respects it will be a model establishment, and as such, if successful— of which there can be no reasonable doubt—will take the first position as a mining company in this or any other country.

The work has grown upon the hands of the Trustees, and it requires enlarged means to complete it according to the plans adopted and pursued thus far. As costly and heavy as the machinery has been, and is, no stockholder would wish to see aught changed. So far the progress made has met the highest and warmest approval of the California shareholders, and is the admiration of all visitors to this section of the country. The Company possesses in real estate some of the best property in Grass Valley, the rapid growth of which place renders it almost certain to become not only the county seat of Nevada at no distant day, but also the largest mountain town in the state. In new buildings alone, during the past four months, nearly one hundred have been added to this town, and in society it has no superior in California. In the success of the Quartz machinery it even now enjoys a high reputation, and when mills like that we are now erecting shall come into operation, employing each from two to five hundred men, it will be demonstrated how prudent was the action of the founders of the Company.

The " claims "* of the Company have been, as will be seen by reference to the Appendix, greatly increased. With the sum of Twenty-five Thousand Dollars expended in opening and proving them, there can be no doubt their value would be Hundreds of Thousands. It is now conceded that our "claims" on *Virginia Ledge* will prove as rich as those of Lafayette Hill, and consequently as valuable. It is but eighty rods distant from the Mill.

J. WINCHESTER, President.

* The number of claims at the organization of the Company was 40. They now exceed 400.

BY-LAWS.

Art. I. The Officers of this Company are such as are designated by Act of the Legislature for Incorporated Mining Companies, and as may be provided for in these By-Laws.

Art. II. The President shall have power to appoint all subordinate officers and agents, and have the general superintendence and direction of the operations of the Company; subject to the control of the Board of Trustees, legally given by vote at any meeting thereof.

Art. III. All vacancies in the Board of Trustees shall be filled by vote of the remaining Trustees at any meeting called for that purpose.

Art. IV. The first annual meeting of the Stockholders shall be held at the office of the Company, in Grass Valley, on Thursday, August 5th, 1852, and thereafter on the first Thursday in August of each year. But special meetings of the Stockholders may be called by the Trustees, specifying the object thereof, on giving three months' notice from the date of the call, by publication in one newspaper in the county of Nevada, one in the city of San Francisco, and one in the city of New York.

Art. V. The Board of Trustees shall meet at the office of the Company, on the first of every month, at five o'clock P. M., except when the first shall be Sunday, and in that case, on the next day thereafter, at the same hour.

Art. VI. The President shall make a report of his acts, and generally of the operations of the Company, at each regular meeting of the Trustees, and also to the annual meeting of the Stockholders.

Art. VII. The Secretary shall keep a true record of the proceedings of the Board of Trustees, and at the annual or special meetings of the Stockholders, which shall be entered in a book kept for that purpose. He shall also act as book-keeper of the Company, and enter up all amounts, and fill all documents and vouchers, and give such bonds for the performance of the duties assigned to him, as the Trustees may at any time require.

Art. VIII. The salaries of the officers shall be fixed by the Board of Trustees, but the President shall have authority to employ such other services as may be necessary to carry on the operations and business of the Company, *Provided: However, that he shall have no power to create any debt or obligation, on behalf of the Company, beyond the amount of funds in hand, not otherwise appropriated.*

Art. IX. The books and accounts of the Company may be examined by a committee of Trustees or Stockholders, as often as may be deemed necessary.

Art. X. The By-Laws may be altered, repealed, or amended, by a vote of a majority of the Trustees, at any meeting, notice of such alteration, repeal, or amendment, having been given at a previous meeting.

In pursuance of provisions of law, and in accordance with the By-Laws, the annual meeting of the Stockholders of the Grass Valley Gold Mining Company, was held at the office of the Company, in Grass Valley, the 5th day of August, 1852, J. Winchester, President of the Board, in the Chair, and L. W. Sloat, Secretary.

The first business before the meeting was to receive the report of the President, which was presented and read:

EXTRACTS FROM THE ANNUAL REPORT.

GRASS VALLEY, Aug. 5, 1852.

*　*　*　*　*　*　*　*

In making a report to the Stockholders of the "Grass Valley Gold Mining Company," of its initiatory operations during the first year of its existence, I shall confine myself to such matters as are more immediately within my own knowledge, or which may concern the interests of the Company.

Soon after the formation and organization of the "Grass Valley Gold Mining Company," that is, on the 16th of August, of last year, in obedience to the authority conferred upon me, I sailed from San Francisco to New York, for the purpose of raising adequate means, by sale of a portion of the capital stock, to procure and erect suitable machinery. An examination of the various kinds of machinery, at that time being introduced into California, for the working of the Quartz Mines, convinced me that none of a sufficient weight of metal, and capacity to operate upon large masses of rock with speed and economy, had yet been got up ; and my inquiries, as well as personal investigations of the extent and quality of auriferous quartz, to be found in convenient localities, also led me to believe, that with powerful means for reducing the ores, and such improvements in amalgamation as were likely to be introduced, Quartz Mining could scarcely fail to realize very satisfactory results, and become, under good management, a source of permanent profit to Stockholders.

As a method of effecting the best reduction of ores, no process has yet been adopted superior to the well known "Chili Mill." On this principle, the rock is much more finely pulverized, and consequently in a better condition to yield up the *flour of gold* it may contain. The improvement on the "Chili Mill," invented by Captain Cram,* by

DESCRIPTION AND POWER OF MACHINERY.

"NEW YORK, Dec. 10th, 1851.

"J. WINCHESTER, ESQ.—Dear Sir : Your favor of yesterday is at hand : contents noted. Herewith find what we suppose is wanted by a ' brief description of the machinery.' Cram's Crusher is, of all machinery yet constructed, in our opinion, THE MOST RAPID AND EFFICIENT IN ITS OPERATION. It consists of a double grooved bed of cast iron, the outer groove being 15, and the inner one 14 feet in diameter, in which moves a wheel 8 feet 6 inches in diameter, with plane faces corresponding to the figures of the grooves. This is revolved by a shaft through its centre, the inner end of which has a square eye that receives a vertical shaft. On the head of the vertical shaft is placed a tooth wheel, with hard face, which is driven by another on the end of a shaft projecting outward beyond the edge of the bed, and where the power is applied that sets the whole in motion.

"We think a thirty-horse power engine will grind to flour a ton of quartz in five minutes. And we further think there will be no necessity to stop the machinery to clear the grooves. Let them fill, and keep feeding the machine with lumps, the flour or dust will overflow the rim, and can be discharged in troughs prepared for the purpose. The' dragging of the outer wheel or face alluded to, assists the operation of crushing, by the chafing motion it at all times has from the difference of diameter. One wheel weighs 50,000 pounds, and from what we saw the other

which an immense mechanical force is brought to bear upon the ore, combining, also, as it does, several valuable points tending to procure a rapid and perfect pulverization, appeared to be the nearest approximation to the wants of Quartz Mining yet brought to notice; and after careful consultation with able machinists and engineers, one of these improved "Chili Mills" was ordered to be made, and contracts entered into by the West Point Foundry, for the manufacture of the same, together with engine and boilers of adequate power to move the whole.

The weight of the wheels, or rollers, for crushing, including the shafts, pinions, and other attachments, added thereto by mechanical contrivance, was estimated at between forty-five and fifty tons; and the remainder of the machinery at about an equivalent weight. The estimates for the cost of the machinery, say of the weight altogether, of one hundred tons, with freight to this place, and putting up, was not to exceed forty-five thousand dollars. As the work progressed, however, it seemed to increase in bulk, and when completed and shipped, was found to exceed one hundred and fifty tons, including an extra bed plate of sixteen tons, and probably three or four tons of other extra parts of the machinery deemed most likely to first give way.

The contracts were made after the first of January, and the amount of one hundred and sixteen tons shipped in the Sea Nymph, on the second of March; and twenty tons more in the ship Monterey, on the thirteenth of the same month. The remainder, twenty-five tons, was shipped in the Fenelon, in the last of April. It will be seen that, in the execution of the order for the manufacture and shipment of such a mass of heavy machinery, a promptitude was secured creditable to the enterprise of the manufacturers, and, at the same time, no more finished and substantial work has been, or could be turned out at any other foundry in the Union.

Having so nearly completed the object of my mission to the Atlantic side, in which I cannot too gratefully acknowledge the invaluable aid rendered at every step by the Secretary of the Company, R. J. RICHARDS, Esq., I left New York on my return with my family, the fifth of February, and after experiencing severe vicissitudes from illness and shipwreck, arrived at Grass Valley on the 10th of April.

The first important object was to secure a suitable location for the erection of the buildings for the Quartz, and saw-mills, and other necessary work. An examination was made of every point unoccupied

day, it will crush pieces of rock, from 8 to 12 inches square, with perfect ease. Hoping the above will prove useful. We remain yours respectfully,

"H. R. DUNHAM & CO., Archimedes Works."

In reference to the amount of power required to operate Capt. Cram's Patent Crusher, we give the following from Mr. Dunham:

NEW YORK, Dec. 13th, 1851.

" A STEAM engine with cylinders 16 inches in diameter and 4 feet stroke, with four boilers, each 30 feet long, 35 inches diameter, having 2 flues through each. The above engine warranted by us to operate the Quartz Crusher at least five revolutions per minute; and in addition thereto, drive an upright saw for sawing logs or boards of largest size and width. We have previously stated, that, in our opinion, Capt. Cram's machine will grind and pulverize to flour one ton of quartz in five minutes, and continue at that rate to grind all day, discharging itself as the quartz is floured by the wheel. We are of that opinion still.

"Very respectfully,   H. R. DUNHAM & CO.,

" To R. J. RICHARDS, Esq.   Archimedes Works."

and unclaimed, where water was obtainable and access easy, within a distance of two miles from the village; and the location fixed on the south side of Wolf Creek, on a gently sloping point of land, at the junction of the north and east branches, and commanding. also, a good supply of pure water; from springs on the property secured by the Company.

The site for the buildings in which to place the machinery, and dwelling houses for the officers and employees of the Company, contain about six acres, enclosed by a substantial post and board fence. The Auburn road from Centreville passes directly in front of the Quartz Mill. To the east of this road another lot of ground was secured by purchase, to which was added a considerable tract of unlocated lands, the whole containing about sixteen acres, also enclosed with a good post and board fence. A bridge has been built across Wolf Creek, between the village and the Company's property, rendering what was previously, and up to the beginning of June, an impassible quagmire, one of the best roads in the country, and now become a leading thoroughfare to Auburn, the county-seat of Placer County, twenty-five miles distant, and to Steep Hollow and Illinoistown, on the Bear and North Fork of the American River—being, also, the old emigrant route from across the plains, by way of Turckee River.

The site of the Quartz mill, and the whole property, is by far the most central, eligible, and valuable of any within the township, of equal extent. Good roads lead in every direction, giving easy access for transportation of rock, and the hills in the immediate vicinity have been opened within the past few months, and found to contain veins of excellent quality.

Operations were commenced on the third of May, towards the erection of buildings, by cutting and hewing the timber in the surrounding forest. The size, in accordance with the original plans, required a heavy amount of labor, in making excavation for the foundations. The work was entrusted to Col. S. C. Richardson, as chief-engineer and architect, who has pressed the erection with energy, and a due regard to economy in the expenditures. The main edifice is now completed and covered in, including a bell tower, twelve feet square, and rising about fifty feet above the peak of the roof. I have no hesitation in saying that this is the best and most substantial structure of wood in the state of California, and while it may be considered an ornament to the village, it is eminently adapted to the business for which it is intended, and will repay any extra expense, by greater durability and less need of alteration and repair. The principal edifice is fifty by eighty feet, with sixteen feet posts, bearing rafters and queen posts so keyed and bolted as to be able to sustain the heaviest presssure.

A dwelling house has been erected, having a front of forty-four feet, by a depth of twenty feet, with other conveniences for a residence.

A building for the saw-mill has not yet been commenced, nor other necessary out-buildings, such as barn, wood-house, kilns for washing the ore, etc., all of which will be necessary before the rainy season.

On the fourth of July, the Sea Nymph arrived at San Francisco;

and commenced discharging cargo on the eighth. A contract was made for the transportation of the machinery by sailing vessel up the river to Sacramento City, at seven dollars per ton, and the contract was completed on the third instant. The machinery arrived in excellent order, and with but trifling breakage.   *   *   *

The prospects for a most profitable business in Quartz Mining, were never brighter than at this time; especially for powerful machinery. The past year has added immensely to the discoveries before known, and an amount of ore even beyond the capacity of a mill such as that of this Company, will be shipped by owners of claims, who have now no way to render them available; the mills now running being unable to perform the work offered. The consequence is, that those who could otherwise open and work their veins, and bring to the mill their rock for crushing and amalgamating, are compelled to lie idle. There is, also, a want of confidence in the processes of amalgamation adopted at most of the mills here, that prevents miners from bringing in their rock. There is now a general anxiety for the machinery of the Company to be put in motion, and offers already have been made that could give it a business equal to *Four Hundred Dollars a day net profit,* which, exclusive of the lumber business, would give fifty per cent. annual profit on a capital of Two Hundred and Fifty Thousand Dollars. One party offers to supply steadily thirty tons per day, delivered at the mill, for which twelve dollars per ton would be paid for crushing. Allowing the capacity of our works to be but sixty tons each twenty-four hours, requiring an expense of labor of not over Two Hundred and Fifty Dollars, *a profit of Four Hundred and Seventy Dollars* would be the *daily result of sixty tons working.* This estimate is simply given to show the profit to be made by a company working *entirely* for others, and is much within what is probable. The rate paid now is Fifteen to Eighteen Dollars per ton; but crushing can be done on a larger scale, at Ten Dollars, and pay handsomely.

But the sources of a larger profit are already secured. It has been an object of the first importance, to ensure to the Company as large a supply of ore as possible, drawn from its own ground. I have, therefore, spent much time in personal explorations, through the immediate region around Grass Valley, with a view to locating claims, and am happy to be able to report that an amount of valuable ground has been taken up, which will hereafter prove of immense value. In some cases, I have deemed the interests of the Company would be best promoted by purchasing " claims" of *known* and *approved* value; and this has been done at prices greatly below the real worth of the veins, consequent upon the inability of the original holders to work them.

A list of the " claims" now held by the Company will be found at the conclusion of this Report. They number over four hundred in all, covering an extent of territory exceeding one hundred acres. They are comprised within a region in which the richest discoveries have been made, and in immediate proximity to ledges now being worked of known richness.

Of these claims, I will mention one of the most valuable, the " Virginia Ledge," situated partly within the enclosed lot, to the east of the Auburn Road, and not more than eighty rods distant from the mill. The property on the ledge consists of sixty-eight claims. The spot selected for the commencement of the tunnel is but twenty-five rods from our mill, and will cut the vein, (near the centre of the original claims,) at a depth of about eighty feet below the surface. The stream of pure water already discharging from the lower edge of the ledge, which will be greatly increased by this tunnel, will be sufficient for the supply of the engine, and, with that attainable from other springs, situated upon the Company's property, be of a volume adequate to the entire wants of engine and crusher. This supply is entirely independent of the water obtainable from the two branches of Wolf Creek, at the junction of which our main building is located.

The "Virginia Ledge" is opened for about one hundred and fifty feet, upon its "outcroppings," and is encased in porphyry in a greatly decomposed state. The vein shows from eight inches to three feet in thickness, and is capable of being worked with great facility, from the nature of the ground. I have made repeated trials of the ore, by water-washing, or "panning," and in no instance failed to obtain a "prospect' equal to Fifty Dollars per ton—much of it reaches One Hundred and Twenty Dollars per ton ; and assays have yielded (of rock in which not a particle could be seen), as high as sixteen cents per pound, or Three Hundred and Twenty Dollars per ton. In my opinion, based upon a pretty accurate knowledge of the quality of the quartz of the principal veins in Grass Valley township, this vein will prove as rich as any, and be worth to the Company hundreds of thousands of dollars. Samples of the rock, from "Virginia Ledge," have been transmitted to New York, and may be seen at the Company's Agency, 107 Fulton Street.

Immediately adjoining Virginia Hill—in fact, another portion of the same hill—we have fifty-one additional "claims," giving the company, *in one body of land,* one hundred and ninety claims, and almost entire control of the hill. To perfectly develop the value of these claims, two tunnels must be cut at different points, involving an expenditure of about Ten Thousand Dollars. This hill is known as "Jefferson Hill."

The next most valuable "lead," is that known as the "Bryan Ledge," on which we have one thousand two hundred feet, including dips and angles. The vein crops out to the surface of the ground, and is distinctly traceable for some four or five hundred feet. I have opened it to the depth of eight feet, uncovering, perhaps, one hundred feet of the vein. The "dip" is nearly vertical, and the width of the lead two feet. So far as tests have been made, the ore from this vein will pay an average of twenty-five dollars per ton, and is obtainable in great quantities, being so situated that it can be cut by a tunnel, at a depth of three hundred feet.

The expenditures up to this time, for machinery, freight, insurance, building, and other expenses incurred, already exceed Fifty Thousand Dollars; and is beyond the original estimates. This is occasioned, in part, by the fact that it was impossible to judge precisely the weight and cost of new machinery; and, also, from the determination that nothing should be omitted that could contribute to the success of the Company. The machinery is mostly at Sacramento City, and a contract made for hauling, at fifty dollars per ton, to this place; which is thirty dollars per ton cheaper than was originally estimated. There is yet to arrive about forty tons additional, and the actual expense yet to be met, before the works can be put into operation, as follows:

Hauling 150 tons, at $50, - - - - -	$7.500 00
Building Foundation for Engine and Crusher, -	3,000 00
Putting up Machinery and Finishing, - - -	2,000 00
Erecting Saw-mill Building, and putting up, -	3,000 00
Reservoirs and Conduits for water, - - -	1,500 00
Contingent expenses, - - - - - -	1,000 00
	$18,000 00

To meet this expenditure, additional stock to the amount of Twenty Thousand Dollars, belonging to the original holders, was ordered to be sold, and which will suffice to complete the works on a scale of power, capacity, and substantial workmanship, that will make this the most valuable Quartz mining property in California.

When completed, it is necessary that there be adequate means and facilities to carry on the operations upon a proportionate scale of magnitude. It is necessary to open the claims of the Company in a permanent and systematic manner. To obtain from any vein the largest supply of rock, it is requisite that a tunnel be driven into the hill, at the lowest water level. Thus, while acting as a drain, the rock can be quarried and delivered at a greatly reduced cost over the methods now adopted, of raising the ore by shafts. To obtain a supply equal to one hundred tons per day, will require the expenditure of, at least, Thirty Thousand Dollars in permanent works, in the mining department.

To provide against the contingencies of the rainy season, the quarrying should be immediately commenced, and pressed with vigor. There should be at least five thousand cords of wood contracted for, so as to secure a stock before the surrounding forests are partially, or entirely exhausted, and the distance from the point of operations increased. For the lumber department, a large force is necessary, to cut and get in logs. The rate at which lumber is to sell, for years to come, will render this branch of the business immensely lucrative. Our proximity to market, if all that was manufactured were turned to Maysville or Sacramento City, would ensure a quick sale of all that could be made. But the rapidity with which Grass Valley is increasing, creates a home demand, that guarantees large profits to this part of the Company's operations. See page 46.

In the purchases I have made, with the sanction of the Directors, the Company have been fortunate. It is now admitted that the ledge on *Virginia Hill will prove not inferior in value to the celebrated Lafayette vein.* I refer, on this point, to the letter of Professor Blake, hereto attached.

The proposition for increasing the capital stock, as provided by the charter, meets my decided approval, and I am convinced that the interests of the Company will be greatly promoted by such increase.

The position already gained, in connection with the capacity and power of the machinery, will give to this Company the first rank in Quartz Mining in California, and render its stock the most valuable. I trust, therefore, if this measure be adopted by the Stockholders, it will be carried into full effect by their united action and influence.

As to the question of success in this enterprise, I have not a doubt. The magnitude of our works, with a comparatively moderate capital, located, as we are, in *the best* Quartz region in the State, are almost absolute guarantees against failure. The geological character of the country in and about Grass Valley, justifies the opinion expressed above, that elements of success are here combined, not found elsewhere, in equal degree, within the bounds of the gold districts of the State.

In concluding this Report, I have the gratification of saying, that *the Company is free from all debts or obligations whatever;* and, at my own instance, the contraction of any debt is strictly forbidden by the By-Laws.

It remains for the Directors and Stockholders to say to what extent the capital and business shall be enlarged; or with what vigor pushed forward to a complete fruition. I pledge them my untiring co-opera-tion, and, if continued in my present responsible position, shall exert every energy to make this, in business perfection and profit, the model Company of California. J. WINCHESTER.

GRASS VALLEY, August 5, 1851.

GEN. J. WINCHESTER—

Dear Sir : I have, agreeably to your request, examined the Virginia Ledge of Quartz, and from the character of the rock, and the nature of the formation in which it is found, I have no doubt but that it will furnish you with an abundant supply of valuable ore. The porphyry in which it is situated, is continued for more than a mile in the direc-tion of the vein, and from its general decomposed condition, will ren-der the extraction of the ore an easy task. As regards the position you have selected for your mill, I consider it one of the best locations you could have chosen, both on account of the facilities it affords for obtaining a supply of pure water, and from its being in the immediate vicinity of that portion of the country in which I believe the richest lodes will be discovered. I remain, dear sir, yours, faithfully,

JAMES BLAKE.

Correspondence of the Tribune.

GRASS VALLEY, Wednssday, August 11, 1852.

The mining interest stands high in favor in the region hereabouts. This is especially the case in quartz operations. Whatever the re-sult of experiments elsewhere, all *fair* and *honest* companies in Grass Valley have been and still are making heaps of money. The Lafay-ette Vein pays better than ever. Last week, Dr. Sheridan, chemist and assayer of the Grass Valley Gold Mining Company, made several assays of the ore from this vein. The product was startling. In rock showing no gold, over $600 *per ton* was given ; and from the *pyrites of iron,* abundant in the ore of this vein, we obtained forty cents per pound, or $800 to the ton. The process of working and amalgamating the rock of Lafayette Hill produces but $80 to $150 to the ton. How rapidly these figures make fortunes for the owners, and yet what larger fortunes are lost in the ungathered gold? A new and very rich vein was discovered, as I believe I told you in my last, in a small ravine near my residence. It is known as the Virginia Ledge, and promises to yield as largely as the Lafayette "lead." It has been purchased for the Grass Valley Company, its proximity to the mill of which renders it of large additional value.

The field of operations for machinery of such power as that of the Grass Valley Gold Mining Company is so extensive that the stockholders voted to increase the capital stock to $250,000. The machinery brought out by the *Sea Nymph*, 114 tons, arrived at Sacramento last week, and eight or ten tons of it reached the ground last evening, a contract having been made for hauling at $50 per ton for 65 miles of land carriage. The main building makes a grand appearance, from the village. It is now completed and ready for the machinery—having a tower for a bell, and surrounded by large and romantic old oaks and pines. It is but seven months since the first hammer-blow was struck upon this machinery, and you may safely put down the progress already made as an evidence of enterprise worth noting.

Mr. F. Argenti, the well-known San Francisco banker, is about to introduce a process patented by a Mr. Longmaid, of London, for smelting the quartz. We expect him in this place shortly to make some practical experiments. It is claimed to be eminently successful, and applicable to large operations. Should it be so, we can make pigs of gold almost as rapidly as pigs of iron are turned out in Pennsylvania. "There is a good time coming—wait a little longer."

The funeral obsequies to the memory of Henry Clay were observed very generally throughout the State yesterday. All day the minute guns at Nevada reverberated in melancholy tones among the peaks of the Sierras.

Yours, truly,   J. WINCHESTER.

Grass Valley, Cal., August 29, 1852.

The continued growth of this and other towns in the northern mines, is attracting, in a larger degree than heretofore, the attention of men of capital and enterprise; and they begin to estimate more truly the advantages to be derived from the construction of works of public utility, to meet the present and increasing wants of probably the most active community within the limits of the Union. Companies have been formed for putting up a telegraph from Sacramento city, *via* Mormon Island, Auburn and Grass Valley, to Nevada city. Also to build a railroad from Sacramento *via* Auburn and Grass Valley, to the same terminus. There are no stocks of like enterprises in the world that would pay such dividends as these companies. The travel is immense, and so long as a mountain region, containing over a hundred thousand people, can be supplied from the plains and seaboard, the freighting business only of a railroad from Sacramento to the mines would of itself pay large dividends. There are two lines of stages running daily between the termini named, at $15 per capita, and yet the travel is but partially accommodated. While capital by the million is seeking investment in like enterprises on the Atlantic side, promising only six per centum, the same invested here in railroads or telegraphs would pay 60 or 100.

In mining there is little of peculiar interest hereabouts. While we have very rich and extensive *placers* in and about Grass Valley, water at this season is so scarce as to render their development or working but partial. Last week a new gold field of several hundred acres was discovered within a mile of the village, near the middle branch of Wolf Creek. The "pay-dirt" is found at various depths below the surface, from twenty feet upward, and "prospects" from fifty cents to two dollars to the pan. The claims are now being staked off by the hundred, but cannot be worked till water can be brought over the hill wherever the diggings are found.

Business in quartz is in a most healthy condition, and while there is an absence of particular excitement, there is no property held higher in value, or so firmly as quartz ledges, of approved quality. Public confidence, greatly weakened by the failures of those who rushed into the business without any means or experience, increases as it becomes better informed; and few are now to be found who deny that quartz mining is destined to occupy the most prominent position in this State—upon which, indeed, will mainly depend the prosperity of the other great interests of the State, in all time to come.

There are many agents of English Companies now in the State, with some of whom I have conversed, and all are satisfied with the richness of our quartz mines, as well as with the titles they are able to acquire *from the miners.* Those rights—of discovery and possession—are the best that can be obtained, and will never be abrogated. A few weeks ago, a party of hardy American miners realized among themselves $100,000 for a vein of quartz near the middle Yuba, thirty miles above this place. The purchase was made for an English Company, who will put up two sets of heavy machinery upon it.

More recently another like purchase was made on the American River for $200,000 for seven claims only, of one hundred feet each. When the most experienced mining engineers of Europe—men who have been educated in the practical working of the richest veins in Russia, South America, or Mexico—are willing to pay our miners thus liberally for their titles to quartz ledges, you may "guess" that they know what they are about. I deem it not improbable that ere many years pass by, the best quartz veins in this State will be owned and worked—with immense profits too—by English and other foreign companies. If our own citizens and men of wealth will not investigate for themselves, and thus secure the working of their inexhaustible deposits of the precious metal, they must be content to see them pass into the hands of those possessing a more far-seeing vision than themselves. Titles derived from Americans, the actual discoverers or possessors of mining claims, will hold good, whether the purchaser be an Englishman or a Russian. The capital required to work vein mines puts it beyond the power of the miner to realize the value of his discovery; and he has no alternative but to take the best offer that presents, even though the amount bears the image of Victoria Regina.

This part of the State will always possess a valuable resource in its forests of pine. The cities below are compelled to receive their pine lumber from the mountains or from Oregon, and rapidly increasing as the State is in population and wealth, it will readily be seen how lucrative a business can be done in the manufacture of lumber. Within half a mile of my house, you enter the pine woods where a thousand saw logs can be obtained on an area of a few acres. The timber is large, tall and straight as an arrow, and not unfrequently eight or nine sixteen feet logs are obtained from a single trunk. There are two species of pines : one called the sweet or sugar pine, clear rifted, and from three to eight feet in diameter, more nearly resembling the white of the Atlantic ; and the other very hard, full of pitch, intractable for splitting, and akin to the yellow or Norway pine. The latter is the most abundant. Large trees of red-wood and fir, as well as several varieties of oaks, are interspersed through the pine forests.

There are but two saws in operation in this town—one upright, the other circular, and neither of them capable of cutting more than five or six M. feet per day. The saw machinery attached to the quartz mill of the Grass Valley Gold Mining Company is Child's patent, running two large circular saws. These saws will turn out ten to twelve M. per day, having a quick market at $40 to $50 per M. It will be seen that this branch of the business is based upon a certainty as to profits, which must be large enough to secure good dividends, independent of its quartz operations.

Labor is steadily rewarded at $5 a day, for common hands without board, which is had of good quality for ten dollars per week. Carpenters get $6 and $7 when employed ; those working in the quartz veins, or cuyote diggings, as " dritters," are paid $6 to $7. These figures do not include board.

The immense emigration to this State, both by sea and over the plains, is exercising a marked influence upon the value of real estate. Farming lands are rapidly appreciating, and the products of the soil bring nearly as high prices as two years ago. Potatoes are quick at ten cents per pound, or $5 per bushel; California barley at $1,50 to $2,50 per bushel. A number of flouring mills will be erected this year, and next season half the flour necessary for home consumption will be manufactured within our own borders. Speculators are making us pay $32 per barrel for flour in this part of the mines, and more than this higher up the hills.

Yours, truly,   J. WINCHESTER.

The President, in a letter dated Grass Valley, September 28, says: " The importance of the lumbering branch of the Company's business has induced the Directors to extend the operations in this department, by the addition of a powerful upright saw, which will enable us to cut about 16,000 feet per day or 100,000 per week. In addition to the large and increasing demand for lumber, it was deemed important to be able to cut logs of large size, no mill here being competent to work those larger than four feet in diameter. Besides giving us a command of the largest timber, we shall be able thus to supply the market in this region, and send quantities to Sacramento. The building of a railroad to Nevada City, through Grass Valley, for which a company has been formed, will, in a few years, render lumbering a most important branch of operations. The change in the plans will require an outlay of $5000, and give an increased capacity to the saw mill department of at least two millions of feet per annum, the profit on which ($20 per 1000 feet) would be $40,000.

"Our lumbermen are felling trees rapidly. We have enough down now, and partly cut into suitable lengths, for 500,000 feet; and by more hands being employed, when necessary, a full supply of logs can be kept always in advance."

[From the San Francisco Whig, Aug. 31.]

GRASS VALLEY, Aug. 28th, 1852.

MESSRS. EDITORS :—From the avidity with which news from the mines in the various sections of our State is read, and the great distrust that generally prevails in regard to that particular branch known as "quartz mining," I am induced to devote a little leisure to gratify the one feeling, and if possible to lessen the other.

Being on a short visit to this most lovely section of country, removed from the din and stirring enterprise of your city, my time has been occupied in gathering mining statistics, and in witnessing the successful operation of the various quartz mills in this vicinity.

The amount of precious metal taken out by these mills weekly, is almost incredible. As an instance, I will mention the result of about thirty hours' crushing of one of them which I had the gratification of witnessing myself. From the washing of forty-two tons of rock, which had been crushed in the time above-mentioned, I saw taken thirty-five pounds of amalgam, which yielded, upon being retorted, the snug little sum of thirty-three hundred dollars, or nearly eighty per ton : being at the rate of one hundred and twelve dollars per hour, as the work of the mill.

If I had not witnessed the above result myself, which may be relied upon as strictly true, and the operation of the mill in question, at present the largest and most efficient one in the valley—efficient, not more for its capacity, than the ingenuity of its amalgamating arrangements, I should have pronounced such a result "all humbug," gotten up merely to operate upon the avaricious desires of our nature. But we are constrained to "give in" to positive facts, attested by our own senses. Here, in Grass Valley, such a result is of so common occurrence, as to excite scarcely more than a passing remark.

The mill to which I have referred, is called the "Empire," after the Empire State, it having been built principally by New Yorkers.

In connection with the quartz department, a large saw mill is attached, driven by the same power, and capable of sawing ten thousand feet of lumber in twenty-four hours.

The crushing stampers of this mill, of which there are twelve, weigh seven hundred pounds, and upwards, each, and the aggregate weight beating upon the bottoms of the mortars per minute is over two hundred tons—a force sufficient, one would suppose, to crush almost any amount of rock; in fact, it is said to have crushed upwards of sixty tons in twenty-four hours. I was particularly interested in this mill, not more for its name, which gave to it a prestige for me, being a New Yorker myself, than because it afforded a striking illustration of what industry and perseverance, in spite of almost insuparable difficulties, can accomplish.

The saw-mill alone, as I have heard from undoubted authority, has paid over ten per cent. on the capital stock, and they have quartz claims on all the richest hills in this vicinity. Their quartz mill at the present rates will pay a hundred per cent. on the stock. That is, as Capt. Cuttle would say, "stock as is stock." Nor is it the Empire Mill alone in Grass Valley that is working such wonders in the way of quartz. The mill of Mr. Conway, a gentleman of the most untiring energy, is reaping for him a golden harvest. I have been informed by Mr. C. that in two weeks' crushing, he has taken out some $12,000. He is now enlarging his mill, by which he will increase his facilities one-third.

The mill of the Gold Hill Co., with eighteen stampers, is running night and day, and crushing rock varying in richness from $50 to $100 per ton. They are incorporated, and paying large per centages upon a capital stock of one million.

A number of smaller mills in this neighborhood, among which may be mentioned that of Woodbury and Parks', and also Mr. Stevenson's, are in active and successful operation.

The world-renowned Lafayette Ledge, which has been so very rich, and which was purchased not long since by our enterprising citizens, Messrs. Baxter and Wells, for $100,000, is still yielding in masses its mineral wealth. There are also several mills in process of erection; but by far the most stately and costly structure is that of Gen. Winchester. This mill, uniting beauty with strength and massive proportions, is being built under the surveillance of Col. Richardson. It is beautifully located upon Wolf Creek, and is intended to be of sufficient power and capacity to crush 100 tons of quartz in 24 hours. This is a gigantic enterprise, and worthy of the mind of Gen. W.

"I have mentioned the operations of these mills, to show that quartz mining is not all "humbug," and to show what an exhaustless store of wealth is locked up here, requiring only a judicious use of capital and labor to make it available. Quartz mining, like any other business into which men rush blindly, will, in most cases, prove disastrous; but that, like any other business, will finally regulate itself, and become a permanent and profitable, if not ultimately the chief, business of the country. Men of capital will become convinced, and the richness of our mountains will be developed.

EYTRAORDINARY YIELD.—Messrs. Martin & Co. have been engaged in mining upon Sandy Bar, since the commencement of the season. The claim has turned out to be the richest we have heard of upon the river. They went to work on Thursday morning last at about 8 o'clock, and at noon had washed out exactly eleven pounds of gold. In the afternoon they realized nine pounds. This seems almost incredible, but the faithless will be more astonished when we tell them that just three weeks have elapsed since they completed their race and dam, and drained the river, so that they could work advantageously in the bed, and the aggregate of their proceeds is over $100,000. On Wednesday they realized $24,000, and on Tuesday $26,000. Their claim is nearly at the head of the bar, and is considered to be the richest now being worked on the river. —*Calaveras Chronicle*, Aug. 1852.

QUARTZ CLAIMS.

Owned by the Grass Valley Gold Mining Company, August 5, 1852.

Name.	No. of Claims.	
Virginia Ledge,	18	100 feet square.
Do. Hill,	50	do. do.
Bryan Ledge,	12	100 feet each on the vein, with dips and angles.
Jefferson Hill,	51	100 feet square.
Empire Hill,	15	do. do.
St. Charles Hill,	19	do. do.
Weehawken Hill,	35	do. do.
Caledonia Hill,	13	100 feet each on the vein, with dips and angles.
Smith Hill,	63½	each 100 feet square.
Grass Valley Slide,	85	50 feet square.
Daisy Hill,*	7	40 by 60 feet.
Ophir Hill,	3	do.
Union Hill,†	30	do.

* The Rev. R. T. Huddart, of this city, and long a resident of Grass Valley, selected various specimens of quartz from Union Hill, which have been assayed by Mr. Warwick, of this city, who stated explicitly to Dr. Huddart, that if one hundred tons of similar quartz were offered to him in a pulverized state, he would be willing to purchase it, after taking an average, at the rates specified below.

Extract from the statement of Mr. Warrick, dated New York, January 29, 1852 :

No. 1, yields 4 grains per lb. or 373½ dwts. per ton of 2240 lbs., or $298 per ton.

"	2,	"	10	"	"	933½	"	"	"	736	"
"	3,	"	33	"	"	3080	"	"	"	2464	"
"	4,	"	46	"	"	4493½	"	"	"	3464	"
"	5,	"	14½	"	"	1353	"	"	"	1082	"
"	6,	"	12	"	"	1120	"	"	"	896	"

Dr. Huddart remarks, that Nos. 1, 2, and 6, before pulverizing, showed no signs of gold, whatever, to the naked eye; Nos. 3, 4, and 5, showed gold in spots, but were by no means what would be called picked specimens.

The above calculations are based upon the value of gold at $16 per oz. In giving the dollars to the ton, the cents are omitted.

With regard to these assays, we cheerfully concur in the remark of Dr. Huddart, that no company should predicate their hopes upon these tests, because there is no machinery in operation at present, competent to extract all the gold, by a process sufficiently rapid to justify working under the present high rate of wages. What is now required is large and powerful machinery, that will reduce and amalgamate one hundred tons, or 200,000 lbs. per day   This being the lowest yield that the most sceptical have estimated, will produce, as shown on page 20, a net profit of nine hundred dollars per day. Now, an additional yield of one mill to the pound would increase the profits $200 a day, which, allowing 300 working days, would of itself produce an additional profit of $60,000 per annum. Most of the mills that have been set in motion have been small, and established to crush rich quartz, and if their expectations, in regard to the richness of the quartz be not realized, as in many cases they cannot be, a failure is the inevitable result. This may discourage some, but the fault lies in the mode of working, and not in the quartz business itself.

A large mill, with powerful machinery, will reduce and amalgamate as much rich, as poor quartz. Hence, the richer the quartz, the greater the profits.

† " We were out on a very rich lead at Daisy Hill. This is a peculiar kind of quartz, is of a light bluish cast, and has the appearance of immatureness, or unripeness. It is semi transparent before it is exposed to the atmosphere, contains much water, has but few crystals of any size, but there are numerous small cavities where minute crystals appear at this time to be in a state of formation. The quartz is very rich in gold. It has never yielded less than $100 per ton by the mill operation, and when the specimens have been pounded up by hand mortar it has yielded as high as $250 a ton."— *Nevada Journal.*

MACHINERY.

THE machinery of the Grass Valley Gold Mining Company has all been constructed of the best materials, and in the most durable manner, by the first mechanics of the country, and no pains or expense has been spared to make it superior to anything of the kind ever before constructed, and the directors flatter themselves that in this they have succeeded. It consists of the following parts, viz. :—

One of CAPTAIN CRAM'S PATENT CRUSHING MILLS, with two double-grooved wheels, running in a double-grooved bed of fifteen feet diameter, with a crushing power of fifty tons, making five revolutions each per minute, calculated to crush one hundred tons of quartz to powder every twenty-four hours.

ONE EXTRA BED PLATE for the same.

FOUR CYLINDRICAL AMALGAMATORS, on a new principle, which, in the opinion of practical and scientific men, will extract the whole of the gold.

THREE PATENT DRILLING MACHINES of a new and peculiarly valuable invention, whereby much of the labor of quarrying is dispensed with.

A POWERFUL SAW MILL, WITH CIRCULAR, PERPENDICULAR, AND MULEY SAWS OF EXTRA SIZE.

The whole driven by a FIRST CLASS SIXTY HORSE STEAM ENGINE, HAVING EIGHT CYLINDER BOILERS.

In reference to the capacity of the CRAM CRUSHER, and the power required to operate it, we give the following from Messrs. Dunham & Co., whose reputation as mechanics is too well established to require any eulogy from us.

"NEW YORK, *Dec. 13th*, 1851.

"A steam engine, with cylinders sixteen inches in diameter, and four feet stroke, with four boilers, each thirty feet long, thirty-five inches diameter, having two flues through each. The above engine warranted by us to operate the Quartz Crusher at least five revolutions per minute; and, in addition thereto, drive an upright saw for sawing logs or boards of largest size and width. We have previously stated, that, in our opinion, Captain Cram's machine will grind and pulverize to flour one ton of quartz in five minutes, and continue at that rate to grind all day, discharging itself as the quartz is floured by the wheel. We are of that opinion still.

"Very respectfully,

"H. R. DUNHAM & CO.,

"To R. J. RICHARDS, ESQ.   Archimedes Works,"

REPORT

ON THE

PLUMAS CONSOLIDATED GRAVEL

MINING COMPANY,

BY

CHARLES W. HENDEL, C. E.

U. S. Deputy Mineral Surveyor for California.

San Francisco :

A. M. SLOCUM, PRINTER, 612 CLAY ST.

1878.

REPORT

ON THE

ℌlumas Consolidated Gravel

MINING COMPANY.

St. Louis, Sierra County, California,
August 1st, 1878.

To the President and Directors:

Gentlemen:

In compliance with your request, made some time ago, I have visited lately and carefully examined the " Buckeye " "Good Hope and Monitor" Companies' consolidated gravel mining property, and have also compiled the different surveys made by me and others for those companies, and herewith present to you a map of said compilation, and the following, as my Report upon the conditions and prospects of said property as a mine.

The mining lands of the above-named company are situated at an altitude of over 5,500 feet above sea level, about one-quarter of a mile northwest from Saw-pit Flat, in Washington Township, Plumas County, California, or in reference to the public surveys of the United States, in Township No. 23 north, range No. 9 east, Monte Diablo base and meridian.

The town of Saw-pit Flat is about one hundred and ninety miles from San Francisco, and is accessible from the latter point, by railroad, to Marysville, one hundred and eleven miles; thence by stage seventy-eight miles by way of Forbestown, Strawberry Valley, La Porte, Gibsonville, and Onion Valley—the latter place being about one mile from Saw-pit Flat—all of which are mining towns of more or less importance, through which the stage passes tri-weekly, to and from Marysville, at all seasons of the year. The mail and express matter, is carried regularly, without delay, from Gibsonville, six miles distance, to which latter place communication with sleighs from below is kept open during winter, the animals traveling on *snow-shoes*, a recent California invention.

The nearest telegraph office is at present in Downieville, the county seat of Sierra County, about twenty miles distance, and, during this coming year, one will be established at La Porte, about fourteen miles distance, which will afford communication with all parts of the world.

The mine is accessible from Onion Valley via Saw-pit Flat by a good and substantial wagon road.

The ground of these companies consolidated is what is termed *"a gold-bearing Gravel Mine,"* and is bounded on the north by the Golden Gate Company ground, on the east by the American Company ground, on the south by the Saw-pit Flat Gravel Mining Company consolidated ground —formerly the New York and Union Companies—(the same having been lately purchased by a San Francisco company of capitalists, who incorporated last fall,)—and on the west by the Golden Gate Company.

As you will perceive by the accompanying map, made by me, the area of the Buckeye Company consists of - - -
92.97 acres.
the Monitor Company of - - - - - - - 120.47 "
Good Hope of - - - - - - - - - - 172. "

containing in the aggregate an area of - - 385.44 acres, besides the tailing claims of the Buckeye Company, situated in Burgh Ravine, a tributary of Onion Valley Creek, emptying into the Middle Fork of the Feather River.

The title to all the above-described ground, as more fully marked out on the accompanying map, is absolutely perfect and complete, the locations were made over sixteen and eighteen years ago, and work has been more or less in progress on the same ever since, while nothing stands in the way of receiving a U. S. patent to all the mining lands of the consolidation, upon application to the U. S. government.

These mining lands are situated and covered by the unmistakable so-called "*Blue Lead*," or "*Ancient River Channel*." A channel reliable beyond a doubt, and in which the gravel invariably improves, and becomes richer in getting nearer the center of the same. The deposit of this rich auriferous gravel strata, on the bed-rock, where the lava has covered the same to quite a depth, has been worked extensively for a number of years, in Plumas and Sierra Counties, which Counties have always been the principal theatres for *Placer Drift Mining* in California, constituting the principal placers for drift and hydraulic mining of the famous gold belt of the Sierra Nevada, which has yielded more treasure since its discovery than any gold-producing region of equal area upon the globe, and, therefore, are now attracting attention, and are the object of renewed operations.

The first workings of all the creeks surrounding these mines, viz: Nelson, Poorman's, Hopkins, Onion Valley, Burgh and Winter's Creeks, as well as the Feather River, in which they all empty, are said to have averaged *one pound of gold per day* to each miner employed, by simple process of shoveling the dirt into sluice boxes. Many of the miners in those creeks, in early days, who could not procure sluices, or "long toms," as they were then usually called, have, to my own knowledge, washed out as high as *two pounds of gold* per day with a single rocker.

The different streams and the front ground of the ancient river channels were easily worked, and in a few years worked out,—have been even worked over several times, and each time paying well, owing partly to the then imperfect, rude mode and manner of working placer mines. The miners found themselves soon working back into deeper and more extensive and difficult ground to open and work, following the pitch of the bed-rock, requiring skill and perseverance in going through the "Rim-rock," by either expensive cuts or tunnels, so as to drain these great, deep and vast main channels of gravel deposits of California, which are as yet comparatively untouched, or but slightly worked, and may be considered as practically inexhaustible. In doing this it requires, however, an organized capital and labor, and an entirely different system of mining, with a more economical, careful and systematic pursuit. The reckless waste of the first few years, which still prevails with many old California Companies must be checked, and improved appliances and methods adopted to obtain and save the gold, so as to declare large dividends. It is proper to remark here, that I have found in all my experience, that all those mining properties which have not been *incorporated*, *pay far less dividends* than those which have so been and are. The reason of this is in the fact that the unincorporated claims, being owned generally by from 6 to 60 men or more, and each one having an equal voice in the management and working all by themselves, so that there is generally such a diversity of opinion, that no intelligent result can be obtained, and changes of superintendency and foremanship are of almost daily occurrence, and each owner, to a great extent, does generally as he chooses. Often but very little work is done by them, for which work higher prices are paid to themselves by one-third than the current wages of labor. And again, many of these unincorported companies never have any definite system in view, neither do they work by surveys or maps, and it naturally follows that they often most wantonly destroy and butcher very valuable mines, and thereupon become bankrupt, as was the case with the former Monitor Company. And again, these deep and extensive basins of auriferous gravel, covering most everywhere many individual claims, none of which can very often be successfully worked by themselves by the construction of long and costly bed-rock tunnels, to secure outlet and drainage. But when several such individual mines are consolidated and worked through only one tunnel, on a grand scale, under a simple business administration, they will invariably insure the largest profits.

Gravel mining in California is comparatively in its infancy, sufficient is, however, now known of these ancient river streams or gold-bearing Gravel Ranges, by actual developements made during the last 20 years, and more particularly during the last 5 years, throughout the State, to prove, that where good judgment is exercised in making selection of mines, it is not only profitable, but also lasting, if enough of mineral land is obtained. Gravel mining uniformly pays well, and enormous dividends are generally realized, while quartz mining has, with but few exceptions, generally proved to be a haphazard investment. And, in consequence, capitalists are beginning to turn their attention in this direction, knowing by this time full well, that this class of mining will, for a long time, be a leading source of our gold product; for the gold that has been produced from these mines forms but a small fraction of what remains locked up, sleeping in the virgin beds in these vast mountain deposits, waiting only the energy and enterprise of man to set it free and send it into the commerce of the world.

There are many places upon these main channels in Sierra and Plumas Counties, to my own knowledge, where the richest kind of gravel mines remain dormant for lack of such energy, enterprise and capital: while, if the matter was fully understood, those mines might be taken hold of with as much assurance of success as though they were fully developed and not worked out—as I have yet to see the first instance of failure where the Main Gravel Channels was judiciously operated upon.

It requires long years of practical experience, study and close observation to enable a person to have the openings into these basins started at their proper places and depths; hence, thousands of dollars are continually spent by thoughtless miners in opeding mines by worihless tunnels, which might be avoided if the matter was generally better understood, or if a competent Engineer of character and experience who has lived years in a neighborhood practicing his profession, and who, being well acquainted with its geological formation, would be consulted before starting into operation. And capitalists would obtain more reliable, solid and

uninfluenced information from such an Engineer in the
neighborhood of the mine, than they generally can get
otherwise—while the majority—nearly all, in fact, of those
men who live at a distance, and who make it their business
to examine mines for the investment of capital, as ''mining experts," are only capable of judging the merits of a
mine which is fully developed, and from the actual product of the mine only, which is *often nearly worked out*,
unknown to them.

I think with my long experiences as a practical miner of
over 21 years past, Surveyor and Civil Engineer throughout this section of California, and where I am at home
and am well acquainted with most every trail, ravine and
hill in our vast mining regions, having traversed these
mountains in every direction, following my transit in most
every drift, incline, shaft or tunnel, and have thereby
become familiar and acquainted with all the mines working
therein, and the mine owners themselves, and from all, I
have for many years past, gathered *very valuable information*, while with them in their works, to advise and direct
them.   Information, which would be of great benefit to
capitalists *not acquainted* in this section of the country.

Having had an excellent opportunity of obtatning *correct* and *reliable information*, as before stated, and being
well acquainted with those infallable evidences, *not* of
where the gold lays, but where it has been taken from, and
knowing often the costs and net profits of the mines—and
the bearings and grade of the channels, as far as worked
by the miners, and after hearing their views, and then
drawing my own inferences from all the facts, aided by
my compiled field-notes, and copies of maps of all my
surveys of over twenty-one years' experience and my personal observation.

As per your request made, when I saw you last in La
Porte, I will state to you all I know about the Buckeye,
Monitor and Good Hope Companies consolidated mines,
after giving you, first, a short sketch of the Gravel Channel upon which the same is situated, and referring you

also to my mineral report on the Mineral Resources of Sierra County, written Jan. 1st, 1873, for Mr. Rossiter W. Raymond, U. S. Commissioner of Mining Statistics in the States and Territories west of the Rocky Mountains, for the year ending Dec. 31, 1872, published by Act of Congress at Washington.

This channel, which underlies the dividing ridge between the waters of Nelson creek on the north and Onion Valley creek on the south, has been not only successfully worked and found to be rich in the Buckeye, Good Hope and Monitor Claims, but also in all the adjoining mines, viz: By the New York Company on the South, who, up to last year, drifted 65,985 cubic yards of gravel, yielding $240,-000, gold bullion, having paid an average of $3.63 per cubic yard. While the Union Company, laying further south of the New York Company, had yielded $180,000,—from 48,741 cubic yards of gravel, on an average of $3.69 per cubic yard. The Franklin, Eagle and Comet Companies, laying southeast, have each taken out over $120,000 —paying from $2.00 to $4.00 per cubic yard of gravel. Some companies below the Golden Gate have found rich dirt wherever they reached the channel, while the American Company, adjoining all these mines on the top or summit of the dividing ridge between Onion Valley and Nelson and Dixon Creeks, being situated on the other side of said Divide, their tunnel starting in near Washington Hill, have worked gravel paying from $1.00 to $20.00 per car load, and have taken out in six years about $80,000, by only twelve to sixteen men working. They are still delving away toward the deeper part of the main channel, toward these mines, the gold being from .930 to .950 fine. East from the American Company are the Union and Washington Companies, consolidated mines, owned by a French Company, paying from $6.00 to $12.00 per day to each man. Opposite the American and said Union and Washington Companies is one of those unfortunate com_ panies which never draws a healthy breath — wrangling among themselves, who have good ground before them, but it is one of the most mismanaged mines I ever saw, and is known as the Mountaineer Company. Here the channel apparently passes on toward Pilot Peak, whence it enters the northwest corner of Sierra county, at the head of the so-called Slate Creek Basin, and splitting into several large channels, the two most westerly ones forming the "Slate Creek Basin," having been worked quite extensively with enormous results. While another branch runs along and under the dividing ridge of the Yuma and Feather rivers, branching out to the right and left, having been more or less worked wherever water could be obtained. The eastern gold-bearing gravel channel of Slate Creek Basin, after entering Sierra county under Pilot Peak, passes through the Pilot Company mine. The channel is next found, and has been worked for years by the North American Company with grand results, having thus far produced over $400,000, in gold. The channel takes thence a southeast course, passing Slate Creek House on the east, near or under Mt. Staffa, whence it takes a southerly course, passing along or under Alturas Mountains, (where its existence has been proved by a tunnel driven in, on the Cañon creek side, which, however, proved too high,) thence toward Table Rock, in a southwesterly course, passing between Gold Cañon on the east and Potosi on the west, in which places this channel has for many years past been opened and been extensively worked with immense profits, by drifting in a direction quartering toward each place and that more in a southerly course.

The Fashion and Sierra Companies in Gold Cañon, have thus far taken out over $750,000.

In Potosi, the Pittsburg Company, now worked out, it is reported have taken out from 9.80 acres of ground breasts $4\frac{1}{2}$ feet high, $152,549.81.

The Hawkeye Company, on the west of one of the aforesaid unfortunate Companies, where everybody was his own master—being now defunct, have taken from 5 acres $365,819.40, and declared *only* a dividend of $25,280, after paying themselves $4.00 per day for wages.

The Monumental Mine, laying northerly from the former two Companies, took out, from May 1st to Sept. 10th, $34,133.30, at an expense of $17,562.76, leaving a clear profit of $16,570.84 for 4½ months on the mine, at $3.50 per day's wages.

The Empire Company, North of the Monumental Company on said Channel, now owned by a Company of San Francisco capitalists, have lately reached, with a long and costly tunnel, the edge of the Channel in their ground, and are now raising an air-shaft of several hundred feet in height, and they will soon begin to open out in the rich channel known to exist in their ground before them.

From the Hawkeye Mine, we find this channel going thence westward toward Howland Flat, as proved by the underground works of the Pittsburg, Monumental and Hawkeye Companies, as with those of the Union, Down East, Erie, Hibernia, Nevada and many other Companies.

The Union Company, (incorporated,) now worked out as a drift mine, has taken from 29.83 acres, $1,187,284.7 , and all the other mines on the Channel have paid about the same in proportion. The Union had to hoist all their gravel, by expensive steam power, upon a 500 feet incline (double-track) to the surface, and had to contend with the troublesome (so-called) "swell rock," thereby increasing dead labor. Neither of which has been the case in the Buckeye, Monitor or Good Hope consolidated mines. *Items in drift mining certainly not to be overlooked.*

The Down East mine, also worked out as a drift mine, yielded $346,000, and divided $146,000 in dividends, all from 6.59 acres, after paying original cost and expenses of working same, all being worked share-owners, and rating wages at $4.00 per day.

From Howland Flat this Channel is easily traced, and successfully worked in Pine Grove, Chandlerville, St. Louis, Cedar Grove, Gardner's Point, Grass Flat, Portwine, Scales' Diggings, and many other places of less note; extending thence by way of Brandy City, Camptonville, San Juan, French Corral, Birchville, etc., etc., on to Smartsville and Timbuctoo, in Yuba County. This eastern channel of Slate Creek Basin, has a grade of 84 feet per mile, from the base of Pilot Peak to Scales.

The Western Channel of Slate Creek Basin also enters Sierra County under Pilot Peak, and passes down the dividing ridge, between Slate Creek on the east, and Feather river on the west.

From a branch of this channel, between Hepsidam and Whisky Diggings, the following amounts have been taken out, viz.:

The Phœnix Co., a drift mine, yielded..........$300,000
The New York Co.,   "   "   250,000
The Iron Bound Co.,   "   "   200,000
The Gem Co.,   "   "   150,000
The Boston Co.,   "   "   150,000
The Redding Co.,   "   "   100,000
The North Star Co.,   "   '.   100,000
The Washington Co.,   "   "   40,000
The Niagara & Fremont Co., a drift mine, yielded 50,000
The Johnson & Co., a hydraulic mine yielded.... 150,000
Other hydraulic companies yielded.... 150,000
Tailing claims in Whisky and Slate Creeks, over. 500,000

Or a total of.............................$2,140,000

Besides the gold taken out by many Chinese Companies, the results of which never could or can be correctly obtained, but which is estimated to have been at least over $100,000, making a total of over $2\frac{1}{4}$ millions dollars of gold, *from less than about 2 to 300 acres of mining lands.*

From Whisky Diggings, the Channel, southwesterly along Mt. Pleasant, Gibsonville, La Porte, Spanish Flat, Secret and Barnard's Diggings, crossing Slate Creek over to Poverty Hill in Sierra County, where it unites with the above referred to eastern channel of said Slate Creek Basin. This western channel has an average fall or grade of 82 feet per mile, and being like the eastern, has an average one mile in width, giving both together an area of 15 square miles through Sierra County alone, of mining ground, to be worked by future generations, of which Slate Creek is the only outlet.

In the before-mentioned channels, the auriferous gravel deposit is exposed on the surface for many miles in Sierra County, proving rich in quality and immense in quantity, for hydraulic washing.

It is asserted by Dr. Brewster, who has been engaged for 16 years in the transportation of U. S. Mails, between La Porte in Plumas County, and Marysville, in Yuba County, and also in the transportation of gold dust and bullion for the different banking and express companies doing business in the vicinity of the *Slate Creek Basin Channels*, that, from books and accounts in his possession, he finds that he has transported for the banking house of John Conly & Co. alone, over 40 millions dollars worth of dust and bullion, and valuing gold dust at $20,000 for the 100 pounds, making 100 tons of treasure for that house alone. Also, that he transported for the banking house of Everts, Wilson & Co., Eve & Crew, Wells, Fargo & Co's Express, and the Union Express Company, at least twenty million dollars worth of dust and bullion, making sixty millions passing down the road, through his hands alone, and it can be safely estimated that one-fourth of the product of Slate Creek Basin passed over the road in private hands, of which no account was kept, which swells the amount of gold produced from this Channel to 80 *millions of dollars*, up to the end of the year 1871.

HISTORY OF THE BUCKEYE AND MONITOR MINES.

1. *The Buckeye Company* ground was located about the year 1856, when they started their first or present Monitor tunnel, and after running it for a distance of about 1100 feet, and having been most all the way in gravel, and not striking bed-rock, this company started afterward their 2d tunnel from near Burgh Ravine, but run the same only a distance of 100 feet, being nearly all the way above bed-rock in gravel. In the spring of 1861, they

started their present third and lowest tunnel below the
falls of Burgh Ravine, and sufficiently low not only to work
not only their own ground, but also that of the Monitor
and the Golden Gate Companies.   In running through
the rim-rock (metamorphic slate) they had to blast through
some bed-rock that cost $50 per foot.   After attaining a
distance of 1750 feet, they raised, in 1867, a shaft, 35 feet
perpendicular, and found that they were sufficiently low
enough for the lowest point of the channel above them,
composed of rich pay-dirt for drifting; in order to be able
to bring the cars to the top of the bed-rock into the
breasts, they run a 90 feet double track incline, on which
the descending loaded car, by an automatic arrangement,
hauls up the empty car.   The company commenced, in the
fall of 1867, to take out pay-dirt, and have been to work
ever since, taking out a great deal of gold, being from
.921 to .931 fine, and receiving $18.45 per oz. at the bank
of La Porte for same.

2.   *The Monitor Company* ground was located about 1856,
and after the Buckeye Company abandoned their above
referred to first tunnel, the Monitor Company bought said
tunnel from the Buckeye Company, giving in exchange the
privilege to use all the water as claimed by the Monitor,
after having used it themselves, which is conveyed in a
ditch from Burgh Ravine to the Buckeye Company Reservoir.   The Monitor Company erected hoisting works in
the tunnel, 490 feet from its mouth, and sunk a double
track incline toward their own ground, by water-power,
using a Fredenburr hydraulic water-wheel.   After reaching bed-rock, at an expense of over $40,000 in opening out
their mine and putting up more costly buildings than
required, it is reported by good authority that they took
out $33,000 in less than 5 months, including one lump of
solid gold of $787.68 value.   After they had blocked out
some ground, a serious cave occurred, which not only filled
up the diggings with water, but also cut off the water of
the springs on top of the ground, by which they had been
enabled to hoist the gravel and keep the mine free from

water. The members of the company who were the original locators of the ground and were very poor men when
they came there, and having for years endeavored to
secure means to develope their ground, and when they
struck rich pay-dirt, would spend all their income, and
when this misfortune came upon them they were without
any adequate means to run a new, long and costly tunnel,
or to obtain a powerful steam engine to free their diggings
from water and hoist the gravel. They run their mine in
debt untll they were sold by the Sheriff to satisfy judgments against them, and becoming, for the time being, dis-
heartened, more so, since at that juncture, in 1859, the
éxcitement prevailed throughout the State over the discovery of silver at Washoe in the now adjoining State of
Nevada, and the former proprietors became scattered,
leaving for some new El Dorado, failing to redeem their
property in due time. And ever since this mine has laid
dormant. The Buckeye Company have in late years
worked their tunnel up to the Monitor line, and to the bottom of the Monitor incline, and consequently have now
perfectly drained the same. Their tunnel being low
enough to work both mines to better advantage, I would
recommend most earnestly the consolidation of both companies, as contemplated by you.

IMPROVEMENTS.

Main tunnel of Buckeye Company.............1750 feet.
Branch tunnel, over.... .... 850 feet.
Incline (with machinery)...................... 90 feet.

Air tunnel, connecting with the New York Company,
several hundred feet long.

Dump-house, with substantial flooring, timber-house,
blacksmith and carpenter shop, coal house, water ditch,
and substantial reservoir, pipes and rubber hose, to convey water from reservoir to dump house.

Three sets of sluices for washing gravel in the aggregate
length...480

Sufficient cars for the transportation of gravel to work

50 men, picks, bars, axes, drills, sledges, and a general assortment of mining tools. (Those of the Monitor alone are valued at $5,000.00.)

CHARACTER OF GRAVEL DEPOSIT.

The pay-dirt is of a light greyish blue color, and is very easily worked and washed, being composed of small well-washed round and smooth quartz pebbles, mixed with yellowish and whitish clay, sand and other earthy matter, and occasionally boulders, washed smooth, from the size of an egg to a ton or more in weight, and, when removed from their places, leave a smooth bed behind, a sign, which is held by all observing gravel miners, as an indication or rich pay.

The channel is confined by a rim-rock on either side, running parallel to it, and varying in width from one-quarter to over one-half a mile.

The gravel, containing the principal pay or gold for a drift-mine, lies directly on or near the "bed-rock," which is, in this place, composed of a soft grey or blueish de-composed metamorphic talc slate rock—sometimes hard. The pay gravel varies in depth, for drifting purposes, from 4 to 5 feet. Above the drifting pay ˙gravel lies finer quartz gravel, from 5 to 50 feet; and which is lighter in color as the bed-rock is left, all of which contains more or less free gold, and would pay well in front, if worked by hydraulic process, provided water could be brought on the ground to do so. On top of this gravel, toward the centre of the hill, from 10 to 50 feet of pipe-clay, of a yellowish color, is to be found, and on top of the same and to the surface is, from a few feet to many hundreds, a bed of "*lava ashes*," or so-called "*mountain cement*," in the mining parlance, invariably overlaying the "blue lead," which bears marks of having gone through a heating process by volcanic action, while the gold-bearing gravel stratas have the appearance of a Neptunic formation. This lava overlies lhe "blue lead," wherever found in this section, and is the only strata from the pipe-clay to the surface, and varies in thickness from a few feet to many hundreds

In these mines the pay channel is in no place less than 50 feet from the surface, while toward the summit of the hill, it is as much as 1000 feet. The channel has, in all cases, a receding grade of nearly 2 feet in 100 toward the centre.

OPENING TO THE MINE AND DRAINAGE.

The opening to the Buckeye Mine is by a regular graded tunnel, which is a fine piece of work, being 6 feet high in the clear, and $5\frac{1}{2}$ feet wide on the bottom, and $4\frac{3}{4}$ feet wide on top, and perfectly straight for 1750 feet in length, running in a direct course from the buildings on the outside to below the rim rock, and will be below the lowest point in the main channel when reached.

This tunnel has a uniform descending grade, from the channel to the outside, of $1\frac{1}{2}$ inch in 12 feet, besides the incline, which has a great fall toward the outside, through this tunnel and beneath the car track, in a ditch or waterway, through which the drainage of the mines finds its outlet.

Although a walk is laid between the tracks, so that mules could find a safe and easy road over which to haul whole trains of loaded cars out of the mine, and then return the empty ones, which would materially lessen the cost of transportation of the gravel, and thereby increas 3 the dividends, still this Company now transport their gravel by men power, at the rate of $4 per day to each man.

VENTILATION.

The air-way connection with the New York Company tunnel, made several years ago, jointly by both companies, connects with all the upper tunnels at a difference of elevation of 35 feet with a main tunnel, creating a draft by this difference of altitude in the tunnels and incline, rendering the air, all the year around, as refreshing and pure as on the mountains, and the ventilation of the mine is secured for all time, wherever it may be worked.

SAFETY OF MINE.

No foul air "damps" or explosions have ever occurred in any of the mines in Plumas or Sierra Counties. Experienced workmen consider that there is no danger attached on that score to tunnel mining in this part of the countiy.

MODE OF WORKING OF TUNNEL GRAVEL MINES.

In all well-regulated mines, after reaching the channel, a tunnel or *main gangway* is run near the center, and generally lengthwise to the pay channel, if practicable, From this gangway, side gangways are branched off, for about 70 feet. After running 30 feet away from the main gangway, openings are made at right angles to these side gangways, and the gravel cut out between them as they are extended. This leaves a solid pillar, on each side of the main gangway, of 30 feet in width for its proper support, less that portion cut away by running the branch side tunnels through. These side tunnels are termed "*breasting gangways*," and the pillars between them, as they are excavated, are termed "*breasts.*" In breasting, or cutting out the dirt, the roof is held up by timbers resting on the bed-rock and reaching up to the roof, on top of which is a cap 2½ feet long, 4 inches thick and 1 foot in width, which is pressed tightly against the roof by the timbers "or leg," and which are in this mine 4, 4½ or 5 feet long, 8 to 10 inches in diameter, and which rests on the bed-rock, as before described, being wedged or driven tightly under it. All the rocks and boulders of any considerable size are separated from the dirt and piled up in pillars or walls back of the dirt, for support and to prevent caving. Breasting commences as soon as the breasting gangways have reached a distance of 30 feet away from the main gangway. These gangways occupy 6 to 10 feet in width on the bottom, 4¾ feet on top, and are 6 feet high in the clear. Thus it will be seen that the mine is cut into strips of 60 feet in width between the gangways, which is divided into

2 breasts of 30 feet each. Two or three breasters are employed in each breast in cutting out the dirt and shoveling it into the cars in gangways.

The number of openings and progress of the main gangways depends upon and are regulated by the number of men employed.

Timbering to main tunnels and main gangways will average twelve inches in diameter, and are usually round.

At a distance of four feet apart, and lengthwise in a tunnel, when required, timbers are placed in sets, with "laying" or "spilings," extending from one set to another, for support of the ground. These spilings are generally four and a half feet long, eight inches wide, and two inches thick.

WASHING GRAVEL.

The Company's dump-house is thirty feet in length and twenty feet in width. A strong, double floor is laid in the bottom, composed of one and a half inch boards, having a pitch on either side of two inches in one foot toward the center, and to the flume or sluice, which extends from end to end of the building. Lengthwise of the dump there is also a grade, corresponding with that of the sluice, of one foot in twelve.

The car-tracks being on a level with the tunnel to the mouth thereof, are twenty-five feet at the upper end, and twenty-seven and a half feet at the lower end above the bottom. The washing flume, or sluice, extends down along Burgh Creek in three different sections (see map): 1st. One hundred and ninety-two feet of sluices, with one foot grade in 12 to a dump, or jump-off of four feet. 2d. One hundred and forty-four feet of sluices, with two feet grade in twelve, to the second dump-off of four feet; thence, 3d, one hundred and forty-four feet of sluices with two feet grade in twelve, dumping the tailings thence into Burgh Ravine, from whence they run six hundred feet with a splendid grade, being one of the appurtenances of the consolidated property. The size of the sluices are sixteen inches wide and twenty inches deep, made of one and a half inch lumber, strongly bound and braced on the outside.

The drainage water from the mine, (at present four inches,) is saved in the company's reservoir, and used in conjunction with the water brought in a ditch from Burgh Ravine, affording four to six inches in the dryest time of any season, and all owned by this Company, as per late decision of the Supreme Court, rendered in the company's favor.

The riffles in the sluices for saving the gold, in the upper sluices, are constructed of " used-up car wheels," and scantling six feet long, two by three inches in size, plated with baud iron, one and one-quarter inch wide by one-quarter inch thick, and which are made into sections by nailing tightly to cross strips with four bars, forming a section riffle, and with the spaces between for saving the gold. Many other devices have been tried, but the above are deemed equal to any, and, for simplicity, they have the preference, except stone pavings, which are used in the two lower sluice sections, in which also quicksilver is used to save the finer gold.

The water for washing is conveyed in iron pipes and rubber hose from the reservoir, which is immediately adjoining the dump-house, and is thrown on the dirt by hydraulic pressure, washing and separating it very thoroughly.

WATER SUPPLY.

The supply of water is obtained, as stated before, from the drainage water out of the mine, which is at present 4 inches, and will be increased to 12 or 15, as more of the ground is worked, and the somewhat lower "back channel" tapped, and from Burgh Creek conveyed in a ditch in which a flume is set, so as to prevent the loss of water by scepage in the dryest time of the year, being 4 to 6 inches, and sufficient to wash all the dirt during the dryest time, which 16 men, and even 25 men, might get out, while the company obtains enough water from said ravine for 6 to 8 months of the year to wash all the accumulated stock-dirt of the other 6 to 4 months, and all the dirt, during the flush-water season, which several hundred men may be able to get out of the mine,

BUCKEYE COMPANY CONSOLIDATED TAILING RAVINE.

The Buckeye Company consolidated *Tailing Ravine* commences about 480 feet in front from the dump-house at the lower end of their third flume, and extends down some 600 feet below the lower end of said washing flume or sluice to Falk, Miller & Robinson Ravine, for tailing purposes. The dirt, after being washed through the flume, is dropped into the ravine, better known as Burgh Ravine, and spreads over a space of some 50 to 100 feet, which, by being exposed to the action of air and water, becomes slacked, the cement more or less of which is contained in all pay-gravel in these channels, is in some degree dissolved, thereby freeing the gold contained in it and in the unwashed clay of the gravel. During the dry season a very large body of this dirt or tailings will accumulate, and being deposited from day to day in thin layers, they are generally increased, and all exposed to the action of air and water alternately. During the wet season this body of tailings will gradually wash away, and the gold will be deposited on the bottom or bed of the creek. The bed of the creek is of hard slate rock, naturally worn smooth by the action of water, but of uneven surfaces, which forms crevices and riffles, into which the gold is lodged, thus saving the finer particles which are washed through the sluices, together with that on which small pieces of cement, gravel or clay adheres, and which is consequently decreased in specific gravity.

The amount of money which such a Ravine will usually pay, situated as this is, will amount to about 5 per cent. on the gross amount taken from the mine on the first 500 to 600 feet below the sluices—or $5,000 on $100,000 washed out in the sluices. An estimate, which I am sure is a low one, having seen in places as much as 25 to 60 per cent yield in 1,000 feet of ravine, below a flume or sluice.

For cleaning up such a ravine, which is usually done once in two or three years, this expense is but very little, and ought in this case not to average more than $200.

It is a settled fact, that *gold which cannot be saved by any process known, can be saved in* RAVINES—*in considerable quantities.* Hence a " *Tailing Ravine"* to a mine is always considered very desirable. And the Company ought, by all means, so as to enlarge its capacity for husbanding the tailings more at pleasure, build dams across the Ravine, and purchase that of the company below theirs, which is about 400 feet long.

TIMBER AND LUMBER.

The timbers used in the mine are obtained from the surrounding hills and flats. There is an abundance of it, at a cost of 20 per cent less than three to five years ago. They let contracts for all sizes of timbers used in the mine, as spilings, breasting caps and posts, tunnel caps and posts, at from 7¼ to 8 cents per piece, all around, delivered at the mouth of the tunnel. Sawed lumber is obtained from the mills near by, at a cost of $30 to $35 per thousand for first quality delivered—no scarcity of timber, for any of the purposes of mining or milling, can ever occur here. Charcoal, delivered, is sold at 25 cents per bushel.

SEASONS.

During the winter season, the snow falls frequently to a depth of nine or ten feet, but the weather is never severely cold.

The timber-house and dump-house, as well as the sluices, being enclosed, the stock for winter use is stored in the former, and is easy of access, while the dirt from the mine is run out and dumped, equally as well in winter as at any other time. No difficulty is found in washing the dirt and clearing up the sluices at pleasure. Winter usually sets in about the first of December, and the snow is pretty well gone by the first of May. This necessitates a stock being laid in, during the summer and fall months for the year.

COST OF LABOR.

When tunnel mining first became a prominent feature in this section, wages rated at $6.00 per day for miners. Since that time they have been reduced in the ratio of $6.00, $5.50, $5.00, $4.50, $4.00, $3.50, $3.00, and at the present time some even receive only $2.50 per day, while many companies still pay old rates, as high as $4.00 per day, for the reason that being all co-operatives, which is the case with the Buckeye Company, the cheap labor cannot be said to have come into universal use.

For many years past a strong prejudice has existed against the employment of Chinese, so much so as to enter largely into all business departments as well as in our State politics, which has incited in many places, a certain degree of lawlessness, and effectually prevented the employment of this class of cheap labor. At the present time, this opposition is all done away with, and this class of labor is rapidly coming into general use for mining purposes. It has been held, they being an inferior race, they were not competent, mentally or physically, of performing what would be required of them in mining. The result has proved that they will average well with white labor, where mere manual labor is required, and are very apt to learn in matters requiring skill.

The rates at which this class of labor can be secured may be set down at $1.50 per day at the present time. Employing one-half of Chinese at $1.50, and the other half of skilled white labor at $2.50 per day, it will give the average of $2.00 per day for each man employed. It may safely be set down that labor will still be further reduced, until white labor will command no more than $2.00 per day. The time is not far distant, and the effect which it will have on mining enterprizes will be very material. The reduction of 50 cents only, on each day's labor, increases the dividends, say 100 men working, $50 per day. This company at present pay themselves $4.00 per day, there being 16 men (shareholders) working. If cheap labor was employed by them, as above stated, and only current wages

paid, the Company would have daily $32 more of a divi-
dend than they now have.

In order to obtain statistics of amounts taken from their
mine, I examined their books, which I found to correspond
with the figures obtained some time ago, when I was surveying for that Company, and from the maps and surveys I
find that they have worked up to June 30, 1878, (their fiscal
year,) 486,228.70 square feet of bed-rock, or 2,000,000
cubic feet of gravel taken therefrom, taking the average
height breasted out, at $4\frac{1}{2}$ feet.

From which they washed, during each fiscal year, as
follows, to wit :

Ending Saturday, June 27, 1868 ....$21,266.88
"   "   "   26, 1869.............. 44,160.92
"   "   "   25, 1870.............. 34,265.10
"   "   "   24, 1871.... .... 33,920.17
"   "   July 1, 1872.............. 27,976.71
"   "   June 30, 1873.............. 31,914.66
"   "   "   4, 1875 .... 58,307.32
"   "   "   4, 1876.............. 67,494.14

            Total....................$319,305.90

Which, if divided by 486,228.70 square feet worked,
would yield a little over $70\frac{15}{100}$ cents per square foot of
ground,or,if divided by 200,000,000 cubic feet of ground excavated, we have a yield of $15\frac{59}{100}$ cents per cubic foot.
Which results I find to compare favorably, taking the easy
working and facilities of this mine into consideration, for,
in examining my estimates of mines on this channel, I find
that the

Hawkeye Mine in Potosi pd. per square yd $9.45
Pittsburg "   "   "   "   "   "   " 7.38
Union   "   " Howland Flat   "   " 8.10
Down East "   "   "   "   " 10.80
Pioneer (hydraulic) in Grass Flat, 22 feet above bed-
rock, pd per cubic yd .... $1.32\frac{14}{100}$
Baker's (hydraulic) at Gardner's Point cub. yd .... $.60\frac{81}{100}$
Old Gardner's Point Claims (hydraulic) "   "   ... 1.14

Union Mine drifting, Portwine pd. per   "   " 12.25

Monte Christo   "   "   "   "   "   "   ... 6.48

The Monte Christo and Union Companies combined average has been, per cubic yard, 8.27\frac{64}{100}$.

The above-named Companies have worked the richest kind of dirt, and all of them had to work under many disadvantages not to be found in these consolidated mines.

In order to convey an idea of the probable daily expenses and yield of the mines, if worked as the same ought to be, and the same being fairly opened (and *not worked nearly out*, like many others, sold for high prices,) with all the substantial improvements in and around these mines, and with their facility of getting out the gravel and being able to wash it daily, I will give you the probable number of men, with the required highest going rates of wages per day, and which will hire No. 1 men throughout.

Superintendent at $2,500 per year, say ....$ 6.85

75 Miners, at $3.00 per day each................   225.00

6 Carmen, at $3.00 per day each...............   18.00

2 Foremen, at $4.00 per day each 8.00

1 Blacksmith, per day 4.00

1 Assistant Blacksmith, per day 3.50

1 Carpenter to frame timbers, etc., per day.......   4.00

1 Washman to wash all gravel, and who can assist
     Carpenter or elsewhere....................   4.00

2 Woodmen to get out timbers, at $3.00..........   6.00

Wear and tear of cars, etc., say 10.00

Incidental expenses, say......................   10.00

Feed for 2 mules, per day.....................   3.00

Giving a total of daily expenses of..............$302.35

Now then, I will say, that so many men will produce at least 400 car loads per day, yielding at a very low estimate, only $2.00 per car load—while the average results have been 3.39\frac{21}{100}$ per car load. Their cars, being 4 feet 8 inches long by 28 inches wide and 24 inches deep, containing 806 cubic yards of gravel, and as they always fill the cars above the basis, I estimate that 1 square yard of ground

4½ feet high will yield 3.10 car loads of gravel. Therefore,
You will have a daily gross income of............$800.00
Take from this the daily expenses................ 302.35

And you have left a net yield of.................$497.65
per day. Multiply this by 26 workings per month, and
you have a monthly net yield of $12,938.90, or $155,266.80
per year on the mine.

In giving the above statement of the mine, I am really
underrating the probable product of the mine, for I find
that the Monitor has worked only 80,000 square feet of
ground, yielding $33,000, or paying over 40_{100}^{12} cents per
square foot, or $3.6108 per square yard, or $5.4116 per
cubic yard of gravel. And, inasmuch as I have said nothing of what may be reasonably expected from the tailings, which will be saved again after their first washings in
the sluices, and accumulate in the before described Tailing
Ravine Claim of the Company, and will yield without a
doubt, at a low estimate, not less than 5 per cent on the
gross yield of the washings from the sluices, which would
amount to $12,480.00 per year, which, added to the other
net amount of $155,266.80, giving a total net income per
year of $167,746.80.

These are estimates at the highest rates of wages, while
any careful business administration will save to the Company and stock owners at least $75.00 more per day on
expenses by employing one-half white labor at $2.50 per
day and the other half Chinese labor at $1.50 per day, thus
giving an average of $2.00 per day to each miner em-
ployed.

For a perfectly safe estimate, we will leave off the odd
thousands of the above net income, together with the additional amount to be obtained by the above-mentioned
lessened expenses in working the mine, and which is certainly more than sufficient for a safe margin to cover all
contingencies, and we still have left the round sum of
$100,000 per yearly dividend on this property.

TIME REQUIRED TO EXHAUST THE MINE.

In the above estimate of expenses, it is set down, that by employing said stated force, 400 car loads per day would be excavated, which would make at 3.10 car loads per 1 square yard superficial bed-rock cleaned up. 129.03 square yards per day, or 3,354.78 square yards per month, or 40,-257.36 square yards per year. By dividing this sum by 4,840, the number of square yards in an acre, and we have nearly 8.32 acres per year exhausted.

These consolidated mines containing an area of 385.44 acres, of which the Buckeye Company has already worked...................................... 6.29 acres

and the Monitor Company.................... 1.83 "

_____

or a total of .... 8.12 "

which would leave a total of 377.32 acres untouched. Dividing this sum by 8.32 acres per year to be worked, we find that it will require 78 years to work the consolidated companies ground. Allowing the ground assumed to be worked in 4.67 years, viz. : 38.85 acres as waste ground along the rim-rock, and we still have 338.47 acres of pay gravel, to be worked in twenty years, before us. Multiply this by $100,000, the lowest net product or income per year, and you have still a total net product of over *three million dollars* during that time.

Another chief value of these consolidated mines is, the late discovery of the so-called " Front Channel " in the New York Company, extending clear across these consolidated mines, which had been overlooked, (as the New York tunnel was like that of the Buckeye tunnel, all under it is bed-rock,) by the chief belief, in early day, that gold was to be found only under the summit of the hills or in the basin of these great ancient river-bed or gravel channels, (which would make an allowance of 38.85 acres as waste ground a reasonable large one.) In January last year, at the time I visited the New York Company mine, professionally, I could see plainly, plenty of free gold in splendid looking dirt or gravel, and was then and there assured that the gravel was good for $12 to $20 per day to each drifter.

While the richest or back channel, worked with enormous results by their neighbors the New York, Union, Franklin, Eagle and other companies, has not yet been reached, but, by all present appearances, I believe they are now near to it, which when worked will produce larger returns than has been the case heretofore.

The great mass of common miners of California have been successful in making large fortunes, and it has been owing more to good luck than good judgment, for, as a class, they are no exception to the general rule all over the world; as, for instance, where a mine has been developed by a company of miners without the assistance of capital, as was the case with the Buckeye Mining Company, and many others throughout the State, they do not appear to comprehend the value of their property. They came to this State with their minds made up and to gratify an ambition for a certain amount of money or "*stake*," as they term it, and when they happen to get possession of a valuable location, they invariable stand ready to accept a certain figure for it, provided it reaches the amount of their ideal "stake"' regardless of its true valve.

Having been heretofore on many occasions employed by the Buckeye and adjoining Companies for many years past to attend to their underground surveys, I had then, as well as at other times, when I have been visiting the different mines, become more familiar with the nature of the gravel and the great extent of the channel passing through this mine and others, as far as the same has been from time to time opened, and I am now, after my recent visit and late thorough examination of the Buckeye, Monitor and Good Hope Companies' consolidated property, as requested by you, more and more inclined to the firm belief that the yield of these mines, *consolidated* as they are and *should be*, is limited only to the amount of work done on the same.

This mine consolidated, being yet nearly a "*virgin mine*," with *nearly all its precious metal in it.*

I am satisfied, if properly managed, and worked by only one company, with all the late improvements utilized, and a sterling, practical superintendent at its head, it cannot fail to become a leading drift-mine of the State of California, having better facilities for working, and a more valuable water privilege, than the majority of gravel mines generally possess in this section of California.

I know of no mining property that I consider as desirable and as cheap as this is, and I have visited nearly all the principal and prominent quartz and gravel mines in Plumas and Sierra Counties, in my official capacity, and after a careful review of all, I think I can safely recommend to you and your friends the purchase of *these consolidated mines.*

Asking your pardon of my neglecting so long to comply with your request to examine this property, and to pass my opinion upon the same, and which was owing to my pressing official duties, and which would not allow me to attend to your request any sooner,

I am, respectfully yours,

CHARLES W. HENDEL, C. E.

U. S. Deputy Mineral Surveyor for California.

I hereby certify that I have carefully read the foregoing report, and from my knowledge of the position of the country, and especially those particular mining claims (the Buckeye, Monitor and Good Hope) to which the report refers—(having been a resident of La Porte and vicinity for eighteen years, and much of that time engaged in buying gold dust)—know it to be correct.

S. WHEELER,

Cashier Bank of La Porte.

TO THE PRESIDENT AND DIRECTORS OF THE PLUMAS CONSOLIDATED
MINING COMPANY.

At your request, we have carefully read the foregoing report of C. W. Hendel, C. E., &c., and having been residents and miners ourselves in this district for the past eighteen years, and knowing something of the history of the several mining Co.'s in the immediate neighborhood of the Buckeye, Monitor and Good Hope claims, we find the report to be correct.

Very truly yours,

DIXON BRABBAN,

Late Dep. Ass't & Col. Int'l Revenue.

B. W. BARNES,

Late Dep. Col. Int'l Revenue and Ex-member

State Legislature.

SAN FRANCISCO, CAL., AUGUST 10, 1878.

I have personally examined the above mentioned property, and can certify to the correctness of foregoing report. The statements of yield of gold have been verified by the books of Wells, Fargo & Co. And the Bank of La Porte.

H. BARTLING.

The
Lightfoot
Gold
Dredging
Company

52 Broadway

New York

The Lightfoot
Gold Dredging Company

INCORPORATED UNDER THE LAWS
OF ARIZONA

CAPITAL STOCK, $1,500,000

PAR VALUE, $1.00 PER SHARE

750,000 SHARES IN TREASURY

OFFICERS.

S. S. LIGHTFOOT - - - - - - *President.*

G. H. TAYLOR, - - - - *Vice-President.*

GEO. H. LIGHTFOOT, - *Sec'y and Treas.*

DIRECTORS.

S. S. LIGHTFOOT, G. H. TAYLOR,

GEO. H. LIGHTFOOT, MYRON L. JUSTIN.

W. GIBBES WHALLEY.

DEPOSITORY.

NEW AMSTERDAM NATIONAL BANK,
NEW YORK CITY.

SUITE 1241.
52 BROADWAY, NEW YORK CITY
PHONE 4206 BROAD

READ OUR OFFER.

WE PUT UP MARKETABLE COLLATERAL TO GUARANTEE OUR STOCK.

Our method of selling this stock is one that insures the investor absolutely against loss in any way as we put up with the stock marketable collateral that is traded in daily on the New York and Boston Markets.

We have about $250,000 worth of such collateral for this purpose.

The original intention of this Company was to hold it as a close corporation and borrow the necessary money on our securities, but owing to the market conditions we were unable to get the loan for a sufficient length of time. This has forced us to place our stock on the market, and, in order to dispose of it quickly, we are placing our collateral with the investors at 75 per cent. of its value as a guarantee with this provision: that if the Dredge is not installed and paying dividends at the end of eighteen months from the time of the purchase of the stock, the Company has either to refund the money with interest or forfeit the collateral.

Our collateral is First Mortgage Gold Bonds on Eastern Real Estate.

Under normal conditions we could borrow 75 per cent. of the value of our collateral, so you see we are absolutely sure of the success of our proposition or we would not risk our securities in this way.

We consider the above offer sufficient for the average person, but we go still further, and offer to take any person or their representative out on the property and prove every statement made in this prospectus, provided we are given a guarantee that they will invest a sufficient amount to warrant our doing so.

IN OTHER WORDS WE ARE WILLING TO STAND ANY TEST YOU CAN THINK OF TO PROVE UP OUR PROPOSITION.

A FEW FACTS
ABOUT PLACER MINING.

The auriferous gravel deposits called "Placers," result from the breaking down, grinding and disintegration, by Nature's erosive forces, of the gold bearing mountain tops and sides, the broken and partially disintegrated material being swept to, and deposited on, the bedrock of the surrounding country by floods and mighty river currents.

Three-fours of all the gold in leads, ledges and quartz veins consists of invisibly fine, or miscroscopic, particles, and this proportion of microscopic gold is increased by the attrition due to the changes from ledge to placer.

Heretofore this invisibly fine gold has been lost by every method of placer mining, and the miner has had to depend on the remaining one-fourth, the **visible** particles, for his profit.

About half of the **visible** gold in placers exists in the form of what the miner calls flake, float, scale and flour gold, which is admittedly unsavable by ordinary methods, and it is therefore evident that placer mining in the past has resulted in the saving of but a small fraction of the total value in the ground worked.

The combination of conditions requisite for successful placer mining by old methods was difficult to find, or supply if lacking, so that, of the 600,000 square miles of placer ground in this country, less than 200 have been worked, and much of this vast, untouched area is quite as rich as any that has ever been worked.

Nevertheless, statistics show that at least three-fourths of the world's present supply of gold has been derived from placers.

Placers are the poor man's mines, because they are easily found, can be accurately and inexpensively tested, are simply and cheaply opened up, pay from the start; their product, often princely, is always **certain,** and can be safely calculated and relied upon. There are no railroads, smelters or middlemen between the placer miner and his product, which is the money metal—the world's standard of value—and not subject to fluctuation. The product, mostly profit, being the direct reward of honest work, without the taint of the tricks and schemes of "high finance," is absolutely "clean money," the volume of which is not affected by hard times, financial cataclysms, political upheavals or the condition of the Wall Street stock market.

Placer mining includes no intricate problems to be solved and none of that delving in the dark bowels of the earth in search of an unknown quantity, with a host of chances for failure, from numerous and unforeseen causes, as is the case in quartz mining. On the contrary, the work is all done in open day, on the surface, and every yard of gravel moved adds just so much to the bank account of the operator.

In a word, Nature has done the mining, eliminated the risks, and left nothing for the placer miner to do beyond the mere extraction of the gold she has placed on the dumps for him.

* * * *

THE LIGHTFOOT
GOLD DREDGING CO.

Own a magnificent body of placer ground situate in Riverside County, California, comprising 640 acres, or 32 full sized mining claims.

These claims lie between two richly mineralized ranges of mountains known as the Chucawalla ranges, and 22 miles east of Salton on the S. P. R. R., connected by good wagon road.

From several hundred pan tests made of this ground, the average value proves to be about $1.10 per cubic yard.

The average depth is about 60 feet, mineralized from the surface down, but of course the greater values being found on the bed rock.

There is abundance of water and wood on the property for all mining and domestic use, and the climatic conditions are such as to permit the working of the property all the year around.

Placer Gulch, included in this property, has been known and worked for the past 20 years by the "dry washers," whose system of gold saving is so crude that only the very coarsest gold and nuggets can be saved.

Locked up in this placer is approximately $64,-000,000 in gold, of which this Company proposes to become the possessor in the shortest possible time.

This ground will be operated by the **best** and most thoroughly up-to-date dredge the market affords. Its guaranteed capacity is 3,000 cubic yards of gravel per day, at a working cost of not over 4 cents per cubic yard, and it extracts practically **all** the values; the flake, scale, float, flour and microscopic gold mentioned herein.

Further—It is conservatively estimated that the by-products, sand-concentrates and platinum, made without extra cost by this dredge, will more than pay all running expenses, so that the gold will all be net profit.

What **one** such dredge operating on the Lightfoot placer will produce, can be easily and accurately determined by a few simple figures, and it is the purpose of the company to have at least three such plants at work within as many years.

The Lightfoot Gold Dredging Company has secured a perfect title to this ground.

The money necessary for the machinery and its installation is rapidly being placed in its treasury. A sufficient amount of its stock will be sold at 75c per share, covered by absolutely sound first mortgage bonds on Eastern real estate and other securities, all of which are traded in on the Boston and New York markets, to insure the early operation of this dredge and consequent dividends.

* * * *

REPORT ON AZTEC PLACER PROPERTY.

Los Angeles, June 25th, 1907.
The Lightfoot Gold Dredging Co.,
    52 Broadway, New York City.
Gentlemen:

In compliance with your request, I visited the Aztec Placer property and herewith submit my report on the same.

The Aztec Placer property consists of 32 full sized mining claims 600x1500 feet each, located about two miles east of the Chucawalla divide in the Chucawalla Mts., Riverside County, California, and about 22 miles east from Salton on the Southern Pacific R. R.

TITLES.

The property is held by regular location under and in compliance with all the requirements of Chapter VI, Title 32, of the Revised Statutes of the United States and the local customs, laws and regulations.

NAMES OF PROPERTIES.

The properties are located under the following names:

The Aztec Placer Mine No. 1.
The Aztec Placer Mine No. 2.
The Aztec Placer Mine No. 3.
The Aztec Placer Mine No. 4.
The Aztec Placer Mine No. 5.
The Aztec Placer Mine No. 6.
The Aztec Placer Mine No. 7.
The Aztec Placer Mine No. 8.

There are four full sized mining claims in each location, or about 80 acres, making in all 640 acres.

SURROUNDING GEOLOGICAL FORMATION:

The mountains surrounding this property are granite, and cutting this formation are large dykes and ledges of quartz, quartzite, and prophyry, with some limestone and iron. The quartz, porphyry and iron are heavily mineralized with gold, silver and copper.

The auriferous gravel deposits on these claims are caused by the breaking down, grinding and disintegration of these surrounding dykes and ledges of quartz and porphyry by the erosive forces of nature.

GRAVEL:

The gravel on this property is what is known as "placer in place," and owing to the conditions that have existed and now exist, the gravel has not traveled far from its source.

The ground measured up shows approximately 64,-000,000 cubic yards, of which fully 80 per cent. is auriferous gravel that carries from a trace to $9.00 per cubic yard.

The average depth to bed-rock is about 62 feet, and from 364 pan-tests made from all parts of the claims, shows an average value of $1.10 per cu. yard in fairly coarse gold.

Placer Gulch, on this property, is about two-thirds of a mile long and averages about 500 feet in width. This Gulch has been worked by the dry washers for the last 20 or more years, who average in the neighborhood of $18.00 per week, working only 4 to 5 hours per day, and handling from one-fourth to one-half a yard of gravel per day.

WATER:

There is developed on this property about 10 miners' inches of water and about twice as much more can be developed at a small expense.

WOOD:

Such timber as Iron-wood, Desert Pine and Pala Verde grow in abundance on and in the neighborhood of these claims.

ROADS:

The old Silver Trail, now the County Road, runs over the property and is in first class condition. This gives a good wagon road to Salton on the Southern Pacific R. R., about 22 miles away.

In conclusion, I am sure that a modern dredge will make this property one of the largest producers in the West.

Respectfully submitted,

F. E. COFFEY, M. E.

Showing how this Dredge t
one side at the rate of 3,0
separating the Gold a
deposits the waste
the clea

the rich gravel banks on
ards per day, and, after
luable by-products,
or "tailings," on
rock.

Estimated Income Per Month From One Dredge.

3,000 cu. yards of gravel per day, averaging $1.10
    per yard $99,000.00
To one Supt. at $10.00 per day....$ 300.00
To two Foremen at $5.00 per day.. 300.00
To two Engineers at $5.00 per day 300.00
To two Electricians at $5.00 per
    day 300.00
To one Blacksmith at $4.00 per day 120.00
To two Firemen at $2.50 per day.. 150.00
To one Teamster at $2.50 per day..   75.00
To four Surface men at $2 per day 240.00
To wear and tear on machinery.. 625.00
To interest on investment of $125,-
    000.00 at 10 per cent........ 1041.50
To Miscellaneous expenses at $5.00
    per day 150.00
    Total monthly expenses.......———— 3,601.50

Net monthly profits.................$95,398.50
About 6 per cent. per month on the entire capitalization.

About 72 per cent. per annum on the entire capitalization.

This shows a maximum cost of 4 cents per cubic yard of gravel handled and a net profit of $1.06 per cubic yard.

Total Cost of Dredge and Installation.

Dredge complete F. O. B. Pittsburg, Pa....$ 75,000
R. R. Freight to Salton, Cal. 7,000
Freight by team from Salton to property... 3,000
5 tons of quicksilver for amalgamation tank 7,500
Bunk houses, kitchen, etc................. 1,200
Wagon, trailer, team of 4 mules, harness, etc. 1,300
Reserve in Treasury for two months pay
    day, supplies and unforeseen incidentals 30,000

    Total amount $125,000

BASIC FACTS.

Your attention is called briefly to a few **basic facts** with which up-to-date Mining Engineers are more or less familiar.

Every process in vogue for the separation of gold from alluvial deposits is designed and operated on the **erroneous** idea that **all** gold is heavier than water.

As a scientific statement, gold has a **specific** gravity of 19.3, while the fact is, that as found in nature, gold **EXPRESSES** in running water, every gravity from 19 to **zero.**

At least 75 per cent of the total free gold contents of the earth's crust exists in infinitely fine particles, invisible to the eye, expressing no gravity in water currents and entirely unsavable by any process heretofore in vogue.

(The truth of this may be more clearly perceived in the quartz veins of the earth, the erosion and disintegration of which results in placers.)

The remaining 25 per cent. of the total is the **visible gold,** fully one-half of which exists in the form of "flake," "scale," "float," and what the miners term "flour gold." These grades of visible gold, **express** a gravity below 7; and are unsavable in sluice currents, or by the devices employed on ordinary gold dredges.

The sluice current (and every modification thereof—as "under currents" and the various devices found on ordinary gold dredges) must necessarily be sufficiently strong to carry off the "iron sand," which expresses a gravity of 6 to 7, and such a current carries with it all the gold expressing a similar or less gravity, including the visible flake, float, and flour, and **of course, all** of the invisible gold referred to above.

It is a well-known rule that coarse or heavy gold (expressing a gravity of 12 or more), is found at or near the bed-rock with large boulders and coarse gravel, and that fine gravel, free from boulders, carries only the finer, lighter gold.

The ordinary dredge cannot be successfully operated where there are large boulders, nor can it save the fine gold constituting the bulk of the value in the fine gravel.

Thus it is evident that the field in which they can be employed with some profit is confined to those few localities wherein there is sufficient gold ranging in gravity from (approximately) 6 to 12 to pay expenses and provide a profit.

This accounts for the fabulously high prices paid for just such ground at Oroville, Cal., and the failure of these dredges, in admittedly rich ground at other points.

The exceedingly imperfect adaptability of the New Zealand type of dredge to the duty required in placer mining, resulting in frequent breakdowns, the impossibility of their doing clean, or nearly clean work on the bed-rock, or of preventing the constant spillage from the ascending buckets back into the worked out pit, and the necessity of their being floated, even on otherwise dry ground, are among the many additional disadvantages under which, owing to their design and construction, this type of dredge must always operate.

Practically all auriferous alluvial deposits carry a proportion of **"iron sand,"** worth approximately $10 per ton; also, a proportion of **mineralized grains** of quartz, often worth several hundred dollars per ton. The Pacific belt, from Alaska to the Cape Horn, in addition to these values, carries **platinum** to the extent of a few cents to several dollars—in one instance as high as $10 per cubic yard of gravel, as shown by over 1,000 tests. All of these values are ignored by the processes in vogue.

In the **New Era System** is presented the final, scientific and practical solution of the entire question of free gold extraction, whether from auriferous alluvial deposits or free gold bearing quartz veins.

In thirty years of field work along these lines we have found no auriferous alluvial deposit presenting any insurmountable obstacle to the successful operation of one or the other type of the New Era system.

In this type the separating apparatus is mounted on the all-steel body of a specially adapted shovel car, on trucks resting on a railway track laid on the bed-rock. These trucks are very heavy and so designed as to provide, while digging, a bed-rock base of 20x26 feet.

This type has a guaranteed capacity of 3,000 cubic yards of gravel per (24-hour) day, will treat 25 per cent. more without undue crowding, requires only a fraction of the water necessary to sluicing devices, which water may be taken from below the level of the ground being worked, and if scarce, may be used over and over continuously.

They are arranged to take current from their own or any power station.

The cost of operation varies from 1½ to 3½ cents per cubic yard.

The New Era
Gold Dredging System.

Which we intend to use consists mainly of an electrically-operated, specially-adapted, all-steel **shovel —or dredge**—upon which is mounted the perfected and thoroughly demonstrated separator, gravitator and amalgamator, together with the various motors operating the whole.

The direct power—electricity—is furnished by a 400 H. P. engine directly connected with a 400 H. P. generator—or by a water power.

The water supply is handled by a power pump, capable of forcing 2500 gallons per minute against 150 ft. head, which is driven by a direct connected 175 H. P. motor.

The sand tailings and waste water are handled by a sand pump of corresponding capacity, driven by a direct connected 40 H. P. motor.

The coarse tailings, including stones from ⅜ of an inch to 2½ ft. in diameter, are systematically piled on the cleaned-up bed-rock by an all-steel carrier, driven by a direct connected 10 H. P. motor.

The **shovel**-type is employed in ordinary placer work, as gulch, bar, hill diggings, etc. It is constructed throughout of steel—largely manganese— is unbreakably strong, durable beyond a life-time, simple beyond comparison, and perfectly reliable for continuous operation at full rated capacity of from 2500 to 3500 cubic yards of gravel per 24-hour day. The shovel and its equipment, as it stands on its 8-foot track, on the bed-rock, weighs approximately 120 tons, and through its side braces, has a base of 20x26 feet on the bed-rock. It makes a cut 60 feet in width by any length, is self-propelling and takes in everything from bed-rock to surface, including boulders 2½ feet in diameter and handling those of 15 to 20 tons each with ease and celerity. Its two-yard electrically-operated and specially-designed patent dipper has a capacity of 140 to 150 cubic yards per hour, which capacity is fully maintained throughout the entire plant, which is so nearly automatic as to require but one man, assisted by two or three common laborers, for its complete operation at full capacity.

In operation the gravel is passed from the dipper into the hopper, thence through a 4-foot opening into the immense revolving manganese steel separator (weighing about 7 tons, and operated by a 25 H. P. motor), wherein each stone, from 3/8 of an inch to 2½ feet diameter, is thoroughly scoured, rinsed and drained, then gently deposited on the carrier which delivers it at the dump; every particle of pay dirt having meantime passed through the separator screens and into the gravitating and amalgamating tank for treatment.

The tank, which is of peculiar shape to adapt it to the requirements, is 25x12x6 feet, of steel boiler plate.

It would be difficult, if not impossible, in the space alloted to describe the operations which take place in this tank. Suffice it to say that, for the first time in the history of free gold extraction, science is applied and the operation is based on the fact that, though gold has a **specific** gravity of 19, it, as found in nature, **expresses** in water every gravity from 19 to **less than 1.**

Each particle that enters the tank is scoured 35 times in a powerful sand blast, by which adhering particles are separated and the coated or rusty gold is brightened or cleaned and thus rendered ready for instant amalgamation.

Every particle which enters the tank is placed in practically **still** water, where it is subjected to the law of gravity, so that particles expressing a gravity beyond that of the common sand settles 2 inches and directly into pockets, of which there are 1200 in the tank, so arranged, with relation to induced, arbitrary currents, that every particle must necessarily have this opportunity to express its gravity **more** than **400 times.** Each pocket is a small "**pan**" or concentrator, per se, and once a particle has entered there is absolutely no escape.

While this is taking place with gold expressing a gravity of 3 or over, the lighter gold, including the invisibly fine particles which are held in suspension in water—and which almost invariably constitutes the vast bulk of the total value—is being brought into **metallic** and **unavoidable** contact with **non-oxi- dizable** amalgamating surfaces from 400 to 1,000 times, always under **ideal conditions** for instant amal- gamation. The infinitely fine gold, thus absorbed from the water, is constantly being deposited with the coarser or visible particles in the pockets, where it rests until the clean-up, which can be made at any time within an hour.

In Conclusion.

If you are thinking of investing in this Company you will find that you must do it quickly as this stock will not take very long to close out. There will be **only** a sufficient amount sold to purchase and install the Dredge and the moment that is accomplished this property will be one of the largest dividend paying concerns in the United States.

This is no idle boast but a thing we can and are willing to prove to you if you will let us. The officers and directors of this Company are men of standing and known as practical business and mining men.

The Secretary and Treasurer of this Company is a member of the Los Angeles Chamber of Mines which has done more to clear the market of "fake mining" than any organization ever organized.

WE HAVE A CLEAN BILL OF HEALTH AND INVITE YOU TO INSPECT THE SAME.

All checks, drafts or money orders must be made payable to The Lightfoot Gold Dredging Co., and NOT to any agent or individual officer or director of the Company.

Personal References of S. S. Lightfoot and Geo. H. Lightfoot.

MESSRS. WHALEY & WALKER,
27 William Street,   New York City;
MR. B. M. CALKINS,
Care of B. M. Calkins, Assayers Supply Co.,
Baker Block,   Los Angeles, California;
HON. L. H. VALENTINE,
Care Valentine & Newby,
Wilcox Bldg.,   Los Angeles, California;
BAVRESTOCK & STAPLES, Mining Engineers,
Los Angeles, California;
and others on application.

Personal References of G. H. Taylor, V. P.

MR. WILLIAM V. NEVINS,
Care Wells Fargo Co.,   51 B-way, New York;
MR. WILLIAM J. BECKER,
Care Bischoff's Banking House,
237 Broadway,   New York City;
CASHIER, PATERSON NATIONAL BANK,
Paterson, N. J.
FORMANS STUMPF & SHARP,
Silk Dyers,   Paterson, N. J.
F. CORRIN,
Manager Corrin Chemical Co.,   Paterson, N. J.

Personal References of Myron L. Justin, Director

MR. F. S. BENNETT, Manager.
New Era Gold Extraction Co.,   52 Broadway, New York;
MR. GEORGE R. SUTHERLAND,
49 Wall Street,   New York City;
MR. J. J. McDAVITT,
German Ins. Bldg.,
Cor. Nassau and Liberty Sts.,   New York City;
MR. E. L. ENNIS,
Manager, Milhaus Sons, Druggists,
205 Broadway,   New York City;
MR. T. S. JOHNSON, Real Estate,
302 Broadway,   New York City.

Personal references of W. Gibbes Whaley, Director.

MESSRS. PICKERING & WALKER,
No. 5 East 42nd St.,   New York City;
HON. WM. A. BARBER,
No. 5 Nassau St.,   New York City.

"There is a tide in the affairs of men,
Which, taken at the flood,
Leads on to fortune."
Julius Cæsar

GOLD

FROM

THE

MOTHER LODE

OF

CALIFORNIA

LOS ANGELES
CALIFORNIA

"It is not enough to speak, but to speak true. Truth makes all things plain."

"A hoarded dollar is like a man after the undertaker is through with him—A dead one."

SOMETHING ABOUT THE

PRUDHOMME
GOLD
MINING & MILLING CO.

OFFICERS

A. C. HARPER .... President
A. C. JONES.............Vice-President
J. R. KLINE ....Secretary
AUGUSTUS D.HARPER Treasurer

DIRECTORS

C. C. REYNOLDS ....Harper & Reynolds Co. Hardware
A. C. JONES ....Los Angeles Furniture Company
J. R. KLINE ....Sec'y Los Angeles Builders' Exchange
A. C. HARPER...........................Consolidated Pipe Co., Los Angeles
J. W. MORRISON......... ....Building Contractor, Los Angeles
F J. HARRINGTON,...........Supt' Quartette Mines, Searchlight, Nev.
A. W. BRYANT ....Sup't Prudhomme Mines, Carters, Cal.

DEPOSITORY
Los Angeles National Bank

OFFICE ADDRESS
532 STIMSON BLOCK   .   .   LOS ANGELES, CAL.

MINE ADDRESS
CARTERS, TUOLUMNE COUNTY, CALIFORNIA

THE
PRUDHOMME
GOLD
MINING AND
MILLING CO.

Is a corporation duly incorporated and organized under the laws of the State of California.

Its charter provides that its stock shall be full-paid.

Its capital stock is 1,000,000 shares of the par value of $1.00 each, 600,000 shares of which is in the treasury.

Its Home Office is in the City of Los Angeles, Cal.

The company have acquired by purchase and possessory title under the United States mining laws, three valuable claims 600x1500 feet each, as hereinafter described, located in Tuolumne county, on the east belt of the famous Mother Lode of California.

The
Men

who are interested in this organization are not promoters or speculators in any sense, who seek to unload their own stock or properties upon the public for their self aggrandizement, but established business men of integrity, experience and commercial standing, who, after the closest scrutiny and careful investigation have invested their own money in these properties, as a purely business enterprise, being fully convinced of the wisdom of their investment.

Mining
is no

longer the gamble it used to be. Modern science has furnished the means whereby the possibilities of reaping

KIDDER PEABODY
G

SUPERINTENDENT'S OFFICE AND STAMP MILL—PRUDHOMME MINE

profit from a mine can be determined to almost an actual certainty. It remains, therefore, for the would-be investor in mining enterprises and stocks, before placing his or her money, to exercise the same ordinary precautions called for when contemplating any other business investment. Reckless investors have been, and doubtless will continue to be caught by the sophistry and glittering generalities employed by unscrupulous promoters. Few there are who would intrust their money to a savings bank conducted by men whose ability and standing was not vouchsafed beyond question.

When about to invest in mining stocks, look well to the ability, character and commercial standing of the men who direct the fortunes of the corporation, and it is seldom you will have occasion to investigate the property involved, since no able business man of good judgment will lend his name, devote his time, much less invest his money in a doubtful enterprise.

With these salient principles in mind, we ask your careful consideration of the contents of this Prospectus, and solicit the most searching investigation into the management and property of this company.

Location of the Prudhomme Mines

The property of this corporation consists of three regular mining claims, 600x1500 feet each, on the Prudhomme vein on the Mother Lode, known as the "Prudhomme," the "Prudhomme South Extension" and the "Clover Valley," comprising a total of 62 1-10 acres.

This group of mines is situated about two and one-half miles southeast of Carters, a station on the Sierra Railway, twelve miles east of Sonora, the county seat of Tuolumne County, all being in the Tuolumne Mining District, which was organized in 1850.

The altitude is 3750 feet above sea level, and 1200 feet

PRUDHOMME HOIST AND ENGINE BUILDING

higher than the railway station, and the mines are reached by a good wagon road four miles in length.

Title

The "Prudhomme" is a patented claim, and the other two are held under location and possession provided for in the mining laws of the United States.

This company is in peaceable possession of the property, and the title is fully vested in it.

The Mother Lode

The Spanish name *Vestas Madras,* or Mother Lode, is conferred upon a long, continuous and well defined belt of mineral producing country, on account of its great size and productive capacity. Commencing on the north at Drytown, near the center of Amador county, our Mother Lode extends thence south 27°, east to the Princeton group of mines, in the vicinity of Mount Ophir, traversing in its course the southern half of Calaveras and Tuolumne and about a third of Mariposa counties. The California *Vesta Madre* is of vast proportions and extreme length, and though a unit, considered in its entirety, does not everywhere con- fine itself to a single channel. At a few points it splits up into several branches—sometimes as many as four or five—which, running nearly parallel for a consider- able distance, again reunite. These deflections, how- ever, are very trifling, considering its remarkable length, the deviation being not more than a mile or so, either way, from an absolutely straight line. In direction this great lode corresponds with the longitudinal axis of the Sierra Nevada range of mountains, running cen- trally along the southern arm of the main California gold-field, being flanked on either side by an auriferous zone varying from ten to fifteen miles in breadth, which carries about all the mines, both vein and placer, in this section of the State. *Nearly every important quartz lode* as well as rich placers heretofore worked, lie to the east of the great vein. On that side are Volcano, West Point, Tuolumne ,and other well-known quarty districts with· Columbia, Sonora and Jamestown, besides several minor localities, all famous for their long years of great productiveness. It is now forty-one years since active operations were first inaugurated on the Mother Lode of California. The famous Amador Mine was first worked in the spring of 1852 and for ten years in succession the total annual production of this mine averaged nearly half a million dollars, and it has always returned a yearly income running into the hundreds of thousands of dollars. In contemplating these *absolute facts* regarding the Mother Lode, bear in mind that the ·Prudhomme Mining property is located on the east belt of this great vein, is a developed and producing mine, with all the characteristics of the other great producers mentioned, the ore of which when ·compared therewith cannot be distinguished apart.

Prudhomme Early History

The Prudhomme mine was first discovered by Mr. Francis Prudhomme in 1879, and was worked by him in a crude way for a number of years. He kept his work confined above the water level by tunneling and short underhand stopes. The total extraction of gold by such work, the ore being worked in Arrastras run by water power, was as shown by mint memoranda $17,000.

Geological

The ore vein of this mine has the following characteristics:

Strike N. 10 degrees east of 62 degrees, dip 68 degrees west, at times being almost vertical, width of vein being from one to six feet, the pay chute of which is from six to forty-two inches in width.

The outcrop can be traced for a distance of 4,000 feet, entirely covering the Prudhomme and extending from both ends into the Prudhomme South Extension and Clover Valley.

The Prudhomme vein cuts the formation, the walls being at times Granite, Porphyry, Slate and Diorite, the foot wall being the same, but being displaced about six feet by eruptive forces.

Oxidized ores extend down 150 feet, and below that depth it is a highly mineralized sulphide, at times running into galena with values running into the hundreds of dollars, the sulphurets or concentrates from the vanners being worth an average of $52.00 per ton.

The country rock or wall is generally granite or diorite, changing often.

The surrounding mines, which are numerous, have the same general characteristics as to formation and strike and dip of veins.

Present Development

On the Prudhomme mine there are a total of 1794 linear feet of development work, consisting of 340 feet of shaft, 490 feet of tunnel, 200 feet of raises and 764 feet of drifts, altogether, having a cost value of approximately $31,000, including stoping and crosscuts not included in above list of developments. The Prudhomme mine has four parallel veins from forty to ninety feet apart at the surface. Before this company acquired the property there was considerable surface word done on each vein by Mr. Prudhomme, the lowest depth attained being forty-six feet. From these workings alone gold to the value of $4000 was taken out. Experts who have examined the mine state that from appearances, and the dip and general characteristics, there is no doubt whatever that these four veins will all consolidate with depth and form a very

STAMP MILL—PRUDHOMME MINE

rich paying mine. The three claims lay lengthways north and south, along the general trend of the Mother Lode. Since purchasing these mines three years ago, the present owners have spent upwards of $75,000 in equipment and development work, their main object having been to first demonstrate the permanent productiveness of the property; though while prosecuting this work of development they have taken out about $20,000, the ore having averaged $18.00 gold per ton.

Very high grade ore is frequently encountered, which is shipped direct to the Selby Smelting and Lead Co. at San Francisco for treatment.

During the six months prior to June 15, 1903, there was shipped three and one-quarter tons of first-class ore, which netted $290.00 per ton. The following communications received speak for themselves:

SELBY SMELTING & LEAD CO.,

Office 416 Montgomery St.,
San Francisco, Cal., June 15, 1903.
Prudhomme Gold Mining & Milling Co.,
Carters, Cal.
Gentlemen: We inclose returns for 456 sacks of ore and sulphurets received from you on June 8th, also our check No. 3582, for $1369.59, in settlement. Please sign and return receipt. You will note we have allowed a working charge of $6.00 per ton on the sulphurets, which is our contract price. We regard this as an extremely low rate, and to avoid any chance of its being advanced, we suggest you enter into a contract with us for a year's output. If this meets with your approval, please advise, and we will forward the contract for your signature.
Yours very truly,
(Signed)   SELBY SMELTING & LEAD COMPANY.
Per Chas. J. Durbrow.

———

THE MINT OF THE UNITED STATES AT SAN FRANCISCO, CAL.

Superintendent's Office.
June 5, 1903.
Prudhomme Gold Mining & Milling Co.
Carters, Cal.
Dear Sirs: As requested in yours of 3d inst., we inclose you herewith Supt. check No. 11629, on the Asst. Treas., U. S., this city, drawn in your favor, for $701.16 covering the proceeds of a gold deposit made for

you June 4, 1903, less $1.35 express charges paid on bullion received.

Memorandum of Mint deposit inclosed herewith.

Very respectfully,

(Sogned)   FRANK A. LEACH,
                                       Superintendent.

THE MINT OF THE UNITED STATES AT SAN
FRANCISCO, CAL.
Superintendent's Office.
July 3, 1903.
Prudhomme Gold Mining & Milling Co.
    A. W. Bryant, Supt.,
        Carters, Cal.

Dear Sir: As requested in yours of the 29th, ult., we inclose herewith Supt. check No. 11692, on the Asst. Treas., U. S., this city, drawn in your favor, for $1,247.62, covering the proceeds of a gold deposit made for you July 2, 1903, less $1.90 express charges paid on bullion received. Memorandum of Mint deposit enclosed herewith.

Very respectfully,

(Signed)   BEN W. DAY,
                                       Chief Clerk.

Equipment

Our present equipment is as follows:

One 2-story mill building.

One large building for hoist, drying-room and storage.

One superintendent's office building.

One assay office.

One boarding house.

Two bunk houses.

One blacksmith shop.

One five-stamp mill, each stamp 850 pounds.

One Dodge rock-breaker with grizzly.

Two six-foot Johnson concentrators.

One ore-feeder.

One 40 H. P. boiler.

One 25 H. P. engine.

One steam hoist good for 1000 feet depth, capacity 2000 pounds.

2000 feet of 3 to 16-inch piping with water ditches and Pelton wheels for conducting water.

Blacksmith tools, mining implements and numerous other incidentals.

PRUDHOMME MINING CREW

Fuel, Timber, Water, Power, Etc.

For fuel, there is a large supply of pine timber surrounding the mines. Mining timbers are cut from the claims at small cost. Water for power is plentiful at a cost of five cents per miner's inch (8.796 gallons per minute), for twenty-four hours, and has sufficient fall to operate ten stamps with vanners and rock-breakers under a twenty-foot head, this power being furnished by the Tuolumme County Water and Electric Power Co. The power company now charge $3.50 per day to operate five stamps, also furnishing all water for boiler and domestic purposes.

By building additional flumes and laying pipe, the above power can be increased, or all the works can be operated by using fuel oil at about the same price as for wood.

Transportation

The mines being located only four miles from the railroad station at Carters, over a good road, with no climatic conditions to prevent easy teaming at all seasons of the year, and the county seat of Sonora being only twelve miles from Carters by rail, where there are first-class supply stores, founderies, machine shops, etc., we have easy access to a nearby source of supply for every want, with rapid, easy and uninterrupted transportation. It is only 152 miles by rail to San Francisco, with daily trains both ways. No mines in the world are more favorably located as regards easy communication and access to source of supply or prompt and sure transportation.

Surrounding Mines

The surrounding and adjoining mines are the "Driesam," with a complete plant consisting of a six-

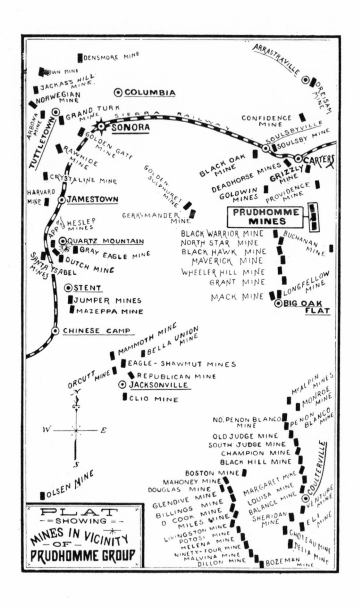

PLAT
=SHOWING=
MINES IN VICINITY
-OF-
PRUDHOMME GROUP

stamp mill, compressor, and water and steam power, with a depth of 450 feet.

The "Providence," with a steam plant, ten-stamp mill, a depth of 1200 feet and a record production of $2,000,-000.

The "Black Oak," with the most complete surface plant that can be devised, composing a forty-stamp mill, vanners, canvas plant, water and steam plant; the depth of the main shaft is 1400 feet. Present production, about $40,000 net per month.

The "Confidence," which has been worked continuously for over forty years and has produced over $5,-000,000. They have a steam plant at present requiring eleven cords of wood daily, a twenty-stamp mill and a cyanide plant of 100 tons capacity, with shaft down 900 feet.

The "Soulsby," which has produced $8,000,000, has a water plant and a ten-stamp mill. The vein of this mine is very small and in granite, but none of its ore has run less than $40.00 per ton. The shaft is 800 feet deep. This mine is located but one and a quarter miles northwest of the "Prudhomme." The "Marble Spring" mine has produced $1,500,000; the "Banderetta," $1,500,000; the "Helso," $1,000,000, and the "Hoyt," $3,000,000. Several other mines in the immediate vicinity have produced heavily, notably the "Grizzly," "Deadhorse" and "Buchanan," all having twenty-stamp mills, etc., and a production record of millions of dollars. Many of the Tuolumme county mines have very large stamp mills. The "Eagle-Shawmut" have 130; the "Jumper," 100; the "App Consolidated," 60, and the "Melones," 120 stamps. In the county there are upwards of fifty gold mines in active operation with a total mill capacity of about 1200 stamps, all producing largely.

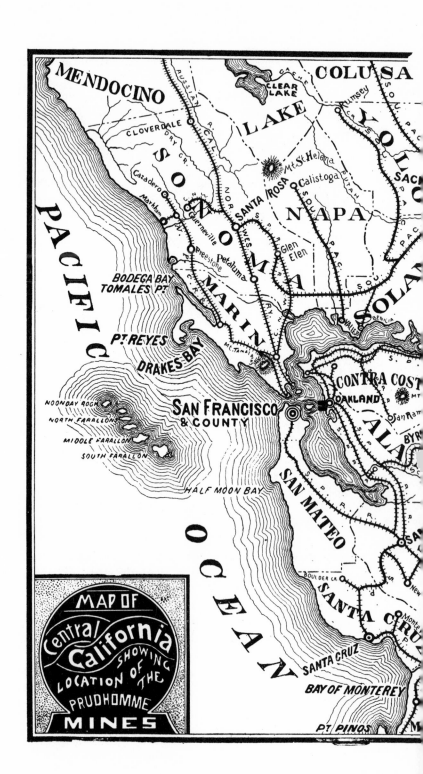

MAP OF Central California SHOWING LOCATION OF THE PRUDHOMME MINES

California Gold Mining

Since the discovery of gold in California in 1848, the State has given to the world $1,425,512,689 in gold. The greatest output was in 1852, when more than eighty-one and a quarter million of dollars worth was mined. For the past twenty years the average annual product has been about sixteen and one-quarter millions. The indications are that the amount will be increased for succeeding years to nearly or quite twenty millions. Improved machinery, more scientific methods in handling raw materials, and more capital intelligently invested, should largely increase the product, as, according to the best mineralogists, there is enough gold-bearing earth now "in sight" to last for a score of years. Gold mining in California is really an "awakened industry," as with the greatly improved concentrators, the chlorinating process and the cyanide process, there has been a remarkable increase in the returns from nearly all mining sections. Under the old system it was known that much of the gold was lost. Under the new, it is certain that nearly, if not all of it, is saved. Where formerly ores and mineral ground were abandoned because they could not be worked with profit, fortunes are now being realized by means of the modern processes. Thus it is that the lottery or gambling features of gold mining have passed away, and it has now become a regular systematic business.

In Tuolumne county, where the Prudhomme mines are located, gold was first discovered about fifty years ago. Up to 1892 its record of gold production was three hundred millions of dollars, making it the banner gold-producing county of the State. A greater portion of the gold mining of the State is carried on by large companies and corporations, as it must necessarily be on account of the amount of capital required for its successful prosecution.

Operating Expenses

The accessibility of our location to the county seat, also the markets of San Francisco in a day's time, the nine hours of labor and the remuneration therefor being more reasonable than that of any other portion of the State, cause us to be particularly favored by being able to operate at a very reasonable expense. The present scale of wages are as follows:

Superintendent, $125 per month; foreman, $3.50 to $4.00 per day; engineer, $3.50; blacksmith, $3.50; miners, $3.00; carmen, $2.50; carpenters, $3.50; top labor, $2.50; millmen, $3.50; timbermen, $3.50; machine drillers, $3.50; hoistmen, $3.00, and cook, $50 per month. Four-horse teams with driver, $8.00 per day. All other classes of labor, $3.00 per day. The officers of the company draw no salary, nor will they until the mine is paying regular dividends. This does not mean that the officers do nothing, on the contrary, they are all heavily interested financially, and have been, and are now, working hard for the success of the mine. The work is under systematic direction, with a highly competent superintendent, mill runs, assays, pay roll, etc., and every item is properly checked and recorded. The books are open for inspection at all times to stockholders or interested purchasers of stock.

What We Want

The Prudhomme is now a fully developed and productive property, ready to pour forth its wealth into the coffers of the stockholders as soon as we are able to economically take out and work the large bodies of rich ore now known to rest in its veins.

Our small five-stamp mill with which we have been crushing the ore from development work, makes our expense, in proportion to the tonnage handled, too

VIEW OF PRUDHOMME SHAFT

great. We are at that stage when we can commence actual production for profit, and desire to do so that the stockholders may reap the harvest due to them from the seed that has been so wisely sown. To do this to the greatest advantage and maximum profit, we want an additional fifteen-stamp mill, an air compressor, two or more air drills and an air baby drill, together with boiler capacity sufficient to operate the same. With these, we can sink the shaft deeper and extend the levels more rapidly, carrying the stopes at several points, and thus handle the entire ore vein on which we are now working profitably to a grade as low as $8.00 per ton, should it ever run as low as that.

In gold mining, the highest proportionate profit is always attained by milling large tonnage.

With the additional equipment, as above ennumerated, the very best possible results would be realized, and the Prudhomme property would soon take its place high up on the list of dividend-paying mines with which it is so closely surrounded.

What We Can Do

Our money and labor has acquired this property and brought it to the productive stage. It is at present in as active operation as our facilities will warrant.

With our small five-stamp mill we have not been able to turn out more than $3200 per month. A larger mill capacity once installed, can be operated at about the same expense as the present one, thus enabling us, while increasing our output, to greatly enhance the proportionate profits of the company, and we have now blocked out large bodies of rich ore, which only awaits adequate and proper facilities to handle and work it to the best advantage.

With the increased capacity and facilities enumerated above, we can handle at least 75 tons of ore daily at a cost of $2.50 per ton.

Working ore averaging $18.00 per ton and saving 90 per cent, would give us the following result:

75 tons at $18.00 per ton.....................$1350.00
Cost of mining and milling $2.50 per ton...... 187.50

Net profit per day........................$1162.50

When this is done, the treasury stock of the company now offered for sale will be readily saleable at several times its par value.

Gold Mining Stocks as an Investment

We have stated that *gold* mining has ceased to be a gamble and an uncertainty and become a stable business, and given the reasons therefor. This being a fact, it follows that the stocks of bona fide, well-managed gold mining companies must be good legitimate investments.

Note particularly that we say *GOLD*. Silver and copper mining stocks fluctuate with the prices of those metals which are ever changing. *GOLD NEVER FLUCTUATES IN VALUE. It is the standard of value.* By it the value of all other metals are determined.

Expectations based upon copper and silver stocks, however well managed the companies may be, can never be realized with any degree of certainty in the face of a fluctuating or depreciating market. On the contrary, given a practical milling demonstration of what it can produce, with a fixed amount of ore in sight, as is the case with the Prudhomme mining properties, and the stock of such mining company is a safe, profitable and legitimate investment. This fact is vividly illustrated by the recent decline of values in Wall street, which amounts to two and one-quarter billions of dollars.

PRUDHOMME BLACKSMITH SHOP

This is many times more money than was ever lost in the mining history of the world, including that occasioned in the Transvaal by the South African war. We quote the following as a valuable opinion by an undoubted authority on the subject:

"The unparalled prosperity of the mining industry at the present time is attracting wide-spread attention. People are beginning to realize that fortune and competency can be acquired by investing in mining properties and mining stocks. In fact, the number who are realizing this and profiting by it is daily increasing. They are beginning to learn that there is an element of hazard *in every business venture*, but not as great a risk in mining as has been imagined in the past. Continued successes have taught them that mining is a business; that improved machinery, scientific knowledge and business management place mining on as safe a basis as the ordinary business enterprise; also that thousands of people are acquiring wealth by judicious investments in mining stocks, the result of their co-operation in the development of meritorious properties of ably conducted, legitimate mining enterprises."

The National Banker, Chicago, June, 25, 1902

Returns from Product

From the returns of the number of shipments of high grade ore and concentrates we have made to the Selby Smelting and Lead Co., at San Francisco, and of bullion deposited with the United States mint, we give below the result of one each, to show how our product runs. It should be understood that the concentrates contain the gold remaining after the free gold has been caught on the plates. This is sent to the refinery for the gold to be extracted. Remember, the rich ore only is shipped away for treatment, the lower grade ore being worked at the mill, thus saving cost of transportation.

Assays

The following assays are of battery samples of ore taken from various sections of the Prudhomme vein, together with that of concentrates and ore shipped to the refinery, covering a period of twelve months to June 19, 1903. They are copied from the records of the assay office at the mine:

GOLD VALUE PER TON

From drift and stope	From 100 ft. level	Concentrates	High grade ore not milled, shipped to refinery	Low grade ore
$14.46	$21.70	$ 45.44	$578.76	$12.40
11.37	13.63	43.41	571.37	7.24
13.70	12.40	50.02	475.38	15.51
15.15.	8.45	54.75	228.40	11.30
7.23	11.37	49.86	214.83	14.46
12.40	9.30	93.14	229.75	9.82
22.72	27.84	95.08	206.70	7.24
15.60	31.40	100.24	190.16	6.20
45.47	21.92	51.67	384.17	6.10
44.34	. . . . . .	44.60	229.44	8.37
28.60	. . . . . .	49.63	231.50	8.89
24.80	. . . . . .	44.34	231.02	. . . . . .
20.15	. . . . . .	62.84	256.40	. . . . . .
16.54	. . . . . .	. . . .	208.65	. . . . . .
25.17				
21.18				
13.27				
9.24	The ore milled, averages $18.00 per ton gold			
9.30				
21.70				
14.52				

Items

January 5, 1903, the U. S. mint received from us one bar of gold bullion weighing 5470 ounces, which, after melting, produced 5467.706 ounces of the value of

GOLDWIN MILL

$797.86 and .271 ounces of silver of the value of $7.05, making a total of $804.91.

June 15, 1903, we shipped to the Selby Smelting & Lead Co. 66 sacks of *ORE* weighing 4950 pounds, which yielded $729.29 gold, being an average of $290.05 per ton.

On the same date we also shipped 390 sacks of *concentrates* weighing 45,790 pounds, which yielded $946.92, being an average of $36.49 per ton. This was the lowest average of any shipment of concentrates made during the past three years.

Why we ask you to Invest

The gentlemen who have invested their money for the purchase, and devoted their time and ability to directing the development of the Prudhomme mining properties thus far, are established merchants in the city of Los Angeles, Cal., whose character and business records and standing in this live, prosperous community are as an open book which all can read who will scan its pages.

While they are men of considerable means, each have large business establishments to sustain and, not being millionaires or capitalists in the strict sense of the word, they wisely decided it would be better business policy to donate six-tenths of the capital stock of this company to its treasury to be used as required in enlarging the plant, etc., and, as the mine is now at the producing stage, push the work vigorously in the most advantageous manner, and thus quickly place the enterprise on a dividend-paying basis. Our faith in our undertaking is amply proven by our past actions and other facts set forth herein.

We are now prepared to convey to those who are seeking investment such interests as individuals may deem it wise to purchase out of the treasury stock of the company, that we may secure the necessary capital with which to successfully bring the enterprise quickly to the point of yielding large returns for small investments, and the low price at which we offer our first block of treasury stock certainly makes the investment an exceptionally attractive one from a financial point of view, both to the small and large investor. The opportunity here offered for a strictly legitimate interest in a developed gold mine is a rare one. We ask your serious consideration of the statements herein. *They are absolute facts.*

Where your Money will go

The Treasury Stock is the property of the company. It is placed there for the benefit of the shareholders. Every dollar realized from the sale of treasury stock is therefore your money in proportion to the shares you purchase. It is virtually banking your money to your credit. You have a right to expect that this money will be honestly expended for the installment of the additional equipment required, and the development of the property to your advantage, and the board of directors and officers of this corporation pledge themselves as honorable business men that this shall be done in the isest manner possible, so that the stock you may now purchase for cents shall quickly grow into dollars.

> "Our doubts are traitors,
> and make us loose the good we oft might win,
> by fearing to attempt."   *Shakespeare*

Do
Not
Hesitate

but fill out the enclosed blank, and send it to us with draft, express or postoffice money order for as much stock as you feel able to buy. The small investor will

GRIZZLY MINE HOIST—DISTANCE 1½ MILES—PRODUCTION $1,500,000—DEPTH 1100 FEET

receive the same consideration and treatment as the large one, and that is strictly fair and honest dealing.

We wish to add, that if any man or combination of men, having sufficient confidence in this proposition to purchase a large block of stock, say 50,000 shares or more, should feel that in so doing they would prefer to have a direct voice in the management of the affairs of the company, doubtless it can be arranged for a representation upon the Board of Directors.

Our Treasury Stock

Out of the 600,000 shares of stock now in the treasury of the company, the Board of Directors now offer for sale 100,000 shares for the specific purposes set forth in this prospectus. Not one share of private stock is offered for sale, neither can a single share be purchased.

Those now holding stock are investors and not stock speculators. They intend to make their money out of the profits of the mine and not by selling their own stock. *They believe in the mine.*

> " Truth is truth
> To th' end of reckoning "   *Shakespeare*

Please Investigate

It is wise for every one when about to intrust his money in the hands of others to handle as an investment to satisfy himself as to the integrity and standing of the men whom he must trust. The names, business and address of the officers and Board of Directors of the Prudhomme Mining and Milling Company are published herein. We recommend and request that every person before investing in the stock of this company will consult the Bradstreet or Dun Commercial Agencies Or write to our references given on back of title page, and satisfy themselves, beyond all doubt, as to the standing of these men. If you have friends in Los Angeles write them for such information. Write us freely for any further particulars you may desire.

Should you, or an representative in good faith, wish to visit and examine the property of this company, apply to us, and we will cheerfully afford you every facility to do so.

Everything connected with this corporation is open for your most searching investigation. Having nothing to conceal and firm faith in our enterprise as a sound investment, when we are approached by an earnest investigator, we know we have secured a sure investor.

Conclusion

Trusts manipulate and water industrial and railroad stocks; real estate booms come and go; manufacturing is nipped in the prime by centralized competition; mortgages do not always secure—there are a thousand besetting evils to all investments, except a gold mine. It is a creative industry. There can be no more legitimate investment. Competition is unknown to the gold miner. His metal extracted, competition does not enter into the sale, for it is always in demand and at the fixed figure of $20.67 per ounce.

We have no preferred stock or bond issue. All stockholders are on an equal footing, therefore,

"If you assist us, you help us,
Thereby help yourselves."

Respectfuily Submitted

Prudhomme Gold Mining & Milling Co.

532 Stimson Block,

Los Angeles, Cal.

Notice

Make all remittances payable to

AUGUSTUS D. HARPER, Treasurer

Prudhomme Gold Mining & Milling Co.

532 Stimson Block,

Los Angeles, Cal.

CONFIDENCE MINE
EUREKA CONSOLIDATED MILL—DEADHORSE MINE

"Screw your courage to the sticking place,
and you'll not fail."—Macbeth

Write us.   Ask questions.   We will cheerfully
answer them.   We want you to learn the truth
about us.

PRUDHOMME GOLD MINING & MILLING CO.

"O Heaven, what some men do,
While some men leave to do."
Shakespeare.

DUSK AT GOLDEN GATE

"An honest tale speeds best being plainly told"
Richard III.

THE

SIERRA NEVADA

Gold and Silver Quartz Mine,

WOOD-RANCH,

AND

WATER-POWER,

LOCATED IN

EL DORADO COUNTY,

CALIFORNIA.

BOSTON:

WRIGHT & POTTER, PRINTERS, No. 4 SPRING LANE.

1866.

LOCATION OF MINE, WOOD RANCH, AND
WATER-POWER.

This valuable property is located in sight of and near to the town of Grizzly Flat, in El Dorado County, State of California, — in the foot hills of the great Sierra Nevadas, and directly within that famous " *Gold* Quartz Belt " and rich " Placer Diggings," from 8 to 10 miles wide, extending North and South, (magnetic) through the counties of El Dorado and Amador,— containing amongst the largest and richest quartz lodes in the State, and probably in the world, and including within its limits the celebrated " Eureka " of Hayward, the " Lincoln Co." of Governor Stanford, the " Mahony, Hubbard and McAdams," " Keystone," " Tibbitts," " Tucker," " Wildman," " Union " of Clinton, "Hooper," " Drytown," "Marlett," "El Dorado," " Crescent City," "Harmon," and many others in successful operation,— all having yielded and do still yield many millions of dollars in gold.

To reach this property, you travel over the finest thoroughfare in California, leaving San Francisco daily, Sundays excepted, at 4, P.M., on a magnificent Steamer, for Sacramento City, the Capitol of the State; arrive at Sacramento during the night. Having slept well all night, at 6, A.M., you take the Sacramento Valley Railroad cars for Placerville, by way of Folsom, and breakfast at Placerville, — the railroad being completed within a few miles of Placerville, and will be finished this coming Spring.

From Placerville to this property is 21 miles, and 1 mile further to Grizzly Flat. You travel over one of the finest wagon roads in the State of California,— this road continuing on over the Sierras into Nevada,— and arrive at the mine between 10 and 11 o'clock, A.M. The scenery in view from this short ride is grand and exhilarating beyond description. Away to your left lie the eternal snow-capped Sierra Nevadas, piercing the very clouds — in front, the undulating " foot hills," "with their charming forests; to the right, the lower green "foot hills," resembling old orchards,— thence westward across the broad and fertile Sacramento Valley, with Mount Diablo in the distance, rising up high to obstruct your view of the City of San Francisco.

GRIZZLY FLAT is a flourishing mining Town, noted for its celebrated "Placer" mines; millions of gold have been taken from them, — they are worked extensively yet, — and immense amounts of gold have been extracted from the quartz lodes located there, by mill process.

PLACERVILLE is the largest mountain City of California,— about 10,000 population,—is the county seat of El Dorado County, and on the direct great Pioneer Overland route across the Sierra Nevada to the noted Silver-Mining Districts of Nevada. It has a foundery and machine shops, contains over a hundred stores,— has fine public buildings, churches, schools, several daily papers, livery stables,— is handsomely built, the fine shrubbery and trees almost hiding the residences from view.

It is one of the most important places in the State. It derives its name from the Spanish word *"placer,"* strictly signifying "pleasure." Any spot in California where gold exists on, or within a few feet of, the surface, is called by the miners "a placer mine."—the term implying that the gold is pleasantly obtained without any labor of deep digging. Mines of this description have always existed very numerously around Placerville, and hence its designation. But Placerville has other claims to distinction. It is the great *enterpôt* of all the riches of Nevada, and the city whence you start for your journey of two thousand five hundred miles across the plains to the Missouri River. The millions of silver bricks taken from out the Gould and Curry, the Ophir, the Savage, the ·Chollar, and all the other silver mines of Virginia City and Reese River, come to Placerville; while from Placerville all the stores required for the flourishing cities of the silver land are transported across the Sierra Nevada. Every necessary, and almost every luxury of life are purchasable at Placerville; and let it be borne in mind, that this important town — this St. Louis of the Pacific — is within twenty-one miles of the rich mine which we propose to sketch minutely in the following pages. But, before we particularize the mine, it may be advisable to say a few words on the conditions under which gold is found in California, with especial reference to the various forms it assumes in El Dorado County.

Quartz is the form of rock in which gold is almost always found, though sometimes it is discovered in granite, limestone, talcose slate, porphyry, trachyte, and greenstone. In quartz, its particles assume all forms and every variety of size. One of the largest pieces ever found was discovered in Calaveras County, California, in 1854. It weighed one hundred and sixty-one pounds avoirdupois, and was valued at $29,000. But some of the most beautiful specimens, in fact the most beautiful ever seen, have been found in El Dorado County. "The most beautiful specimens of crystalline gold," says Blake (*U. S. Pacific Railroad Report*, Vol. V., p. 300), "are those in which the crystals are combined with an arborescent or dendritic growth of the metal, like the leaves of ferns or the foliage of the arbor-vitæ." Now, at Irish Creek, a very few miles from Placerville, one of the largest specimens of this arborescent foliated gold was picked up. It was twelve inches long by nearly thirteen broad. Another, found at the same place, weighed thirty ounces, was free from quartz, and resembled a bundle of fern leaves closely matted together. Rain had washed these treasures out of their quartzose beds. Weather is the great miner; for rain, wind, frost, heat, and every change of temperature, tend to decompose, disintegrate, and break up the quartz rock, exposing the golden treasures it conceals. Storms descend, and wash down the soil from the hills and mountains to the flats below. Along with the soil are swept away the golden particles from the lodes or ledges in which they were imbedded to the rivers and gulches, where, sinking by the force of its gravity to the bed of the streams, the gold forms "placer mines." The experienced miner, finding a rich placer, knows well that productive veins of gold must exist in the adjacent hills. The existence of one is the result of the other. The placer indicates the wealthy quartz vein, and the auriferous quartz, the proximity of productive placers. Placerville would never have been famous for its placers, had not the hills around Placerville literally perspired with gold.

CLINTON, south of this property, is a village of about one hundred dwellings, has several stores, a large hotel, mechanic shops, cultivated ranches, extensive orchards of all variety of choice fruit, over 200,000 full-bearing grape-vines in its vicinity, — has several immense quartz lodes and quartz mills in successful operation — had fine "placer mines," plenty of wood and water, and within one mile of the Moklumne River, noted for its rich placer "diggings."

Within this "Quartz Belt" are also the flourishing quartz-mining towns of Volcano, Jackson, Sutter Creek, Amador, Herbertville, Drytown, Puckerville, Lower Rancheria, Fair Play, and other mills through the country.

EL DORADO is the most noted and historic mining county of California. At Gen. Sutter's old saw-mill, gold was first discovered. The effect of that discovery has revolutionized the business and financial world. It has added to the coin, multiplied millions of gold. Its inexhaustible quartz mines will add millions annually. It abounds in magnificent forests of the choicest timber for lumber and building materials, lying easterly from Placerville, and easy of access; has good soil for the cereals, grass, fruits of every variety, and the choicest grapes cultivated with great ease and certainty. It has now twenty-five extensive vineyards and wine cellars extensively engaged in the manufacture of the choicest California wines. No better grape or fruit country exists under the sun. Its water-power for milling, mining, manufacturing and irrigating purposes, is abundant beyond every conceivable demand. It exports gold, copper-ore, lumber, marble, hay, wine, pitch, and supplies Nevada chiefly with apples, peaches, pears, grapes, nectarines, apricots, melons, and vegetables.

Lake Bigler lies in its easterly boundary, the sparking gem of the Sierra Nevadas, and the resort of thousands of pleasure seekers during the long dry seasons. Its climate is salubrious, and most salutary for invalids. Its pure water — cold as ice during the long hot summers — from the melting snows and mountain springs, flows down thousands of ravines, in rivulets, with astonishing velocity, forming the creeks and rivers of the county, free from all mineral substances,— a most delightful, exhilarating and healthy beverage.

Near the centre of this interesting and wealthy section of country, is located the "Sierra Nevada" mine.

THE MINE, AND DEVELOPMENT.

The "Sierra Nevada" mine was located by Colonel Knox and his partners, prior to 1853, and then and long afterwards known in the county as "the Knox Claim." It contains 3,600 feet, lineal measure, and favorably located for working it.

The explorations made on the lode were as follows:

An "open cut," uncovering the lode, . . . 1,000 feet,
Depth about . . . . 25 "
One incline sunk in the lode, . . . 130 feet deep.
" " " " " " . . . . 95 " "
" " " " " " . . . . 90 " "
" " " " " " . . . . 40 " "
" " " " " " . . . . 40 " "
Inclines connecting shafts run on the lode,— one of 140 feet
" " " " " 100 "
" " " " " 70 "
" " " " " 60 "
" " " " " 30 "

and another not measured.

These proved the following important facts : —

First — a mine of *great richness.*
Second — a mine of *great width.*
Third — the walls of proper geological formation, leaving no doubt as to its being a real quartz ledge.

Fourth —The ore solid and compact, every pound of it between the two walls fit to crush and easy to quarry — a single blast breaking down from five to twenty tons; and the vein of such thickness that no wall rock need be quarried; thus quarrying and hoisting nothing but pay rock all the time — a most important consideration,— the lode growing wider and richer as you go down.

These facts and the flattering results produced from the crudest mill built by Col. Knox & Co. (which mill would not now, from the improvements on mills, be taken as a gift), soon established the good character of this lode, and the following extensions were located on this ledge; viz., The "Steely," "Eagle," "Powers," and "Treat" Locations — the Ledge being traceable, and successfully prospected the entire distance of all these locations; the Steely worked more than any of the others — having an "open cut" of over 2.000 feet long and 100 feet deep, besides sundry tunnels and shafts, and owned by D. O. Mills, and other bankers of San Francisco.

No ledge in California, Nevada, or the territories has yet been discovered that can be traced so far and easy as this without a break or fault.

By those best informed, it is believed to be a part of "that great gold-bearing quartz vein of California of which Mr. S. V. Blakeslee says: "A thorough geological survey of the State would reveal one great leading vein running along the Sierra Nevada, which, though broken at intervals, and irregular, yet extends along a good portion of the length of the State. Vast quartz-mining operations are going on at different points, and we do not doubt that this vein will in time yield more gold than the present circulating currency of the world."

There is mining ground enough in this location to form two mammoth Companies, owning 1800 feet each, with wood and water, and every facility to successfully mine the same for a hundred years to come. The alloy of the gold on this lode is silver, a most desirable feature. Gold quartz veins, like silver extend downwards into the bowels of the earth beyond the capacity of man to work them. Some of the mines in California are now mined down from 900 to 1300 feet deep, and the lodes growing wider and richer, and no evidence of exhaustion.

Spurs and bastard ledges give out. So they do in silver and copper; but a real vein, never.

YIELD.

A mine in California that will yield from eight to ten dollars per ton, worked with our modern quartz mills, will and is netting large profits.

The average yield per ton of the Sierra Nevada is over $20, gold.

Much of the ore worked on the imperfect Knox mill produced, per ton, over $75, gold.

A large quantity, per ton, over $50, gold.

And none *less*, per ton, than $10, gold.

The proper assay of these ores, showing *all* the gold and silver, would go far above these figures, but none were made.

The present owner took several tons of the ores lying about the " dumps " (not fair average quality), to San Francisco, and had them reduced on the mills now in operation there, which yielded over $28 per ton, gold.

The former owners realized over $200,000 in gold, from operating their miserable imitation of a mill, which was washed away by the high floods in 1862,— even rented out a part of the time and worked with profit to the lessee.

It was one of the few mines that paid profits to the early quartz miner of California. Hundreds of other quartz mines had been open afterwards, and worked with the same kind of machinery, with loss and abandonment of the property, that have since been relocated with modern mills and machinery erected on them, and now worked with immense profits. Had these former owners let outside speculations alone, which was a *mania* in that country, and kept up with the improvement in mining machinery, they would all have been rich, but their outside losses forced them all into insolvency. Still they held on to this property until it fell into the hands of the present owner. The ores they reduced were principally taken from the " open cut."

No accurate data exists from which to estimate the amount of gold taken from this lode by all the companies above mentioned; but, from the books and oral evidence, it is placed at many hundreds of thousands.

In proof of the high estimation in which this ledge is held, it is proper to say, that ex-Governor William Bigler, of Pennsylvania, visited the silver mines of Nevada, and California gold mines, last year,— spent most of the year there,— and with his brother, ex-Governor John Bigler, of California (John knowing all about the mining interests); and, after surveying the whole mining field, with a view to good investments, this lode attracted the strongest; and Wm. Bigler, with Messrs. Hopkins and Melton (the latter old Californians, and well informed on mines), purchased the "Eagle" Location above named, and paid Mr. Davis, of Grizzly Flat, for his $\frac{1}{8}$ interest, $10,000 in gold. (The Eagle has less property than the "Sierra.")

This lode is directly contiguous to the immense "Placer Diggings" of Grizzly Flat, which have yielded their millions of gold.

Please read the Report, on this mine, of James F. Eddy, a practical mining engineer, who frequently reports on mines for San Francisco bankers. His report is historic and interesting.

WOOD RANCH.

1,000 ACRES of as fine timber for lumber, building material, timbering mines, and fire-wood, belongs to this mine — in sight of the mine — as can be found on the Pacific coast. Some of the standard varieties are the sugar-pine, cedar, spruce, pitch and every variety of pine, with live oak, black and white oak — enough in quantity to supply fifty one-hundred-stamp mills for one hundred years to come; besides, this portion of the county is now beginning to furnish the great Sacramento Valley with building and fencing lumber. Being so easy of access, and having a magnificent road, gently descending to the Sacramento Valley, this ranch can furnish an immense amount of clean, clear lumber, of great value. The land, too, is fine soil, as the immense unsurpassed forest on it shows — good to raise the cereals, all kinds of fruit and vegetables for the mines, and in great superabundance.

WATER–POWER.

The original and only water-power right on the Steely Fork, running by the southerly end of this mine, belongs to this property. Its supply is ample all the year round to drive a hundred-stamp mill of 600 pound stamps, and four or five of such mills could be erected on it; thus giving a choice of either running a water mill, or steam mill or mills, at less cost than in any spot in California.

2

TITLES.

To the mine and water-power, by location and uninterrupted actual possession.

To Wood Ranch the title is acquired under the "Possessory Act," by surveying, recording, &c.

These sources of title are well fortified under the mining laws, b, legislative enactments of California, and the uniform repeated decisions of her highest judicial tribunals. Also by the Possessory Act of Congress, passed last year.

CLIMATE,

winter and summer, at Grizzly Flat, is not surpassed, probably, anywhere. Snows melt as they fall, or lie scarcely a day. Water is perfectly free from all mineral substances, and healthy to drink, always being cold from melting snow.

HEALTH.

Society, churches, schools, comforts of life, and civilization, are all here; and living easier than in the Atlantic States.

FREIGHT

is from $\frac{1}{2}$ to $\frac{3}{4}$ of a cent per pound to this mine. Contrast this with Nevada, Colorado, Idaho, and Montana.

WOOD

can be cut, hauled, and corded in the wood-house for $1\frac{75}{100}$ to $2.00 per cord.

LABOR

is worth from $1\frac{1}{2}$ to $3.00 per day in gold.

PRICE FOR REDUCING ORES.

THE QUARTZ FROM THIS MINE CAN BE QUARRIED, HAULED TO THE MILL, AND REDUCED, FOR $3 PER TON, AND NOT TO EXCEED $4.

The common price in California for doing the same thing does not exceed from $5 to $6, when they pay for wood $5 per cord.

FORTY–STAMP MILL.

The owner of this property has propositions at San Francisco, to build him, on this mine, a complete new forty-stamp mill, including complete new steam-engine and fixtures, with all the best modern improvements to reduce the quartz on this mine successfully, and place the mill and mine in complete working condition, for $35,000 in gold.

CALCULATIONS.

California ores are not "base" or "rebellious"; hence worked with great rapidity. This mill will reduce fifty tons (and more) of ore per day (24 hours).

Average value per ton estimated at $20 in gold.

YIELD.

Per day, fifty tons at $20, ...	$1,000	in gold.
Per month, ...	25,000	"
Per annum, ...	300,000	"
Mr. Eddy puts gross yields at . . .	350,000	"

ALL COSTS.

Price of labor, including Superintendents to mine and mill, fifty tons per day . . .	$60 00,	gold.
Board, &c., per day	45 00	"
Wear and tear of mill and other machinery .	35 00	"
Powder, fuse, oil, candles, drills, &c. . .	35 00	"
Total expense per day for fifty tons . .	175 00	"
Per annum	52,500 00	"

PROFITS.

Deduct expenses from gross yield . .	$300,000	
Will *net per annum*	247,500	in gold.
According to Mr. Eddy, net . . .	297,500	"
If the ores yielded only half this sum; viz.,		
$10 per ton, then the net would be .	123,750	
On Eddy's basis	148,750	

Even if it netted only $5 per ton, the profits would be immense.

As the ore is unlimited in quantity, the above results can be practically increased, just in proportion as you increase your mill and working capacity.

To appreciate gold quartz mining in California, in comparison with silver mining and mining in other States and Territories, please read the following

REMARKS AND COMPARISONS.

The four great enterprises of our nation are the Commercial, Mechanical, Agricultural, and Mining for the precious metals.

Are the profits and proportion of successes in mining greater than in the other pursuits? If so, where, and in what kind of mining is it best to invest?

All nations and peoples, from the earliest antiquity, mined for the precious metals, and gold and silver coin is made the standard of value by all enlightened nations. The history of nations on this subject is replete and most interesting. We will refer to a few noted mining countries only.

The *Freiberg* mines, located in the Kingdom of Saxony, from 1524 to 1550 (26 years), produced the enormous amount of 208,000 TONS of pure silver. These mines have been worked over 700 years, to a depth of over 2,800 feet, and still they yield large returns. Spain and Austria are renowned for their immense yields of gold and silver.

Baron Humboldt estimates, from official statistics, that the mines of New Spain, from 1550 to 1790, produced $5,000,000,-000. That the Potosi mine alone, since 1545, produced over $1,500,000,000. That the mines of Mexico, from 1537 to 1731, produced $2,579,000,000, of coin in gold, silver, and copper.

The "SAN DIMAS" mine, in twenty-five years, yielded over $25,000,000.

The "PAVILLON" yielded $20,000 per day, and divided amongst its stockholders over $6,000,000 per annum.

The "ZORALLO" produced $2,000,000 per year.

The "SEMPRERATE" in seven months paid its stockholders, in clear profit, $5,000,000.

"The 'SAN AVASCO' gave its stockholders $54,000,000 in three years."

The "GALLEGO" in six years yielded $11,000,000.

The mines of gold and silver in South America and Mexico have been worked over 300 years; they yield largely yet.

But mining for gold and silver in the United States domain, on the Pacific coast, during a few years only, far eclipses mining in foreign countries.

The San Francisco "*Mining and Scientific Press,*" under date of Jan. 2, 1864, sums up to 1863, by saying:

"California has astonished the world, and almost revolutionized commerce, by the produce of her mines of the precious metals. The enormous production of the mines of the Pacific coast, for the last fourteen years, has indeed been the marvel of the age. From 1849 to 1862, the sum of $750,000,000, in coin and bullion, was shipped from the United States to foreign countries, — chiefly to England, — nearly all of which has been the product of this coast. Great has been the reality of the past; the promise of the future is still more abundant."

President Lincoln's Annual Message to Congress declares, from statistics, that the yield of gold and silver from our mines amounts to more than $100,000,000 bullion annually.

It is safe to estimate that the product of gold and silver in the United States, for the last sixteen years, exceeds the enormous sum of $1,050,000,000. Another compiler says : —

"By the receipts at the various United States mints and assay offices, banking houses, and express offices throughout the mines, together with foreign shipments, it is estimated the yield of gold and silver for the year 1864, from the Pacific coast within the United States, was, in round numbers, $100,000,000, as follows: From California, Idaho, and Oregon, $75,000,000; Nevada Territory, $25,000,000." (Idaho and Oregon did not produce $5,000,000.)

Bowles' book, "*Across the Continent*," last page, 438, says (he quoting): "Over $1,000,000,000 of gold have been exported from California since 1856" (though this is much too large).

Ure's Dictionary (Supplement) contains the statistics of California gold coined and assayed at all the United States mints and assay offices for a series of years, running from $35,000,-000 to $49,000,000, gold,' annually. This does not include shipments of crude gold dust in private hands, or uncoined bullion shipped to foreign countries.

Bowles, "*Across the Continent*," p. 308, says: "There are no rights which mining respects in California. *It is the one supreme interest.*" Page 310, "The mines here are receiving enlarged attention just now." (He only visited two localities in California.)

Now, those who may say mining, — legitimate mining, — is carried on at a loss; "that the cost exceeds the product," are mistaken.

It is supposed the people of the Pacific are entitled to some share of intelligence. Are they producing this $100,-000,000 yearly at a loss, and still embarking in it deeper every year? What country, since man began to till the soil, has sprung, by the magic of its incalculable mineral wealth, into such vast importance and development, as California, Oregon, and Nevada have done; where usury laws have never obtained, and money has readily commanded from 2 to 20 per cent., in gold, per month; where labor is so amply paid, and the whole country growing into greatness?

What is to make the Pacific Railroad a paying institution, but the untold millions of wealth of the mountain ledges of the rich, glittering ores of gold and silver, converted into coin by an empire of people settled and to settle there, to do all this. He who says mining on the Pacific is not a highly remunerative enterprise, with a greater ratio of individual success than in any other calling, is simply not informed.

But where, and in what kind of mining, is the most certainty of success?

The answer is: *In* GOLD QUARTZ MINING *in California.*

Remember, that California yields over $50,000,000 of gold, annually; that its yield is much greater, yearly, than *all the other States and Territories put together.*

Now put to yourself this question, and then seek the true answer: —

Why are the Eastern markets full and overflowing with mines and mining stocks from Nevada, Colorado, Idaho, and Montana, and there are none, or comparatively none, from California? The answer is: the California mines yield the most regular and largest dividends upon the capital invested, of any mines in the known world, and are mostly held and owned by capitalists and operators in California; and because their money pays them bigger and more permanent returns there than in other mines or business.

Mr. Bowles, pp. 312 and 313 : —

"Mining in California, of all kinds, is now much more systematically and intelligently conducted than ever before. * * * The cost of production is cheaper here than in the newer and more remote fields; new and valuable fields are being discovered and opened among the Sierras; *and I am inclined to the belief that investments in mining in California can be made with better results ; at least, with more certainty of profit, if less possible gains, than in any of the fresher and more fashionable regions."*

The veins in Idaho are narrow, "like those of Reese River, pinching sometimes as low as four inches to four or five feet." Bowles, p. 314. "The country is very barren, having the same general characteristics as Eastern Oregon and Nevada."—*Ibid.* Price of labor, $6 a day (gold), and goods and provisions are in proportion. Montana is claimed to be rich in mines; but its quartz interest is not yet developed, and it is 1,600 miles from railroad or steam communication." Bowles, p. 41.

If the quartz there should prove rich, the immense costs of freights and supplies will prevent their present development.

The gold veins in Colorado are narrow. "Good ore yields about $100 in gold per cord (eight tons make one cord), being $12 per ton." "Choice ores yield $300 a cord; but these are rare." "The difficulty is not in separating the gold from the pure copper, iron, or lead, or the quartz with which it is composed; but the sulphurets of these metals, which suffuse and coat the whole, are a plague and mystery. These cover and hold the gold in a stern chemical lock; how to break which in a simple, effective way, is the great study of the mineralogist and mining capitalist." "Various processes are on trial." Bowles, pp. 36, 37. "Not more than 20 or 25 of the 100 stamp mills in the territory are now at work," with labor and food from three to four times as high as at the East" (Bowles p. 35), and freights enormous. The yield has been decreasing for several years, and last year was less $1,500,000, gold, from the whole territory.

Until freights and supplies, and labor are greatly reduced, and some practical mode for reducing the rebellious ores of Colorado shall be discovered, mining the quartz of Idaho, Colorado, and Montana must be postponed, and the capital embarked therein must prove a failure of immediate returns.

The choice lies entirely between California and Nevada, they having the most extensive gold and silver mines on the globe. The Reese River are the richest silver mines ever discovered. Most of the eastern capital embarking in mining is going to Reese River.

Now then let us compare an investment in a silver mine in Austin and the "Sierra Nevada" gold mine in California.

In Austin,

a 25 stamp mill, with roasting furnaces, amalgamators, retorts, fixtures, steam engine, &c., all complete, will cost in gold $150,-000. Wood, lowest price per cord $7, now $15, gold, will be scarce in a few years, and will then rise in proportion to scarcity. At Virginia it is from $16 to $25. Freight, from ten to fifteen cents per pound. Board, $9 to $10 per week, cheapest. Labor, $4 to $6 per day. Provisions, all tools, traveling expenses, shipping your bullion, &c., and water rents, high in proportion.

In Grizzly Flat, California, $150,000, in gold, will build complete, with all modern improvements, two 80 stamp mills, viz., 160 stamps.

Mining and milling of gold quartz is $3\frac{1}{2}$ per ton. Labor, $1\frac{1}{2}$ to $3 per day. Freights, $\frac{1}{2}$ cent per pound.

Wood, for all time to come, from $1\frac{75}{100}$ to $2 per cord. Water for mill, free. Vegetables and all supplies, cheap in proportion. Board, cheap. Travelling expenses light, &c.

Compare Results.

The 160 stamps will crush . . . 180 tons per day.
  at $20 per ton, low average, . . . $3,600 in gold.
Deduct cost of mining, milling, &c., $3\frac{1}{2}$ per
  ton, ... 630 "

Net yield per day of . . . . . $2,970 "

25-stamp silver mill will reduce per day 7
tons to every ten stamps, ... 17½ tons,
At $200 per ton, high average, . . $3,500 00 in gold.
Deduct mining and milling, lowest $65 per ton, 1,157 50 "

Net yield per day of . . . . $2,342 50, silver.
Difference in favor of gold mine in California is 627\frac{50}{100}$ per day, and in one year, 300 days, will be $188,100 in gold.

This difference of result is produced by using the same amount of capital in each mine, but should be a still greater margin in favor of the gold mine, for it will yield $25 to $30 per ton, average, as readily as the silver mines will $200. " Comment is unnecessary." Silver mines in Nevada do pay profits; so do gold mines in California.

Quartz is the mother of gold. " The gold quartz mines are mostly in the same neighborhood, with present or past gold-washings (Placer mines) in the hills back and above the rich stream-beds and gravel-banks." (Bowles, p. 309.) Mr. Bowles is not reliable in his mining statistics, nor his judgment on Reese River mines; as, for instance, he calculates the yield of gold and silver on the Pacific, by the shipments made through " Wells, Fargo & Co.'s Express," while there are several other expresses carrying bullion and gold-dust, and a great deal is carried by private persons. Nearly all the silver from Reese River is shipped by the Express of the First National Bank of Austin. But he is about as correct as a man would be who gathers facts in a flying trip through a strange country.

FACTS SHOWING THE PROFITS OF A FEW GOLD MINES IN
CALIFORNIA.

The Allison Ranch Gold Mine, in Nevada County, California, has enriched the whole town of Grass Valley. It is owned by private individuals, and is one of the Pioneer Quartz Companies in California.

The Rocky Bar Quartz Mining Company divided, for 1863, between the three brothers, owners, $750,000.

The Emperor's Lode sold $400,000 in gold, its product for 1864. Many other companies there have produced largely.

The actual amount of gold taken from the quartz mines within Grass Valley District, since 1854, is over $20,000,000
From the Placer Mines over 8,000,000

Total over $28,000,000
The production in 1855, was $3,300,000
or $275,000 per month.

The Saulsbury Quartz Mine, of Tuolmne County, is now clearing up $50,000 per month.

The Crescent Quartz Mining Company, of California, pays $50, in gold, dividend, on each share of $100, per month.

Amador County, in California, is producing between $3,000,-000 and $4,000,000, yearly.

The great Gould and Curry Silver Mine, in 1864, yielded near $5,000,000, gross, and netted $1,080,000. Dividends per month, $75 per foot, and 2½ per cent. per month on its actual capital. Its vein is 70 feet wide, and commenced to be opened in 1859; average ore per ton, $65.

Take the Eureka, Hayward's Gold Mine of Sutler Creek, California, opened in 1859. Mine down now 1300 feet; vein 23 feet wide; ore averages only $14 per ton. He has cleared $3,000,-000 since, and realized 27 per cent. per month on his actual capital invested.

With improvements equal to the Gould & Curry's capital, he would take out more dollars than the Gould & Curry.

"EL DORADO.— A quantity of picked quartz was recently crushed from the Blue Bank Lead on Webber Creek, which paid at the rate of $25,500 to the ton. The Company have one hundred tons of rock of extraordinary richness at the mouth of their tunnel. Persons desirous of examining the rock will have no occasion to use magnifying glasses."

"EL DORADO BULLION.— Some idea of the amount of bullion now being taken out in El Dorado County may be formed from the fact that 23,918 ounces of bullion passed through three assay offices in San Francisco during the month of January. Since that time the weekly yield of bullion in that region has largely increased, as will be noticed from the fact that 6,600 ounces were received at two of those offices only during the first three days in February; a very encouraging increase."

"GOOD RUN.— A bar of gold, valued at $10,618.25, is the result of one week's run of the Crescent City Quartz Mill, in Indian Valley, Plumas County. This, it will be recollected, is a regular dividend-paying Company. Their last dividend was $50 per share, payable on the first of the present month. This Company is worthy of a more general notice than it receives, as a productive California mine."

"LOOKS WELL.— Thirty-one tons of rock from the General Grant Ledge, recently crushed at the French mill, cleaned up $28 per ton. Eighteen and a half tons from another ledge on Little Deer Creek, yielded $37 per ton."

"Sharp, Smith & Co. last week cleaned up from sixty tons of rock from the Union Ledge, $6,600. They are confident their next crushing will yield at least $125 per ton."

The Union Mine, near the town of El Dorado, in El Dorado County, with a ten-stamp mill, has produced over $1,000,000 in the last two and a half years.

ITEMS FROM CALIFORNIA PAPERS.

"The quartz mines in El Dorado County have attracted a large share of attention during the past season, and an unusual degree of activity appears to have prevailed among the claimholders in the development of their lodes. Some of the most industrious miners have erected hand-mills for crushing the float rock, which is quite abundant, and the results quite profitable. These temporary institutions can be counted by scores in some parts of the mines, showing conclusively that the hardy discoverer is not entirely dependent on the capitalists for machinery to work his ore. Though commencing with float rock, they soon begin to put them up for legitimate purposes, many mines paying the whole expense of building mills, sinking shafts, and running tunnels, by crushing select rock taken out."—*Alta Californian*, November 11th.

"The return to California, during the past summer, of a large portion of the prospectors who crossed the mountains eastward during the past three years, appears to have given a renewed impetus to our quartz mining operations. Especially has this been the case in the neighborhood of Placerville, in El Dorado County, where many mines, which had been either entirely abandoned or greatly neglected, are now being worked with most extraordinary success. The great change which has thus been effected has been mainly brought about by the great improvements in the mills, and by going down to a greater depth on the lodes ; showing it to be an established fact, that the deeper you go the richer the ore.

The constant increase in the receipt of bullion from the interior of the State shows that the miners have by no means been inactive.— *San Francisco Bulletin*, December 11th.

Between 500 and 600 mills, good and poor, are operating now on the California quartz ores.

"FROM THE BLUE LEDGE.— A bar of gold has been received in this city the past week from the Blue Ledge, El Dorado, valued at $1900 — the result of a crushing of forty tons of rock — about $48 per ton."

"QUARTZ MINING FOR GOLD IN CALIFORNIA.— Quartz mining in California is now being carried on more extensively than for the past five years. California has sent her millions for the last fourteen years, which is sufficient evidence of her metallic riches."—*Pacific Index*, of New York, January 30th, 1866.

From the Editorial Review for 1865, of " *The Mercantile Gazette and Prices Current*," of San Francisco, January 9th, 1866, we extract:—

" In magnitude the quartz region of California is already even more than commensurate with that of the Surface mines."

"Vast and munificent as are the other resources of California, none are so promising and pregnant of lasting and certain wealth, as are the fields of auriferous gold quartz."

"To the prolific character of this class of our mines, and the advantages of the business, our people seem to be waking up." "Having for the past six years been investing money in the mines of Washoe, Mexico, and other newer places, they are now wisely turning their attention home to these mines, from which a more shrewd and contented class of citizens have meantime been quietly amassing fortunes.

"The value of this description of property being established, and the obstacles to cheap successful reduction being removed, it only requires now, as a general thing, a moderate amount of capital and good management to make it both safe and lucrative." "After the experience had elsewhere, the conviction seems to have obtained with all classes, that California mines present the most eligible field for the labor and capital of any place on this coast." "Reviewing the whole field of quartz operations, it is evident that this branch of mining in California has not only received a new impulse the past year, but that its rewards have been steadily on the increase, and confidence in its future established."

Some say, "Show us results; if they are satisfactory, capital will flow into the enterprise."

Do not the statistics on mining convince the judgment?

What other business can exhibit such results, such speedy and high profits, and such *property* itself, which, by development in one, two, or three years, augments in value from one hundred, three hundred, five hundred, to eight hundred per cent. *above* the capital invested?

These are facts susceptible of every-day proof. The business world thinks.

Now, *look at the property* in railroads, in manufactures, in shipping, &c., depreciating by daily use and the elements until it wears out and becomes valueless. Look at the iron interest, and merchandising. All these vast enterprises constantly fluctuate; even their profits or products constantly fluctuate: sometimes highly profitable, at other times carried on with heavy loss. Some clogged with high and low tariffs, heavy taxation, and high insurances: most profitable when all prosper, and when assuming the *speculative character*, which never *lasts* in any business. Look, too, at the unremitting attention these interests require in their many sundry details, and then look at *final results*.

History says, seven merchants in a hundred have succeeded.

History further shows, that by far the largest number of men in the other enumerated vast enterprises have failed finally.

Not so with gold quartz property. Your mine requires no insurance: it cannot burn down; it never wears out; every year *increases* instead of decreases its value; it grows richer and wider the more and deeper you work it; it yields a product which never fluctuates,— which is gold; its yield is constant, its profits are constant; it requires fewer details to carry it on successfully; its products fixes values to every other thing; and, after you have extracted from it for a life-time, it is the richest legacy to descend to your children. Sink our gold and silver mines out of existence, if you could, and then what is the value of your currency, your property, or the credit of your Government?

Quartz mining is not a *" speculative enterprise."* Its honest side is real, solid, and its successes larger, in proportion, than any other business.

Speculative Mining is dishonest; and, like every speculation, is at the loss or expense of others, and never lasts. It injures the solid enterprise, and ought to recoil on its adventurer. Let thinking men separate the real from the speculative, and avoid the latter; and then success is almost certain.

It is believed that no property has been offered in this market with so many good points.

First — The mine offered is rich, and lode very thick, and ground enough for two immense companies.

Second — The wood ranch and land is of great value.

Third — The water-power is a fortune to this mine, and every other element and facility at hand to make this mine a success immediately after the erection of a mill and hoisting engine.

A. F. Mitchell, the owner of this valuable property, is now here to sell a portion of this mine, ranch, and water-power, to get an adequate working capital. He feels satisfied, if he can get the attention of capitalists to investigate the merits of this property, that he will accomplish his object in getting his necessary working capital, and that his liberal terms will meet with favor.

He has maps, abstracts of titles, ores, and all facts necessary to show what this property is.

He respectfully refers to the accompanying Appendix, for a full report of this mine by Mr. Eddy.

REPORT OF SIERRA NEVADA MINE.

BY JAMES F. EDDY, Mining Engineer.

A. F. Mitchell, Esq.

The town of Grizzly Flat was settled, in 1851, by Colonel William Knox and others, who made, at that time, discoveries of the richest placer mines that had been found in the State. The result was, that although two years behind other towns in El Dorado County, yet, in one year after its settlement, it bid fair to become a successful rival of all others, and, in fact, at a period of six months subsequent to that time, its voting population was the third precinct in the county. Large quantities of gold were taken from the mines by means of artificial streams drawn from Steely's Fork, until during the year 1853, when, by working off the surface, rich deposits of gold were found in ledges of rock. This was an entire new feature in mining, and the prospectors commenced work under the disadvantages which would naturally surround the first work of extracting gold from quartz rock in the United States, as up to that time the precious metal had not been found to exist in that manner. During that year, Colonel Knox and associates, twenty-three in all, commenced work upon what was called the "Knox Claim" (afterwards known as the "Sierra Nevada"), by opening and uncovering the ledge for a distance little short of 1000 feet, commencing at the north end of the run, and at a point where the Steely Ledge commences, making an open cut about twenty-five feet deep, and apparently about ten feet wide. The ledge through this cut was very open and fissile, showing much free gold, and being very easily worked, and of varying width, ranging from three to eight feet. The following summer they constructed a mill upon "Steely's Fork," at the south end of the claim, carried by the waters of that stream. That mill, in itself, was a novelty, and in fact so was the entire manner of working all the mines in that country at that time. An abundance of power could have been had upon that mill site to carry a hundred stamps of 600 pounds each, with all the machinery necessary to complete a mill fitted for all modern improvements, yet a small affair of ten stamps was made, each stamp weighing about 150 pounds. The gold that was saved was confined to the battery, the pulp being run to an Arastra. The only wonder to the intelligent quartz miner, is, that they saved any gold at all; yet the company became rich under the rude process. They then struck a class of ore, showing less oxidization, and the presence of a variety of mineral substances with which they were unacquainted, consisting mainly of gold pyrites, with occasional indications of lead. However, this was a small obstacle, for that class of ore could be thrown out. But the rock also was becoming hard, and not readily reduced; so they abandoned their immense cut, and sank shafts in various places, and run tunnels, as indicated on the annexed diagram, in search of more easily worked ore. The figures indicate the order of work; yet in all of these tunnels and shafts, the general character of the vein is the same, being everywhere very solid, and *in no case* broken; and in no instance has rock been taken from the mine that has not yielded more than ten dollars per ton, and in many instances has it produced from fifty to seventy-five dollars; and this large yield was kept up for months together, during the progress of the work in the open cut. I am satisfied the tunnels and shafts are securely timbered. The shaft marked No. 9, on diagram, is a double 4×8 feet in the clear, heavily timbered with spruce, which will keep its position for half a century. This shaft is perfect from the top to the bottom, with but little water in it. This shaft was dug by Capt. Tulles, the discoverer of the famous Cosumnes Copper Mine, situated three or four miles south, during 1863, and marks the line between the Sierra Nevada and Steely mines, and is an admirable piece of work. Fine ore was taken from this shaft from top to bottom, and paid fine dividends to Capt. Tulles, who dug the shaft and worked the rock in an arastra upon shares. He left the work to attend to his copper works, and unfortunately died a few days after that mine had attained a celebrity second to none upon the coast. Intelligent men who worked in different portions of the mine uniformly speak in highest praise of it, and all assure me that not a pound of rock was ever taken from the vein, but it paid to work, and that they never saw a spot of the ledge that was less than three feet in width, and running to eight or nine feet. The shafts Nos. 7 and 8 are forty feet deep, and about two thousand feet from the north end, where the main work was done; they stand close to each other and are connected by a drift of fifty or sixty feet, to purify the air by currents. About 1856, Colonel Knox purchased the interest of the other owners, and kept on with the work until 1858, when he was compelled, from outside adventures, to surrender it to creditors — Messrs. Hulbard Brothers. An examination of his books, however, shows a yield of more than $60,-000, saved by his improvident manner of working. The Colonel is still an honored citizen of the town of Grizzly Flat, and has held for a long number of years the highest office in the gift of the citizens of the township, and you are at liberty to refer any one to him for information concerning the mine in question. In 1860, H. S. Hulbard, who had become the owner of the mine, became an insolvent debtor, and assigned all his property for the benefit of his creditors; and in the list was the "Sierra Nevada Mine." During the time Messrs. Hulbard & Brothers worked the mine, they took out a large quantity of gold; but the books are in the hands of other parties, and not to be found, so that the exact amount cannot be ascertained. It is understood, however, that the mine has yielded more than two hundred thousand dollars, and the affidavit of Colonel Knox shows the vein to be in as good a condition as it ever was, only richer by far. A. F. Mitchell is now the legal owner of the mine and other property.

FACILITIES FOR WORK. ALSO LOCATION.

Grizzly Flat is situated twenty-two miles south-east of Placerville, the County seat of El Dorado County, California, and at an altitude of 4200 feet above the ocean, in a broken country, with a fine wagon road connecting it with railroad and steamboat communication with San Francisco, being at present thirty miles distant from the railroad, which will be reduced to twenty-two miles, within one year. The Sierra Nevada mine is situated about one mile west of town, and in the midst of the finest timber I have seen in the State, consisting of spruce, cedar, sugar-pine, and oak, in abundance; it is sufficient to say that its only cost is to cut it, and haul it a few rods to the mill. There is enough within a distance of twenty rods of any place on the line of the vein, to supply an one-hundred horse-power, engine with fuel for ten years of constant service. Water can be had in any quantity. Labor and provisions can be had as cheap as at any other place in the mountains.

The Ledge upon which the " Sierra Nevada Mine " is located is traceable from Steely's Fork to the Cosumnes River, and has been successfully prospected during the entire distance, by the "Sierra Nevada," "Steely," "Eagle," "Powers & Co.," and "Treat" Companies, who claim as laid down in diagram Nos.

1 and 3. Of all the five companies, the most work has been done upon the "Steely Mine," it having an open cut like the one described in the "Sierra Nevada," over 2000 feet long and 100 feet deep near the entire distance, besides any quantity of tunnels and shafts. Four mills have worked upon it at a time. It is owned by D. O. Mills & Co. and other wealthy men of Sacramento, who I understand are intending soon to construct extensive works thereon.

Next, north of the "Steely" mine is the "Eagle," which has been in the same condition as the others, until a few months, when they commenced working it in a more systematic manner, with a small five-stamp mill, and one Varney pan. They use water power which they obtained from a ditch leading from the river, which they purchased at high rate. The power is insufficient to drive the stamps and run the pan at the same time, yet it now pays the owners very good profits for work.

On the 3rd of August, 1865, it was purchased by ex-Gov. Wm .Bigler, of Pennsylvania, and Messrs. Hopkins and Melton, of Sacramento, they paying Davis, of Grizzly Flat, for his ⅛th interest, $10,000 in gold coin. They continue working the old mill, and will immediately construct a new twenty-stamp mill, with all the modern improvements, to be run with water power, which I think will be more expensive than a good steam mill, as they will have to purchase the water from a ditch company, and not so reliable.

Still further north is the "Powers & Co. claims," which is made to pay with an arastra and horse power.

Still further north is the "Treat" claim, which is said to be a good claim. However, I did not visit it.

All the rock of the four claims first spoken of are of the same character, being all highly oxidized at the surface, and growing hard as you go down on the ledge: all the rock in the ledge seems to pay the same, being very evenly diffused through it. No books of the last company can be found, they having been carried to Oregon. I will send you an affidavit of Col. Knox, showing what he has done.

The length of this lode, known as the "Sierra Nevada," contains 3600 feet; the course of this lode is nearly north and south, the walls being well defined, pitching on an angle of 10° (degrees) east, showing it to be a true vein or lode, and with my experience in quartz mining it is my belief that at a depth of 400 feet, the "Sierra Nevada" will stand second to none — Hayward's of Amador included — in the State of California. The hanging wall is of coal black slate, with a small gouge, which is a great advantage in producing the quartz, it being composed of a mixture of clay a few inches in thickness.

THE CAPACITY OF A FORTY-STAMP MILL.

We will take it for granted that we can crush one and one-half tons every twenty-four hours, with each stamp that wi'l weigh 600 pounds, and a mill of the most modern improvement, to be constructed with not less than 40 stamps; and, the average of the rock being $20 per ton (which I consider to be a low figure), then the productive capacity of the mine and mill will be $1200 per day, or about $350,000 gross, per annum, in gold.

Money in California is worth five per cent. a month, or sixty per cent. per annum, and is the income a mine ought to return on its capital: the "Sierra Nevada" should on the basis of this report represent a capital of nearly $500,000, in which sum must be included all the cost of purchase, and at least $50,000 of free cash to carry into efficient and early operation all the works of exploration and construction such as I would recommend, viz : The building of a No. 1 forty-stamp mill to be driven by an one-hundred horse-power engine, placed over the mine so that it can be used for hoisting and pumping the mine.

That the "Sierra Nevada" mine, thus developed, and with sufficient capital judiciously used, will pay large dividends, is the honest belief of

Your obedient servant,

JAMES F. EDDY.

PART II
Alaska, Arizona, Colorado, Idaho, Utah

What——
The Klondike & Boston Gold Mining & Mfg. Co.

Has——
Accomplished
In a
Few Months.

OFFICES :

244 Washington Street,
Boston, Mass.

.. PROSPECTUS OF ..

The Klondike & Boston —
Gold Mining & Manufacturing Co.

Operating in the Mynook Creek and Cook Inlet Districts, Alaska's Richest Gold Fields.

Incorporated Under the Laws of Colorado.

Capital Stock, $1.000,000.   Divided into 1,000,000 Shares.   Par Value, $1.00 Each.

Full Paid and Forever Non-Assessable.

OFFICERS.

JUDGE THOMAS E. GROVER,	President.
JOSEPH H. ALLEN,	First Vice President.
JOHN R. NEWMAN,	Second Vice-President.
EDWARD C. DAVIS,	Treasurer.
GEORGE F. CLOUGH,	Secretary.
GEORGE M. REED,	Manager of Mines.

GENERAL COUNSEL.

THOMAS E MAJOR, Boston, Mass.

DEPOSITORY

INTERNATIONAL TRUST COMPANY, Boston, Mass.

DIRECTORS.

THOMAS E. GROVER, (Judge, District Court)	Canton, Mass.
HENRY A. STEARNS, (Ex. Lieut. Governor of R. I.)	Pawtucket, R. I.
JOSEPH H. ALLEN, (Broker)	Boston, Mass.
EDWARD C. DAVIS, (Broker)	Boston, Mass.
JOHN R. NEWMAN, (Boston Merchant)	Winchester, Mass.
ARTHUR M. BRIDGMAN. (Editor Legislative Bulletin)	Stoughton, Mass.
WILLIAM J. SHEA, (Brooklyn, N. Y. Daily Citizen)	New York, N. Y.

OFFICIAL BROKERS.

EDWARD C. DAVIS & CO., 244 Washington St., Rooms 8, 9 and 10, **BOSTON, MASS.**

The Klondike & Boston Gold Mining & Manufacturing Co.

N the following pages will be found brief reports of Mr. George M. Reed, the general mining manager of the Klondike & Boston Gold Mining and Manuturing Co., and of Captains E. J. Meagher, O. G. Herning and W. O. Cutter, manrs of Expeditions Nos. 2, 4 and 6, who have purchased and located for the Company tal of FIFTY (50) PLACER MINING CLAIMS, equal to 1000 acres, in the richgold mining districts of Alaska.

The securing of this vast mining territory, both by purchase and by location accomplished in less than 12 months' time, as Mr. Reed did not leave Seattle il Aug. 5, 1897, while Captains Meagher and Herning did not leave with their ties until April 12, 1898. Since this latter date two additional parties have been t to the gold fields of Alaska under the management of Capt. Charles L. Wilson, l Capt. William O. Cutter, the former leaving Seattle, June 21, and the latter g. 4, equipped with steamboats, fifteen months' provisions, etc. These last two ties going so late in the season will not be able to report their success for some nths hence, but as they have been sent direct to Rampart City, to assist Mr. Reed working the rich claims he has secured there, (twenty-five in all,) they cannot to reap a rich golden harvest, as the Company's claims are on the richest eks and gulches in the district and many of them are on the "Old river bed", the st and richest discovery made in Alaska.

With this magnificent record--fifty rich placer claims located d purchased, with forty good sober and industrious men to work em on shares, no salaries to pay, and three steamboats, forty ns of provisions, large supply of mining tools, placer mining achines, boilers for thawing gravel by steam, with everything id for, it is no wonder that the Company holds an enviable posin among the Alaska Mining Companies.

With forty men at work on the Company's claims, vast fortunes are sure to be ured during the coming fall and winter. The directors are not content to stop re, but are arranging to send at least 100 men, fully equipped and provisioned to rk these mines ; and to procure funds to do so, we have been authorized to conue the sale of the stock for a short time longer, at par, $1.00 PER SHARE, in blocks suit. This stock offers the greatest safety and profit of any on the market, and believe it will equal in point of profit and dividends any of the leading Boston copper cks which have made millions for their stockholders during the past few years.

We call special attention to the officers and directors of this company. They : all staunch New England business men, thus insuring an honest and business-like ministration.

Send all orders for stock and remittances to the company's financial agents,

C. DAVIS & CO., 244 Washington St., Rooms 8, 9, 10, Boston, Mass.

EXTRACT FROM LETTER OF GEORGE M. REED, GENERAL MANAGER OF THE COMPANY.

Rampart City, Alaska, June 25, 1898.

Messrs. E. C. Davis & Co.
244 Washington St., Boston, Mass.

Dear Friends,—

On April 20 I received your letter dated Sept. 4, 1897, in Windy Jim's mail vi. Dawson, the first mail I have received since leaving Seattle, Aug. 5, 1897, and witl the letter came a prospectus of the Klondike & Boston Gold Mining & Mfg. Co. which is very finely gotten up. I have worked very hard since I landed on thi shore, locating and buying claims and doing the assessment work necessary to hol them. There has been a great discovery here in locating an old river bed up o the mountains from 200 to 1000 feet above the creeks and I spent three day tracing it.

This old river bed crosses several gulches in which I have a number of claim: Discovery was made by following up a small gulch off No. 9 on Little Mynook. A the surface gravel was struck paying from 25 cents to $2.00 per pan. Two me washed out $67.00 in a few hours. I have already secured several claims on thi old river bed where there was a big rush, but I got there just the same. The gol in this river bed is identical with that found in the creeks 1000 feet below and is u doubtedly the source of the gold found in the creeks of this section. The ridg where discovery was made is called Idaho Bar. My conclusion is that this o river, which was a monster, existed when Alaska was a tropical country and sporte the elephant and the mastodoi vhose bones are found in large quantities a couple hundred miles east of us, and a few bones have already been found here.

Since my arrival here it has been one grand rush locating and securing claim on new creeks and the consequence is I have so many claims that I have been u able to do but little real mining beyond the necessary assessment work (equal $200.00 per claim) to hold them. In your letter of Sept. 4th you speak of sendii in men in the spring to help work the claims I might secure, which I hope you ha done or will do as I can work them to great advantage on the many claims whi I have secured on Dawson, Julia, Alder, Leonora, Russian, Rampart, Hiyu, Chic go, and the old river bed above referred to.

I have some of the best claims in this part of the country, which should yie fortunes for the company, and a full report of which I will send you in my next l ter. Now that the real source of the gold supply has been located (old river be the gulches will be prospected more vigorously and in a different manner. The s is the greatest prospector in this frozen country. It melts the snow on the sun side of the mountain causing it to wear away and deposit its slide of dirt and roc below in the gulch and push the creek further over each year. I have no dou that good bench diggings will be discovered this summer and the pay streak lo ted in many of the other gulches next winter from the very fact of the recent d covery on the mountains. Boats coming down the river lately report that very r

CAPT. E. J. MEAGHER,
Manager of Expedition No. 2.

CAPT. C. G. HERNING,
Manager of Expedition No. 4.

GEORGE M. REED,
General Mining Manager.

CAPT. CHARLES L. WILSON,
Manager of Expedition No. 5.

CAPT. WILLIAM O. CUTTER,
Manager of Expedition No. 6.

bench diggings have been discovered on top of the monntains there. If this is tru
is possible and very probable that the gold in the Dawson district all comes from
cient river beds or possibly enormous glaciers.

Minook Creek district gold is worth $18.60 per ounce, $3.00 more than Daws
gold. A nugget cleaned up to-day on No. 9 Little Minook weighed $184 ; anot
on No. 5 was worth $104; and this gold came down from that old river bed j
as sure as preaching ; and there is lots more of it to be found, for I know that
the gold found in these lower creeks and gulches comes from the old river t
which is the fountain head. New diggings have been discovered this spring
Quail, Willow and Troublesome creeks in this locality, but the greatest discov
of all is the old river bed crossing the mountain tops for many miles and sweep
across most of the creeks on which I already hold claims as above mentioned.

It is now ten minutes past one o'clock at night and perfect daylight. I ha
used no candle in writing this letter—the land of the midnight sun sure enough.

There has been so much snow this winter that the river was higher than ever
fore known here—rising to 65 feet above its level before the ice broke. I send y
a very correct map of the mining district here and it would be well to have some tr
ings of it made.

Our camp is building up very rapidly; cabins are springing up on every s
and several large buildings are being erected. The North American Trading
Transportation Co., is putting up a very large store and one of the finest on
river. The future prospects of Rampart City look bright and it will undoubte
be the metropolis of the American side of the Yukon. As distributing point t
town is well located and I own either wholly or in part seven city lots, some w
cabins on them in the best part of the town, which will become very valuable this s
son. The town has had a population of 400 this winter and on account of the r
discoveries made here this season and the wide publicity given the camp, I ant
pate a population of at least 5000 before fall.

The month of January proved the coldest for the year, averaging 17 below ze
Our coldest day recorded 60 below. While on the temperature subject I will
that the average temperature by months was as follows ;—October, 16 above ; I
vember, 1 above; December, 3 below; January, 17 below; February, 10 belo
and March, 20 above.

Some small boats came down today and one party came in over the pass
Dawson and thence down the river to Rampart City. They report that at the ti
they crossed the pass there were about 15,000 men on the trail and many of th
were bound for this camp preferring to locate on the American side owing to the m
ing laws of Canada.

In conclusion I will say that I am in good health and working hard and beli
that I shall make a big fortune for the company this year, and if you send me
some good men to assist me in working our large number of claims, so much
better and the greater will be our success.

Sincerely yours,
GEORGE M. REED.
General Mining Manage

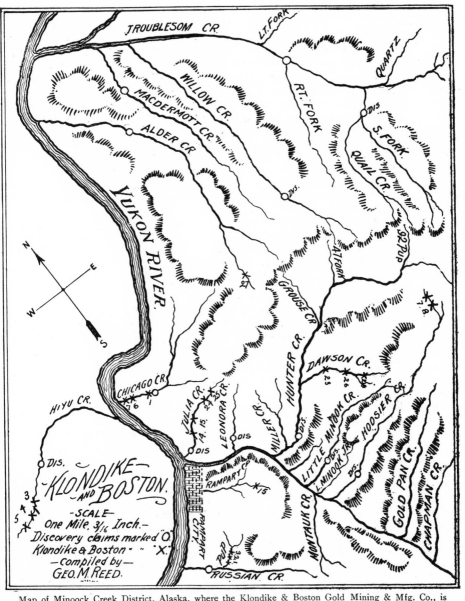

Map of Minoock Creek District, Alaska, where the Klondike & Boston Gold Mining & Mfg. Co., is carrying on such extensive mining opperations.

Extract from Mr. Reed's Letter.

Rampart City, Alaska, July 6, 1898.

E. C. Davis & Co , Boston, Mass.

Gentlemen:—Yesterday the steamer "Seattle No. 1" brought down a little mail from Dawson and I received two letters from you. There was a government mail agent aboard who is establishing post-offices along the river. He established one here, and we are supposed from now on to receive mail twice a month. I see you are hustling, getting the 5th expidition ready. I have not said much about the machine as I have had no opportunity to use it, but since the old river bed or glacier was discovered a couple of months ago, I could see an opening for it, and I have had it out on exhibition for some days now and it is causing a sensation. I see you are using in connection with the machine an apparatus for thawing the ground and also for drying it. This is all that is necessary.

I located a bench claim on Hunter Ridge, 1000 x 600 feet. I have also located another claim on Dawson Creek, No. 32, and still one more on the new creek called Leonora Creek, next one to Julia, claim No. 3 above discovery. The last two are 500 foot claims, about 10 acres each. This makes 40 acres more for you to list. The Reed Dry Placer Machine is all right, and with the appliance for drying and thawing the dirt cannot possibly fail on rich claims. I am expecting No. 5 expedition to show up any day now. You will hear from me often.

Yours sincerely, GEORGE M. REED.

Extracts from Mr. Meagher's Letters.

Alaska Commercial Co's. 1st Post,
25 miles from mouth of Sushitna River,

Messrs. E. C. Davis & Co.,   60 miles from Tyoonak, 12th June, 1898.
244 Washington St., Boston, Mass.

Gentlemen :

This is written on the forward locker of the steam launch, E. C. Davis & Co. No. 1, which has gained the proud distinction of being the first steam craft of any size that has crossed the bar and ascended the waters of the great Sushitna River.

The stanch little boat has now an historical name and character as this achievement of hers marks an epoch in the history of steam navigation in this part of Alaska, and as she must be considered today and for all time a pathfinder and pioneer, that has made possible the navigation of this great stream by steam craft (which will be followed in a very short time by all kinds and sizes of steam ships.) It must be a matter of great pride and satisfaction to you, gentlemen, and an honor and distinction for her commander, Capt. E. J Meagher, Capt. Frank Churchill, Engineers Isaac I. Fonda and Fred Woodward, who made the trip.

I shall soon start out again, and shall try this time to reach the falls of the river, 150 miles or so above its mouth. The meagre reports we are getting from the interior are not at all reliable ; but from a report made to me privately on good authority it appears that some rich finds have been slyly and privately made somewhere between here and the falls, and if I have not lost too much of my old-time

Members of Expeditions Nos. 2 and 4 of the Klondike & Boston Gold Mining & Manufacturing Co., with a portion of their supplies as photographed just before leaving Seattle, April 12, 1898, for the COOK INLET gold fields of Alaska.

grit fighting flies on my last trip, I will get into the swim before another fortnight and locate on ground that will send the stock of the Klondike & Boston Gold Mining & Manufacturing Co. skyward and up to the satisfaction of all stockholders and particularly to every member of the party I am heading, not forgetting the *old boy* himself.

I crave indulgence, I must be brief; writing with one hand and fighting 1 ½-inch mosquitoes with the other, does not inspire either poetry or good nature. So let me close, and say that my next (in all probability) will be dated from the very head of navigation on the great Sushitna.

Kindest regards to all in your office and remembrances to all friends.

Yours very truly, Capt. E. J. MEAGHER

Tyoonak, Cook Inlet, Alaska, 27th June, 1898.

Gentlemen :

I borrow a postal on the beach, to say that our party has staked off 160 acres of good placer ground on the Sushitna river, 40 miles up from the inlet, and 60 acres on the Matson Creek, a tributary of the same river. I go with four men up the Sushitna tomorrow, and will try to reach the falls, 150 miles up. A schooner goes out on 1st July. This is to catch her. I write on a rock, so I must be brief. All well.

Yours truly,

Capt. E. J. MEAGHER.

Tyoonak, Alaska, Aug. 22, 1898.

E. C. Davis & Co., Boston, Mass.

Gentlemen :— The steamer "Dora" which brought out my last letter to you is expected in again either tonight or some time tomorrow, therefore I will commence this letter in time to have it ready to go out by her when she leaves here. Today I take the greatest pleasure in giving you news that will gladden your hearts, and send joy and comfort into the hearts of every shareholder in the stock of The Klondike & Boston Gold Mining & Mfg. Co., and the assurance of success and large profits and benefits to every investor large or small in the stock of your company. Yesterday I saw a Mr. Andrews who had just returned from his holdings on a creek which bears his name — a tributary of the great Sushitna river, and less than fifty miles from its mouth, who showed me two sacks of coarse gold taken from one of his recent discoveries, which yielded by sluicing in the crudest way over one ounce per day to the man. Mr. Andrews is on his way to Seattle and San Francisco to place some of his claims on the market, and he told me that just before he left his camp (the same day) he had seen and spoken to a Mr. Malcom Cameron, the advance guard of the five men I sent in there about a month ago or over, and that he, Cameron, was to stake and locate in the name of the company the full complement of ground allowed by law, and that the other four men of the party, namely, Falconer, Grover, Churchill and Hayes, were following up with all the provisions and outfit they could carry. Mr. Andrews assures

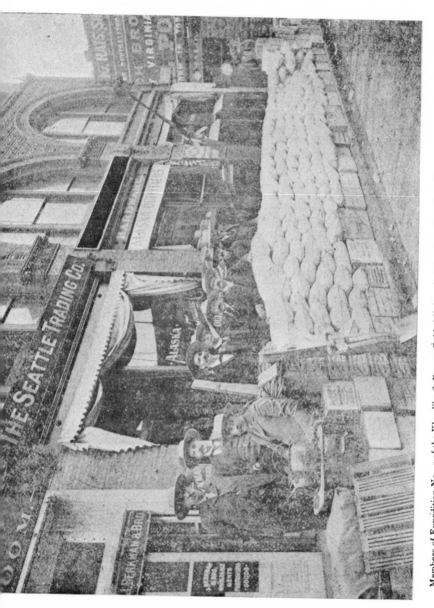

Members of Expedition No. 5 of the Klondike & Boston Gold Mining & Manufacturing Co., with a portion of their supplies, as photographed just before leaving Seattle, June 21, 1898, for Rampart City, (Minook Creek District) Alaska.

me that the creek is rich in coarse and fine gold, and that our party are on best paying ground in that section of the country. I saw and handled so of Mr. Andrews' gold myself, and saw Mr. Hanmore of the Alaska Commer Co's. store weigh one nugget which turned the beam at 4 oz.; the balance of the g was coarse, pieces weighing from 25 to 85 cents being common. This creek is be rapidly staked off and will be a very important point in a very short time. It is co paratively easy of access, and not so far into the interior as to make it difficult very expensive to reach, points of very great consideration in this almost inaccessi country. Every man of the party is well and full of hope, the brightest of hope, a we are impaciently waiting the propellers which are expected daily, and when t arrive the balance of the party will board the E. C Davis & Co. No. 1 and h her for the new Eldorado. Believe me, yours very truly,

E. J. MEAGHER, Manager, Expedition No. 2

Extracts from Mr. Herning's Letters.

Tyoonak, Cook Inlet, Alaska, June 20, 1898
Messrs. E. C. Davis & Co.,
244 Washington St., Boston, Mass.,
Gentlemen :—

It is with pleasure that I can now pen you a few lines of quite encouraging n ing news. I have just returned from the prospecting and investigating expedit that I wrote you about the 25th of last month. I have staked and located fift placer claims of twenty acres each (300 acres in all) on what is known as "Wil Creek" and its gulches. I could get anywhere from 5 to 50 colors on any one these claims, of good wire gold, and as the formation was so good I decided stake at once ; 45 cent pieces have been taken out just below me. This prope is located between the big Sushitna and Knik rivers, about 75 miles north of head waters of Cook Inlet.

One good thing about our location is that we can go to bedrock, as the frost o goes down about six inches. I consider this ground will prove one of the b hydraulic propositions in this part of the country, and I will send you some gold fore winter sets in.

On my trip I was chairman and helped to organize two different mining tricts, "Willow Creek" and "Knik." It has cost us a lot of cash to locate get into this district. I got in with two old timers, who are located on Will Creek, and are the only men that know how to get into the mines. They w trappers and agents for the A. C. Co. I consider that their experience is worth m to me than a five years' residence in this section. I am furnished with map guides and they have great control over the Indians. A short way up the mouth Willow Creek off the Sushitna is a box canyon, which is impassable, and wh turns away all prospectors. The Indians will not guide white men in for they spoiling their hunting grounds. I think the Sushitna will be the only route o in the Tanana and Yukon District, while the Knik River is the only way to get i the Copper River District. These former owners were afraid that they would l

Members of Expedition No. 6, of the Klondike & Boston Gold Mining & Manufacturing Co., with a portion of their supplies, as photographed just before leaving Seattle, Aug. 4, for Rampart City (Mynook Creek District), Alaska.

most of this ground, and the only way was to turn it over to a company like ou
They have great confidence in No. 4 (I hear it come from all sides.)   We are m
ing great preparations for next summer's work.

Now to be short I consider we have a good paying proposition for
pany, and I am confident our "Martha" group is worth $40,000, and wh
back to the mines I shall prospect and locate all the paying ground I can find.
have no doubt that there will be a big rush next year in this new district, and as m
all the ground will be located, mines will sell at a good price.

I will write you and keep you posted on our movements.   Can only get mail c
here once a month, April to October.   We are all well and feel more than confide
Look for sample of gold next month.   With best wishes. I am

Most sincerely yours,

CAPT. O. G. HERNING.

Mgr. Expedition No. 4

Knik Store, Cook Inlet, Alaska, Aug. 12, 1898.

Messrs. E. C. Davis & Co., Boston, Mass.

Gentlemen :—I have just arrived from the mines.   I located and recorded
claims (300 acres.)   The two Mexicans are taking out ounce pay per day per m
and Mr. Andrews, next claim adjoining ours, did likewise.   I have a nice sample
the gold for you.   I am now going to locate two town sites and the only deep wa
harbor on Cook Inlet where steam boats can land at any time with safety.   There a
no wharfs this side of Keni and Homer.   This harbor I will locate is within a f
miles of the Govt. summer trail that leads through from Cook Inlet by way of K
River to Manuska, Copper and the Tanana districts, and the Government now has
trail opened 75 miles up to timber line, and are now going over the mountains wit
pack train of 25 mules, headed by Capt. Glenn.   All the creeks along the trail
located, and next year there will be a big rush through here.   We can easily ru
pack train in to our mines and must have one for next year; we expect a stampede i
our mining district.   The Mexicans above referred to have taken out a large amo
of gold this season and expect to work 25 men on their claims next year.

Now, Gentlemen, if there ever was a chance to make a fortune it now prese
itself.   The Government will surely open up this district, and it is the only route throu
Cook Inlet, and our town site will be so located at the mouth of Knik Arm that v
sels can land at any time, and from there can go to any tributaries prospectors desi
It is only a short distance from placer mines that are actually a success, and a big bo
will surely come next year.

I have done all in my power to further the interests of our company and I w
to see a dividend declared and make this one of the banner companies of Alaska.

Believe me. gentlemen, I am

Yours most sincerely,

O. G. HERNING,

Manager, Expedition No. 4

tracts from letter of Wm. H. Thorne, member of E. C. Davis & Co's. Expedition
No. 4, to J. W. Sweeney, Winchester Mass.

Tyoonak, Cook Inlet, Alaska, July 17, 1898.

Well, friend Sweeney, I received your welcome letter, today, and was glad to ar from home. I knew the war was in progress; but you want to know about this intry. Well I will give you straight information. In the first place we landed e the 1st of May, and I think it is the finest country in the world. It has been e ever since we came with the exception of one or two warm rains. There are hun-ds of tons of hay as fine as you ever saw growing here that they call blue joint. the next place there has been 24 hours' daylight in a day ever since I came here. m not sorry I came. I am five inches smaller 'round the waist, and only three unds lighter than when I came. Well, there has been a lot of men come here as as Cook Inlet and go home afraid to venture the rivers. I saw 85 start home in e vessel, and I believe over 300 have gone; and they will give this place a bad me without knowing anything more about it. As far as we have gone it has en very trying; but we have located 15 claims, 20 acres in a claim, and we have me rich diggings. We would not take $50,000 for one of our claims. In prospect-g them we got 50 to 75 pieces of gold out of one shovelful of dirt. It is called re gold, some of the best. But we do not expect to get out any this fall, or but ry little, as we have lots of work to do. We have to get our goods 148 miles by at, and packing, and to build a house to live in for the winter; and it will be about we will be able to do. But next spring we shall sock it to the claims. These ims run from the Sushitna river to the mountains; and I think there is a lot of ld up there. We have one of the best propositions for hydraulic works that was er seen. If we had hydraulic machinery we could take out from $10,000 to $20-o a week or more, for it is a great chance. But we will have it here before we give up if we do not get enough without it. But I think we will get all we want easily xt summer.

There is a lot of game here . moose, bear and it is the greatest place for fish in e world. I saw more salmon caught yesterday than I ever saw in my life. The vers are full of them. You can buy a salmon that will weight from 40 to 85 lbs. r ten cents up here; and if you have a spear you can get all you want and all you uld give away. And there are all kinds of birds: geese, ducks, parrridges, prairie ickens, woodcock, and everything but turkeys. There are mountain sheep that eight 100 lbs. when dressed. Well, friend John, let me know what information u want when you write and I will try to give it to you.

Yours truly,

Wm. H. THORNE.

Extract form Mr. Cutter's Letter.

Messrs. E. C. Davis & Co., 244 Washington St., Boston.

Gentlemen :—On board steamer "Piotection" 6th day out from Seattle.   I co
mence this now as the weather is very fine and sea smooth and all hands have j
fairly gotten over the seasickness, also I know we shall be extremely busy when
reach St. Michaels, and I wish to send you some word of our progress.   All is wo
ing very smoothly thus far. We are all well and in best of spirits. There is a young C
man on board who has put in one year up in the vicinity of Rampart City, and is n
going back with about ten tons of stores.   He has several claims there and he gives
all the encouragement in the world, and you know the Germans are not enthusias
All they say that is needed is "sand" and if any more sandy people can be found tl
in old Massachusetts I shall be obliged to enquire where, and I feel sure it is not la
ing in our party.

Dutch Harbor, Aug.

I regret to say that after leaving here yesterday and three hours out the crossh
to pump broke, compelling us to return here for repairs, but they expect to get out so
time tonight, thus delaying us about 36 hours.

There was a passenger on the Brunswick lying here bound for 'Frisco with a n
bag of "nuggets" from Little Mynook. Two of them were $37 nuggets and the Myno
gold brings $19.20 an ounce, and of course he talks more than encouragingly.   C
boat's boiler and tank are full, and we can start in 24 hours after arriving at
Michaels, weather permitting.

St. Michaels, Tuesday, Aug.

All well.   Will probably start up river tomorrow, Aug. 17, weather permittin
All packed, coaled, etc.   Yours in haste, W. O. CUTTER.

Seattle, Washington, August 29, 1898.

Messrs. E. C. Davis & Co., Boston, Mass.

Gentlemen :—

Herewith we send you Outfit List which we nave compiled for the u
of the KLONDIKE & BOSTON GOLD MINING & MANUFACTURING C
based upon our experience in outfitting for the Arctic regions and the requiremer
of the several parties we have outfitted for you this year.   We believe this is t
most complete list yet published.   Your outfits this season were, in our opinic
among the best that went out from here; and it is seldom that we find those out
ting, that are so thoroughly alive as you to the very important feature of this out
ting trade—that miners in Alaska require the best, and that the best is the cheape
Here is where your plan, it seems to us, brings to a common centre the interests
both the miners and the company they represent;—and under these conditions, wi
the same conservative management that has characterized your dealings with t
your company cannot help but succeed. We believe that Alaska has a great futu
and we trust all business we have done with you this year will prove so satisfacto
that we may depend upon your future valued patronage, to which we promise o
very best efforts.   Yours truly, THE SEATTLE TRADING CO.

By F. S. Sylvester, Manager.

The Conquest Mine,

ARIZONA.

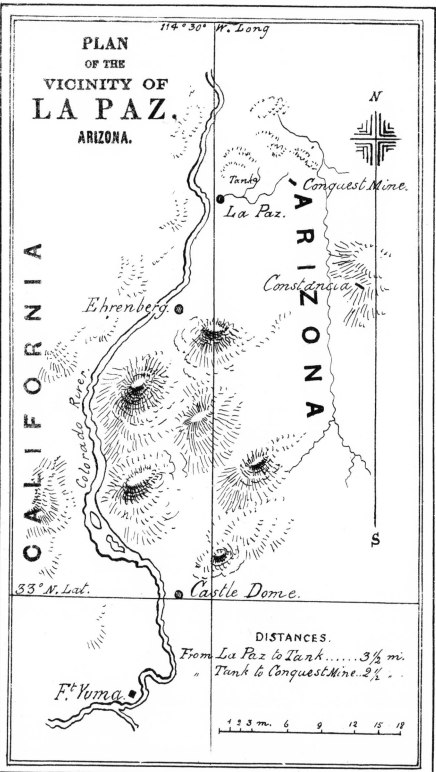

PLAN
OF THE
VICINITY OF
LA PAZ.
ARIZONA.

114°30' W. Long.

N

Tank

La Paz.

Conquest Mine.

ARIZONA

Constancia.

Ehrenberg.

CALIFORNIA

Colorado River.

S

33° N. Lat.

Castle Dome.

Fᵗ Yuma.

DISTANCES.
From La Paz to Tank......3½ mi.
„ Tank to Conquest Mine..2½ „

1 2 3 m.   6   9   12   15   18

Litho. J. Conder.

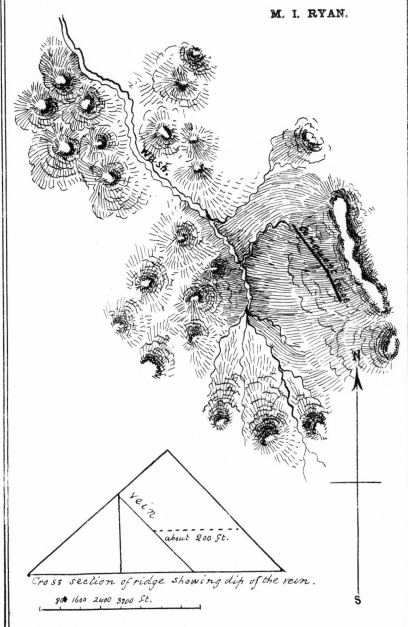

SKETCH
OF THE
CONQUEST LEDGE
BY
M. I. RYAN.

about 200 ft.

Cross section of ridge showing dip of the vein.

80 1600 2400 3200 ft.

THE CONQUEST MINE,

ARIZONA.

————:o:————

REPORT ON THE CONQUEST LEDGE, LA PAZ MINING DISTRICT, ARIZONA.

THE Conquest Ledge is situated 6 miles east of the village of La Paz, in the La Paz Mining District, Territory of Arizona. The extent of the location is 1,600 feet, with 100 feet on each side of the ledge. The present road runs for the first $3\frac{1}{2}$ miles over a gently ascending *mesa*, or gravelly plateau, and, with the exception of a few sandy stretches, is a hard road. At that distance it touches a water-tank in a deep ravine, the banks of which down to the tank are composed of granite, and from the tank down of stratified lime-rock of tertiary formation. A limited supply of water can be procured here at all seasons of the year. By building a dam, 15 feet high across the ravine immediately above the tank, a large reservoir can be formed at little cost. The banks of the ravine approach each other at a height of 15 feet to within 30 feet, so that, estimating the fall of the ravine at 3 feet per 100 feet, the mean slope of the banks 1 by 2, and the mean distance across the surface of the water 50 feet, the reservoir would hold about 98,000 gallons. Such a reservoir would probably fill twice every year, if not oftener, and its construction would be advisable in the absence of water at the mine. Until such time, however, as very extensive operations would make this improvement desirable, the mine might be supplied with water hauled in sheet-iron tanks by teams going for ore. The Vulture mine, 15 miles from Wickenburg, has been supplied with water in this manner for years, at a slight additional expense over the cost of hauling their ore.

This same ravine intersects the road to the Conquest ledge, and it will be necessary to throw a bridge of about 30 feet span over it at a suitable point. From the tank the road is hard. At about a mile from it a descent of, perhaps, 70 feet can' easily be reduced to a proper grade, and from here the road ascends gradually in a stony ravine, or wash, to the mine.

A more direct road from the mine to La Paz, leaving the water-tank to the north, can be laid out with an uninterrupted gentle descent.

The Conquest ledge runs in a N.W. direction (see Plan) on the westerly slope of a granite ridge, which rises about 300 feet above its base. The side walls consist of talcose slate, and are very thick ; at no point could I measure their width. The dip of the vein is about 45 degrees. I will here transcribe some of the notes taken by me on the ledge, commencing at the N.W. end of the location :

Shaft No. 1. This shaft, or cut, is 16 feet long, 15 feet deep, with the ledge 8 feet thick at the bottom of the cut.

Shaft No. 2. Cut 10 feet long, 5 feet deep, the ledge showing clearly 3 feet in thickness, in talc slate.

Shaft No. 3. Under this head note 2 cuts 8 and 10 feet square, 20 and 8 feet deep, with the ledge 4 feet thick and well defined.

Shaft No. 4. Cut 8 feet square, 16 feet deep, 3 feet thick.

Shaft No. 5. Cut 8 feet square, 20 feet deep, ledge 3 feet wide ; continues visible in places to next shaft.

Shaft No. 6. Cut 40 feet long ; shaft 10 feet square, 64 feet deep ; ledge 20 feet thick. There is another shaft, almost adjoining, 30 feet deep, with the ledge 15 feet thick and well defined. A small ledge, which I take to be a spur, makes into the main ledge at this point. It is located under the name of "the Diamond," and owned by the same party.

Shaft No. 7. Cut 24 feet long, 7 feet deep ; ledge 5 feet thick, well defined in talcose slate.

Shaft No. 8. There are 2 shafts almost together, 45 and 25 feet deep, with the ledge 12 feet wide.

Shaft No. 9. Shaft 5 feet square, 26 feet deep; ledge 10 feet wide. There are a number of cuts on the ledge not named in these notes in which the vein appears to be from 4 to 15 feet wide.

The ledge is visible on the surface for a distance of 1,200 feet, or three-fourths of the entire location. The richest ore is at the deepest shaft, although at several of the shallow cuts very rich decomposed ore was abundant. These shafts, I am bound to say, appear to have been made more to demonstrate the permanence of the vein than to develop it.

From the foregoing notes, the existence of a quartz ledge, imbedded in talc slate, of more than 1,200 feet in length, is proven. Outcroppings of the ledge are visible to the N.W. of it, as indicated on the map by the dotted lines ; also on the S.E., where I examined a cut at a distance of about 150 yards from the S.E. end of the Conquest claim. It was impossible to determine the width of the ledge at all the shafts and cuts ; at some of them, the quartz is much decomposed and mixed with talc slate. At different points, where the quartz appeared very compact, I broke off pieces, and found them on the inner side honeycombed or decomposed, impregnated with the oxides of iron and containing more or less gold. I do not wish to convey the idea that none of the quartz was compact, and without gold, but I saw pay rock piled up at most of the shafts and cuts, and estimated it to amount in all to 200 tons.

The width of the ledge is at different points 20, 15, 12, 10, 5, 4, and 3 feet. We may, therefore, including the branch veins which furnish the same kind of gold-bearing quartz as the main ledge, take its mean width to be 10 feet. Then 10x1,200x25 would make 300,000 cubic feet, which at 15 feet per ton of 2,000 lbs. would give 20,000 tons for the first 25 feet from the surface down, or 80,000 tons for the first 100 feet. As one of the shafts is 64 feet in depth, and several more than 25 feet, it must be conceded that this is not assuming too great a mean depth as actually in sight for three-fourths of the location. Besides, where the ledge appears narrowest at the surface, it is usually intermixed more or less with talc slate. At my suggestion, a slate horse was removed from the top of the ledge, where it was 12 feet wide, and proved it to be, on removal, 20 feet wide. I have every reason to believe that on attaining a depth of 150 or 200 feet, a very large ledge will be found. In this connection, I may say that the dry placers of this vicinity, which proved so remarkably remunerative from 1862 to 1866, and which continue to turn out good wages to industrious miners, are all situated below the Conquest ledge and the apparent line of its extension. As placers are but the detritus of auriferous rocks, they must be soon exhausted. The production of gold in California by gulch or placer mining diminished from $60,000,000 in 1853 to $20,000,000 in 1868. Public attention turns therefore, from surface deposits to the separation of gold from its native matrix of rock as the only permanent means of production. Now, the slightest prospect cannot be obtained above the ledge, and, consequently, we must come to the conclusion that the source of supply of these placers lies in or near this ledge. This is not my own theory only. I have conversed with a number of experienced mineralogists, who expressed their belief that a tunnel run into the Conquest ledge would strike the source of the riches of the Campo Ferra placers, and others in this vicinity.

From the most S.E. shaft, the angle of elevation of the ridge is 46 degrees ; the altitude of its crest above this shaft about 100 feet. On the eastern slope, the angle of elevation from a point about 200 feet below crest is 40 degrees. A horizontal tunnel, therefore, of 200 feet length drifted from the eastern slope towards the vein would probably strike it (see cross section).

A steam quartz mill may be erected in La Paz itself, near the slough, from which water can be obtained, or on the *mesa*, where water could be had from wells. Fuel costs the labor of cutting and hauling in the immediate vicinity of the slough. There is enough willow, iron-wood, mesquite, and cotton-wood in the river bottom to last many years. The expense of keeping one six-mule team with driver is, at present, $10 per day. The team could make two trips a day from the mill to the mine. Mexican laborers and miners can be had from $30 to $50 per month, with board ; American miners command fiom $40 to $60, with board, and are worth the difference.

The Indians of the River Region of Arizona are friendly, and have been so for a number of years. The Reservation is 40 miles above La Paz, on the river.

However improbable it must appear, to any one who has visited or examined the ledge, that it could give out at a depth of 25 feet, let us assume so for a moment. Then we have, at a minimum calculation, 20,000 tons of ledge rock. I can conscientiously say they are in sight.

The samples of ore selected from the rock at the shafts and cuts speak for themselves.

M. I. RYAN,

Engineer.

La Paz, Arizona,
June 18, 1870.

Similar samples to those referred to in the report may be seen at the office. They are mostly of honeycombed rock or decomposed quartz, and show considerable gold, visible to the naked eye. Parties who take an interest in such matters are invited to call and examine them. Specimens of the ore may also be seen at the School of Mines, Columbia College. When pulverized, it readily yields the gold, and is as easily worked as any of the Grass Valley ores. The ore is frequently pulverized in a druggist's mortar, and washed out in a horn spoon by parties at La Paz who wish to prospect its richness. The gold is very similar in character to placer gold.

CERTIFICATE OF A U.S. DISTRICT JUDGE AS TO THE VALUE OF THE MINE.

Territory of Arizona, }
Yuma County. }

I CERTIFY that I am personally acquainted with Mr. Manuel Ravena, a citizen of Yuma County, in the Territory of Arizona, and know him to be a gentleman of unexceptionable character and integrity. I further certify that Mr. Ravena is the owner of what is known as the " Conquest Gold Mine," a quartz lode situate in the county and territory aforesaid, and about six miles east of the town of La Paz. The public records of this county show that Mr. Ravena's title to said mine is in all things regular and absolute, not only under the laws of the said territory, in that behalf made and provided, but, also, under those of the United States. Mr. Ravena has owned and worked this mine continuously for the period of more than five years ; during which time he has uncovered and developed said ledge for a distance of twelve hundred feet upon the surface of the ground, and has shown the ledge to be from three to twenty feet in width along the whole distance, with an extension of four hundred feet not yet developed. He has sunk many shafts on said lead of various depths, from thirty to seventy feet, and at all points has found the ledge well defined and continuous.

The rock from this mine is all gold-bearing and very rich, and will pay, when properly worked, from fifty to five hundred dollars per ton. The mine is situated in a district of country where wood and water are plenty, facilities for transportation good and comparatively cheap, and labor in abundance and at reasonable rates.

The facts herein stated are within my personal knowledge, and I take pleasure in recommending the Conquest Mine to the favorable consideration of all persons as, perhaps, the richest deposit of gold-bearing quartz on the Pacific coast.

Witness my hand and the seal of the U.S. District Court.

ISHAM REAVIS,

U.S. District Judge,

2ND DISTRICT OF ARIZONA.

La Paz, June 27, 1870,
(Seal of the U.S. District Court,
2nd Judicial District, Arizona.)

CERTIFICATE OF COL. GEO. W. DENT, LATE SUPER-INTENDENT OF INDIAN AFFAIRS IN ARIZONA, NOW APPRAISER-GENERAL OF THE PORT OF SAN FRANCISCO.

SAN FRANCISCO, CAL.,
July 22, 1870.

I ENDORSE everything stated by Judge Reavis in relation to Mr. Ravena (whom I personally know) and his title to the Conquest Mine, near La Paz, in Arizona Territory, under the laws of that territory.

I am not apprized of his having obtained title from the United States under act of Congress, though know of no obstacle in the way of procuring title, as he has complied with the necessary requirements in work, and expended largely in excess of the amount in money required.

The mine is doubtless a good one ; metals assaying from $50 to $500 per ton. It is nearly a year since I visited the mine. I have learned, however, from reliable authority that it is now fully developed, and producing metals of great richness.

GEO. W. DENT.

THE PROPERTY CLEAR OF INCUMBRANCE.

A CERTIFICATE from the County Recorder of Yuma County, dated June 15, 1870, declares Manuel Ravena to be the sole owner of the property, and that there are no incumbrances thereon.

A U.S. patent to the mine has not yet been obtained, because it has not been applied for. The title to the property being so clear, and the ledge being constantly in the possession of Mr. Ravena, it has been unnecessary to obtain a clearer title to the property than he has at present.

MINING AS AN INVESTMENT.

There are on this side of the continent many persons who look on the mining of the precious metals as inimical to the general interests of the nation, on account of its hazardous fluctuations and the contempt it often begets for slower modes of making money. Their view is nearly correct as applied to mining at an earlier day, or to the stockjobbing speculations of a few years past. But the objection does not hold to mining directed by skill and capital, and conducted in as systematic a manner as are manufacturing or mercantile pursuits. This kind of mining promises to become one of the main sources of our national wealth. And we hazard nothing in saying that the immense deposits of gold and silver found in our Western domain are destined to make quartz mining as safe and legitimate a business as mining for coal and iron is to-day in Pennsylvania.

Were it not for mining, the states and territories of the Pacific slope would be but little more than barren wastes, or, at best, mere cattle ranges, instead of powerful states and growing territories. But for the necessities created by the development of our mineral wealth, the Pacific Railroad would be uncommenced, and the steamship line to China unthought of.

Agriculture, manufactures, commerce, and mining go hand in hand. In the Atlantic States, it is commerce that leads ; in the Eastern States, it is manufactures ; in the Central States of the West, it is agriculture ; in the Western States and Territories of the Pacific slope, it is mining.

The mineral discoveries in Nevada and Colorado have given an impetus to mining, and greater confidence than ever exists in the profits to be derived from this pursuit legitimately conducted. The general depression of mining stocks is a healthy indication, in so far as it shows that instead of any actual decline in the value of the mines themselves, the era of wild speculation has come to a close. It simply shows that a system of mining based on stockjobbing speculations must, in nearly every instance, result in failure. Wherever we find mines worked by individuals or companies as carefully as other branches of industry are looked to, we find the average success to be as great in this business as in most others.

The following article commends itself to the attention of capitalists by its sound logic and practical handling of the subject:

MINING, AS A SCIENCE AND AN INVESTMENT.
(From the London Mining Journal.)

IT may be safely asserted that at no period of the history of mining has the art drawn to itself such extensive consideration as at the present moment—from the man of science, as a subject calculated to afford ample scope for inquiry into the theory of metallic deposits and other natural phenomena; or from the man of business, as an opening for investment, and far exceeding all others in the lucrative return on the capital employed

That mining always has been, and ever will be, a highly remunerative industry to those who engage in it circumspectly, and with due caution, may be inferred from the fact that from the earliest ages it has been unremittingly practised, and, it may be said, with a good degree of success. Evidences are easily obtained that even before the invasion and occupation of our island by the Romans mining was extensively prosecuted, and the metallurgic arts not indifferently understood by the early Briton. It would, doubtless, be a most difficult task to assign to their true causes the motives which led the primitive and barbarous inhabitants of Cornwall to seek for the metallic treasures lying hid in the numberless veins which traverse their native hills and valleys, in the face of difficulties which to them must have appeared well nigh overwhelming, but it may reasonably be presumed that profit of some sort or description was the power that urged them to their exertions, more especially if we judge them by our knowledge of the savage tribes still remaining on the earth, whose appreciation of the merits of a profitable transaction is as keen as, and in no way inferior to, that of their civilized brethren.

These causes must naturally give an explanation of the extraordinary revival of mining on all sides, and how the untiring labors of eminent geologists in teaching how to select the most favorable localities, and the skill of engineers in the preparation of most elaborate works and machinery, have wrought this great and welcome change—a change which bids fair to place mining in its true position as a medium for profitable and safe investment.

The great interest now taken in the mineral resources of this and other countries, induced by science in the selection of districts and by skilful appliances in surmounting difficulties which at one time appeared insurmountable, induces us to refer to the rapid progress which mining is making, and we cannot be venturing too far in saying that mining is one of the finest fields for speculation that can be found, although often looked upon by capitalists with prejudice and distrust; but if every transaction were fairly elucidated, and openness and candor practised, mining would become far more popular than it has been, and the adventurers would be far more benefitted. But here it is necessary for us to remark that if capitalists will only take the precaution of making full inquiries as to the persons who are to have the management of the mine, as well as those who are to be some of the shareholders, they will be better able to judge of the manner in which the management of the affairs of mining companies is likely to be conducted.

A good number of very promising undertakings have recently been established, and we hope and think they, or at least some of them, are based on a solid foundation, and if so they will be some of the greatest contributions to the wealth of the nation, and will secure for themselves a high position in the estimation of the public; and it requires the united energy and assistance of mining men to bring back the days of yore, when mining was looked upon with more favor. The almost uniform success that attends the development of well-selected and properly-managed mines is naturally enough daily attracting more attention on the part of capitalists, and by those acquainted with legitimate mines it will be allowed that, when properly conducted, mining is neither so uncertain or speculative as many have been led, either through ignorance or prejudice, to imagine; on the contrary, it frequently offers the most profitable advantages to the capitalist, great or small.

WHAT THE PRESS SAY OF THE CONQUEST LODE.

From the "Arizona Miner," June 25, 1870.

CONQUEST MINE, LA PAZ.—Work has recently been resumed on this well-known mine, by the proprietor, Manuel Ravena. Arrastras are now in course of construction, and we hope to be able shortly to give the result of some crushings. This ledge shows free gold in abundance, is visible for 1,200 feet of its length, and has eight shafts sunk on it, besides a number of cuts. There are hundreds of tons of valuable ore already taken out, with a large amount of ore in sight in the shafts. It is a great detriment to the territory to keep such mines as the Conquest lying idle; and yet this mine, notwithstanding its known richness, and the fact of its attracting the attention of capitalists several years ago, has remained almost perfectly quiet during that time. We can only attribute this to the fact ot its proprietor being above the want of ready cash, and consequently too independent of outside capital. Ross Browne refers to this mine in his report, and Ehrenberg and Waldemar, both good engineers, agreed on its great value.

From the "Los Angeles (Cal.) Daily News," July 9, 1870.

FROM ARIZONA.—We learn that ore has been struck in the Conquest lode, near La Paz, that produces over $1,000 per ton. Much of the ledge is decomposed, and is filled with both fine and coarse gold. The proprietor of the mine, Mr. Ravena, formerly of this county, let the mine remain idle for a long time, but recently recommenced working with the above result. He has at various times been offered from $60,-000 to $100,000 for the mine, but neither sold the mine nor worked it; consequently, instead of proving a benefit to the section, it may almost be said to have been a detriment. Such mines as the Conquest should be worked by their owners, or they should be transferred to some parties who would work them.

From the "San Bernardino (Cal.) Guardian," July 9, 1870.

FROM LA PAZ.—We have intelligence from Arizona that ore has been found in the Conquest mine that produces over $1,000 per ton. Mr. Manuel Ravena, formerly of Los Angeles, is the proprietor of this mine, and has but recently recommenced working his ledge. There are eight shafts on the ledge, but no mill, as yet. Some years ago Mr. Ravena was offered $60,000 for the mine, but would neither sell nor work it himself. Ross Browne refers to this mine as one of the best in the territory, and we hope it will prove so by turning out the gold bullion.

From the "Scientific Press (Cal.)," July 23, 1870.

At the Ravena Conquest mine at La Paz, ore going over $1,000 a ton is being taken out. Shipment of a few sacks of this ore has recently been made to San Francisco and New York.

LETTER FROM ARIZONA.

We condense the following correspondence from the *Engineering and Mining Journal*, of New York :

WICKENBURG, ARIZONA, July 22, 1870.

You hear very little in New York of the Vulture mine, as it is not an incorporated company. Moreover, it appears to be the desire of its owners to keep their affairs as private as possible, and, therefore, they make no boast of the immense yield of gold bullion constantly furnished from their mill. An idea of its importance, however, may be formed from the fact that about one-half of the currency of Arizona is in Vulture bullion. The Vulture Mine is fifteen miles from the village of Wickenburg. The mine has been opened to a vertical depth of 250 feet, at which point the vein is 30 feet in width. The richest ore at the present writing is taken from the upper shaft, but no experienced miner can for a moment doubt the richness and extent of the mine after a careful examination of its developed ground. There being no water at or near the mine, the ore has to be hauled fifteen miles, to Vulture City, in order to be crushed. The mill is a 40-stamp mill, with power for 60 stamps, and is one of the finest on the Pacific coast. The average crushing is 80 tons per day, and I doubt if there is another of its size in the world that turns out more bullion.* The hauling of the ore from the mine to the mill costs the company $7 per ton; it formerly cost $9 per ton. You will ask, What does the ore pay? Of that we cannot speak to a certainty; but we may say that for several years it yielded $7·50 per ton, clear of all expenses.

But there are other big mines in this territory besides the Vulture. Ross Browne, in his report, speaks of the Conquest mine, near La Paz. This mine was for a long time considered richer than the Vulture, but the latter fell into the hands of an energetic set of men, who went to work to develop it, while the former, being the property of one man, was allowed to remain almost idle for several years. The Conquest shows much free gold in the surface ore, and has several shafts on it. Ore was recently shown here and in Prescott that goes over $1,000 a ton. The Conquest is not in the Apache country, but it wants a mill badly. Were it up here, there would be more excitement about it.

I close this letter by giving a few notes as to the route from San Francisco and cost of travel : San Francisco to San Pedro, steamer fare $20, time 48 hours; San Pedro to Los Angeles, railway fare $2·50; Los Angeles to San Bernardino, daily stage, 65 miles, $5, 10 hours; San Bernardino to Prescott, Arizona, stage leaves every Thursday morning,

---

* From Nov. 1, 1866, to Sept. 1, 1867, 4,834 tons, which produced $145,633, an average of about $30 per ton.—*Browne's Report.*

From the report of Professor Raymond, Commissioner of Mining Statistics, we take the following : "The continuation of working results from Sept. 1, 1867, to Aug. 31, 1868, 12 months, is as follows : During this period, the mill crushed 10,640 tons of ore, producing $254,110, gold, an average of about $24 per ton.

via La Paz, Wickenburg, and Date Creek, arriving at Prescott, 410 miles, the following Wednesday, noon, through fare $80.

EXTRACTS FROM THE REPORT OF J. ROSS BROWNE TO THE GOVERNMENT ON THE MINERAL RESOURCES OF THE STATES AND TERRITORIES WEST OF THE ROCKY MOUNTAINS.

(See p. 452, et seq., on the Colorado River Region.)

Colorado River.

The valley of this great river, " the Mississippi of the Pacific," may justly be considered one of the natural divisions of Arizona. Ascending the river from its mouth it is a distance of 150 miles to Fort Yuma, where the mineral district may be said to begin. Opposite to the fort, on the Arizona side, is the town of Arizona City. The Gila road to Tucson, and across the Territory to New Mexico, begins at this place, and the supplies for the military of southern Arizona are forwarded from here, coming from San Francisco via the Gulf of California.

Castle Dome, 50 miles above Arizona City, is a well-known mining district, so called from an isolated mountain bearing a close resemblance to a dome. The lodes are in a range of mountains from 15 to 30 miles back of the river, but, as in the Eureka district, they are not very easy of access, and water is exceedingly scarce. A number of lodes have been claimed, and several companies organized in San Francisco for their development. Those opened are from a foot to five feet in width, and well defined. Professor Blake states that the ores of Castle Dome are argentiferous galena, in a vein-stone of fluor spar, and that they contain 30 to 40 ounces of silver to the ton.

The next district is that about the town of La Paz, and bears the same name. It was first explored in the Colorado gold excitement of 1862, and, indeed, little was known of the mineral resources of the Colorado valley until that year. Mr. A. McKey, member of the territorial legislature from La Paz, has furnished the annexed account of the discovery of the placers which caused the upbuilding of La Paz, now a place of considerable importance, and a favorite shipping point for goods for Central Arizona ; Prescott, the capital of the Territory, being at a distance of less than 200 miles in the interior, and Wickenburg at a distance of but a little more than 100, over remarkably good roads.* *

Of the yield of these placers, anything like an approximation to the average daily amount of what was taken out per man would only be guess-work. Hundreds of dollars per day to the man was common, and now and again a thousand or more per day. Don Juan Ferra took one nugget from his claim which weighed 47 ounces and six dollars. Another party found a "chispa" weighing 27 ounces, and another one of 26 ounces. Many others found pieces of from one or two ounces up to 20, and yet it is contended that the greater proportion of the larger nuggets were never shown for fear of some evil spirits, who infested the mines at the time. It is the opinion of those most conversant with the first working of these placers that much the greater proportion of gold taken out was in nuggets weighing from one dollar up to the size of the "chispas" above named. I have often heard it said of those days that "not even a Papago Indian would work for less than $10 per day.

As has been seen from the above, the gold was large, and generally clear of foreign substances. The largest piece (above mentioned) did not contain an apparent atom of quartz or any other base matter. The gold from the different camps varied a trifle in its worth at the mint in San Francisco, and brought from $17·50 to $19·50 per ounce. But all that was sold or taken here went for from $16 to $17 per ounce. Since the year 1864 till the present, there have been at various times many men at work in these placers, numbering in the winter months hundreds, but in the summer months not exceeding 75 or 100; and all seem to do sufficiently well not to be willing to work for the wages of the country, which are and have been for some time from $30 to $65 per month and found. No inconsiderable amount comes in from these placers now weekly, and only a few days ago I saw myself a nugget weighing $40, clear and pure from any foreign substance.*

As might be supposed, the richness of these placers suggested the existence of valuable quartz lodes in the vicinity, and prospecting began in 1863. The result was the location of a number of gold, silver, and copper veins within an area of 30 miles about La Paz. Of these several have been opened, and the ores well tested.

CONSTANCIA MINE —A gold mine 12 miles east of La Paz has a shaft of 75 feet, and some 20 tons of the ore worked by arrastras yielded $30 to $50 per ton. The vein is five feet wide in a granite formation and regular. The Las Posas is a similar vein.

CONQUEST MINE.—This is a gold mine, otherwise known as the Ravena mine. It is situated east of La Paz, some six miles, and has been well prospected. A number of shafts and tunnels have been

---

* These placers continue to be worked (1870), and yield fair wages to the miners, most of whom are Mexicans. It is a fact worthy of note that the placers are all below the line of the Conquest ledge, not the smallest prospect of gold being to be obtained above it. The natural inference is that as gold comes from quartz, the source of supply of these placers is that ledge.—M. I. R.

opened, and the vein is found to be well defined and promising. The width is from 3 to 20 feet. Some silver is found in the ore which is free from sulphurets. Gangs of men are now employed, as they have been for several years, in preparing this mine for working upon a large scale and its owner, Mr. Ravena, is confident that he has a valuable property. He has already, it is said, been offered $100,000.

ASSAYS OF CONQUEST ORE.

ASSAYS made by Goldsmith Bros., San Francisco, of samples of rich ore from the Conquest lode, yielded as follows, as per certified certificates on file in the office :

No. 259, gold, $400·22 ; silver, $13 08 ; total value per ton of 2,000 lbs., $413·20. No. 260, before melting, 1·26 oz. ; after melting, 1·20 oz. Fineness of gold, 0·686 ; value of gold, $17·01 per oz. Fineness of silver, 0·301 ; value of silver, 46 cents per oz. Gold, $377 78 ; silver, $10·22. Total value per ton of 2,000 lbs., $388·00. This was the result of the working of 90 lbs. of ore.

NEWARK SMELTING AND REFINING WORKS,
NEWARK, N.J., Sept. 15, 1870.

I HEREBY certify that I have assayed 173 lbs. of ore for M. I. Ryan of New York, marked Conquest ore, and find the yield to be in—

Gold........................value	$9	09
Silver........................ "	0	21
Total.....................	$9	30

Mint value per ton of ore of 2,000 lbs......$107 50

ED. BALBACH, JR.
F. FOHR, *Supt.*

° Governor McCormick, in his message dated Nov. 16, 1868, says : " The Wickenburg gold mines are worked without interruption, and steadily yield a large revenue The Vulture lode, the Comstock of Arizona, now has a wide and merited fame. ° ° ° From the Eureka district there is a steady and profitable shipment of lead ore to San Francisco ; and work upon several silver lodes in that district is vigorously prosecuted, as it is upon several gold lodes near La Paz."

THE CONQUEST MINE NOT FOR SALE : ONLY WORKING CAPITAL WANTED.

THIS enterprise is offered for consideration in the confident hope that it will, after a careful examination, be deemed a good investment. No mining property, proved as rich as this, has ever been offered for sale in New York—much less, only for working capital. The owner of the mine does not ask a single dollar to be paid him. Sure of the value of his property, he is willing to take his pay in the stock of a properly organized company, and only requires a fair guarantee to be given that, if the property be legally transferred to them, work will be commenced vigorously, without unnecessary delay.

By reference to the report it will be seen that operations on the mine have progressed so far that success appears not only certain, but almost attained.

WHAT IS NECESSARY TO BE DONE.

THE work necessary to be done at the mine, before a steady return from it can be expected, may be briefly summed up as follows :

1. Two of the deepest inclined shafts on the ledge should be continued to the depth of from 150 to 200 feet, in order to determine, before the erection of a mill, whether the ledge continues as rich as it appears to be at present.

2. A road to be made from the mine to the mill-site.

3. A steam quartz mill to be erected. If the ledge continues as rich as it appears now, this mill should be of 20 stamps, with power for 40 stamps.

For further information apply to, or address,

M. I. RYAN,

544 Broadway, Room 11.   NEW YORK.

A LETTER

COLORADO MATTERS

TO THE

STOCKHOLDERS OF EXCELSIOR CO.

AND OTHERS

WHOM IT MAY CONCERN.

BY

JOHN WETHERBEE.

B O S T O N :

J. E. FARWELL AND COMPANY, PRINTERS,

37 CONGRESS STREET.

1 8 6 7 .

To the Stockholders of the " Excelsior Mining Company of Colorado."

INTRODUCTORY.

Though this communication is especially addressed to the stockholders of the Excelsior Company, and for the purpose of giving briefly, but, as far as practicable, detailed information of the progress of that enterprise, now at last at the producing point, — it will necessarily comprise also the progress to perfection, or rather practical and profitable action of the " gold saving process" in use at that Company's mines, which being applicable to the general and refractory ores of Colorado and elsewhere, will interest not only the friends of that enterprise, the Excelsior Company, but the public also, especially those who are, or may be, interested in the mining operations of Colorado or elsewhere ; and therefore careful and critical attention is asked to its subject-matter from the public, to whom it is also respectfully submitted.

I will say further that the statements of facts and the inferences, made with much care, which I propose to offer, can be relied upon, having been carefully considered, and whatever associations with monetary matters may be connected with my name or specialty, I assure the reader this communication has no reference to a speculative action, and is not sent with that object in view, or even desired; but is simply a statement, briefly but very plainly made, of matters of vital interest, in connection with finance and commerce. In some of its features, as the reader will see in perusing the following pages, I shall conflict in some respects with the records of science, but I feel sure I am right notwithstanding : and to justify myself for being so positive in this introduction and for my boldness, allow me to say the subject has been my specialty for four years and I feel competent to say what I do, hence I challenge refutation, and invite criticism. I know I make myself liable to the accusation of egotism, and I feel that I ought to say, in apology for this rather unusual preface, that it is written for strangers, rather than those associated with me in the *enterprise* that has called for this letter ; if it were for them alone the matter would have been sent without this preliminary comment.

COLORADO AND MINING.

In A. D. 1867 a description of this territory will be superfluous, it has been so prominently before the public for the past four years; and besides being near in a peculiar sense, by the planting of capital, "for where our treasure is there is our heart also," it is getting nearer and nearer to us in another sense, and at the rate of two miles a day, by railroad construction already completed to within thirty odd hours' stage ride of the base of the Rocky Mountains, which will be reached during this year; then Chicago will be the half-way house between its Eastern and Western termini, and it will be our neighbor.

The mineral wealth and other advantages of this region, occupying the central point between Chicago and San Francisco, have been too often spoken of to need a word here; and yet a very brief reference to them, at least to the *dynamics* that have impressed Colorado on so many brains, seems to be somewhat necessary for the better understanding of the subject which I propose, under a few distinct heads, to give you in the pages that follow.

In brief then, the discovery of gold has attracted a population to this region, and 40,000 would not be far from its number at the present time ; in this respect it has not *materially* varied since 1863, though an increase of good sense is quite marked. The years from 1859 to 1862 were years of activity, and in a certain sense the country has been living since on the momentum it got during that period of legitimate production and healthy activity. Local governments had become established, with their laws and regulations ; wealth had accumulated ; many had their pile of the yellow dust, nuclei blossomed into cities ; *Denver, Golden, Black-Hawk and Central* are well-known, and will be more so, as the territory develops its wealth, which is one of the things which may be written down as certain to happen. I am no prophet, but on the fulfilment of that, viz., the great yield of gold from the locality in question, I am willing to risk my reputation. I see practically the sources for my statement and to me it is simply a mathematical calculation. I am not writing this letter, as I have already said, for any speculative purpose, have no such object in view, and am happy to know, that the time has passed when any man's letter, or story, however well told, can galvanize a Colorado gold stock, and I write this letter with more satisfaction, I am so happily satisfied *with* that conviction, and I hope to receive attention on altogether different than speculative grounds or objects.

It was found after some of the usual experience of mining localities, that " all was not gold that glittered ; " that perseverance and frugality, as well as good luck, were essentials to success. Still many got their nuggets who never would, had they stayed at home — people here were also lucky and unlucky, persevering with varied success ; accident often doing for some, what industry failed to do for others. Here, as elsewhere, skill, economy, and judgment were as marked elements of success as rich diggings and the labors of these years and the gold obtained established the value of the locality as a gold field. Without here going into a detailed account of the transition period, from legitimate mining to speculative conditions, I will state, what is now well known : — it had been discovered after, in a measure, exhausting the gulches and the surface ore of the lodes that had been so profitably worked, that there were peculiar features to these ores : that the proportion of *free* gold was less, though the ores themselves were richer, as a whole, by assay than in any other locality. The modes of saving gold practised in California and elsewhere, — the stamp mills, the most popular, — were found to be inadequate to get the gold from most of these ores, and this was irrespective of what assay gave, as being in the ore. For instance, in two lodes of equal value by assay, one would yield little or nothing, the other would pay a profit ; and again, sometimes ore that would assay comparatively small, would yield some profit, while another rich by assay test would yield none, or so little as to pay no profit, and even a loss; as the miners learned by experience these facts, there were many disappointments, mills erected at considerable expense, abandoned and sold, and the question how to save the gold from these refractory ores, as they were called, was an important one. At this time there were a few lodes that paid something, but they were growing less by the increase of mining and milling expenses, and other causes which are well known, and need not be enlarged upon in this communication.

It is difficult to say now what might have been the condition of Colorado if the speculative action of 1863 and 1864 had not sprung up in conneetion: very many and good judges say to-day, it was the worst thing that could have happened to the territory. I think I realize fully the injury of attracting industry from legitimate channels, to short and generally fallacious roads to wealth; but still I think the injury has been so far severer on the eastern invester than on the territory in question; and I think growing out of it I see a successful future for Colorado, that, without it, it would at least be much farther off. Be that as it may, at this time property was changing hands, sales were being made to people for speculative purposes, and numbers sold their lodes and mills for sums not dear, if they had been remunerative; but under the circumstances, $ 20,000 to $ 50,000, and even more, seemed large sums for unproductive enterprises on future expectations; and sometimes these sums paid were treble what any native would have given, or the seller have obtained, but for the advent of this new order of purchasers. That was a new vein that paid well, and it was worked with vigor—no one knowing how soon it would run into *cap*, using a local term. Then had almost entirely ceased the work of getting gold, *prospecting* increased, and lode claims found quick sales, often at larger prices than the estimated value of the best and popular lodes in their palmiest days. The years of which I am speaking, 1863 and 1864, may be said to have been the speculative period of Colorado history; almost every man of any *spread*, if I may use the word, had made sales of property, and often these properties were sold at sums that made the seller smile in private at the prodigality of eastern people. Yet, when that property was resold for double and treble the sum first paid, he was inclined to say to himself again: I am the man that needed education, and especially when the latter purchaser had watered it, and in its extended or diluted state it moved round in stock form, representing from a hundred thousand to a million dollars, as was frequently the case, which was apparently dear, and very likely now is at the

original sum of say $30,000. You can imagine the
effect such operations had upon the mining people of
the territory. They felt, as well they might, that the
veins struck of all others lay in the east, and may be
called the *Wall Street* or the *State Street* lodes, and
prospecting turned wholly in that direction. That
brought into prominence a class of people, agents, or
men who had financial influence, and knew how to
manipulate such movements. These, affiliating with
the mining population, combined, by no means villain-
ously, to run the thing as long as the pay lasted:
legitimate work was abandoned, and in consequence
the product of gold entirely ceased. Who could run a
stamp mill with doubtful success, when by telling
actual truth of what *had* been done, and show certificates of assays, that by the rule of three, plus improved
equipments, would eclipse their ancient actual work,
and thus easily, by a sale, get at one full swoop the
sum that years of toil might fail to produce? Without
reflecting upon any, this was natural, and, I think, in
a commercial sense, right; at least, under the circumstances, I am willing to admit it, for by and through
almost this only course has the wealth of Colorado been
placed within the reach of this generation. That it has
been so placed, I feel that I shall convince the reader
when all the facts that this letter carries have been
stated, and he has given them the consideration that

their truthfulness, and importance, and reliability deserve.

In the speculations referred to, thousands, in the form of stockholders, became interested in these high-tide purchases, and who expected returns of profit from legitimate work in a few months, or in a year's efforts; and yet, mark you, this was on a million dollars, and but little of that, often none, working capital, which cost, it may be, about one-tenth of the sum represented, and a fair income on its real cost would be reckoned a failure, when veneered over such extended surface. I think the love of gain, regardless of consequences, rather culpable, in the strong assurances made,—many no doubt were honestly made; figures were made upon past experience without sufficient regard to new conditions. They also took miners' words for it, who are at least no better than the average of men, who are ever disposed, the world over, even if honest, to be sanguine, and strain their facts in the direction of self-interest; but very many knew better, but they knew also how few would plant their money if its gestation was for years; and Colorado success *depended* upon the sowing of that kind of seed, and did not advise the best course for the parties becoming interested, even if from selfish action they did what proved, or will, I think, prove, for the benefit of Colorado. The consequence was, money was indiscreetly spent in equipping

these good, bad, and indifferent properties, which had
now been converted into stock companies; incompetent
men often made superintendents, and they were forced
by eastern pressure and ignorance to do something,
even if they did wrong, and they exhausted their several working capitals, small at best, in mills and
machinery, &c., before they knew what they wanted.
If they had simply developed their lodes, or even done
nothing at all but wait till some process had been discovered and *proved*, some companies that have gone
under might have been saved; but a superintendent, as
I have said, was expected to be doing something, even
if doing wrong; because working the mines for legitimate profit was the last thing thought of. There are
very few companies that have proposed to make their
investments remunerative by getting out gold, and
making dividends with it, but have aimed to make their
money by the rise and sale of shares, by strong statements and puffing, and other modes of speculative
action; and in keeping with this, false representations
have been conveyed by even truthful statements of
specimens of ore.

I never knew a property sold, or converted into a
Company, and the stock for sale, that the movers did not
have specimens of ore, and certificates of assays, won-
derfully rich, and they were generally *unselected* specimens or a fair average; every lode was in such hands

equal to *Bobtail* or *Gunnel*, or some *star* lode. The country is rich enough in gold, on practically truthful statements, if the gold can only be saved from the ores that contain it : but the fallacy of assays from $200 to $2000 a ton to base any legitimate calculation upon is now learned, and pretty much given up : there being a great difference when a working assay is made ; or ore in the mill, by the ton, and not an average specimen. It may be descending some to step down to the actual, from such high sounding certificates, but the ores or lodes that will in a mill in a large or working assay, show $50 a ton, are very few. I even mean *in* the ore not out of it, and no man competent to judge, having a regard for truth, will place the average of the ores of this country at more than $35 to $40 a ton : and that is double the average by experience of the ores of California. I make this statement very deliberately, wishing to give a golden expression to Colorado, and for fear some may think me unfortunate in my locality, allow me to say, besides having interests in different places, I am especially interested in a locality where the ores, though refractory, will bear comparison with the best in the territory. It is a pity to touch the nerve, but the time to fool and be fooled is past, or ought to be, in reference to Colorado, and, as sensible people having done many foolish things, some more and some less, we may as well pick up our pieces, do the best we can with what we have, profit by past experience, and we shall heal without much of a scar.

Here let me say that all companies and all individuals having lodes refractory or unrefractory, galena, pyratous, quartz or any other of the varied compositions that constitute a vein of ore, that will assay $15 a ton, that they can be worked at a profit; not as much profit as if the assay was $30 or $100 dollars a ton, but at a profit. I refer not now to special assays of an *unselected* specimen but of a working assay : that is, take ten ton of ore, as refractory as you can find, that has $150 in the said ten ton, and put it through upon principles referred to under the head of " process ;" it can be worked and the $150 can be saved, or at least $140 can be, and if properly handled by men who know the value of time and money, the cost will be from $70 to $100 ; the richer the ore the greater the proportion of profit, as lean or rich, refractory or unrefractory, the cost of working is irrespective of these terms, of course there will be differences in cost of working, growing out of depth, width, distance, hardness, &c., but these differences bear no relation to the quality or richness of the ore as a general thing, hence all there is over the poorer quality that will pay, will be clear gain.

Now if this be so, and I assure the reader it can be depended upon, there is encouragement for the long list of mourners who have been foolish enough, as the expression goes, to have invested. He need not take my say so, take my facts and draw his own conclusions. — I make a point always to be sure of my facts and then stick to them, and so I advise others to do ; any man who has got good sense, the facts being settled, is as capable of coming to correct conclusions, as if he were a *professor*, I sometimes think more so, owing to the prejudice that education often has to innovations, that is, supposing the facts of which we are speaking are in any respects different or counter to custom or prescription. My object in calling your attention to these remarks, even if you are not a stockholder in the Company which I shall under its appropriate head speak of, is because you are interested, if I state the truth, especially if you have any investments in Colorado stocks, allow me to say I have, and shall state nothing else, and commend what I say much more for its truth, than for its beauty. What follows under the head of *Excelsior Company* for its stockholders may be read with profit also by those who are not stockholders, as illustrative of the difficulties a pioneer company labors under, and seeing the frictions overcome and the road by this experience, made easy for others, it should, if I am plain enough to convince you, be a source of encouragemen to all who have interests lying in this direction.

THE EXCELSIOR MINING CO.

It will not be surprising after reading the foregoing pages, if this Company, now to be a little while considered, should be included in the same order of spuriously begotten schemes that have been referred to in speaking of Colorado and Mining; I shall find no fault, there would be reason for thinking so, for as yet it has borne no fruit, though it is now full of blossom, and something more than promise, and I think the day is very near when the fact will speak for itself and need no argument.

Under this head I am not pleading its case to outsiders, and to them its perusal is only recommended as an illustration of some of the difficulties that all the Companies have labored under, and as a source of hope to others who are still struggling, and its necessary connection with the general drift of Colorado enterprise,— *but to the stockholders of this Company* for whom it is especially intended, I submit it as a brief report of what has been done, and how it has been done, and its condition and prospect now.

The Excelsior Company was about the first stock company organized in the territory and of course has seen a great many expand into certificates and fade and be forgotten almost, even in its short life of four years. It has had its drawbacks, and suffered for want of knowledge by its management as well as by association, and has had its share of the difficulties that have been general and referred to under another head, in fact, I think more than its share, because in many respects a pioneer, and its success is encouragement for all. By careful attention it has survived its ills and reached perfect health with a good show for a long and profitable life.

I think it due to the long and respectable list of patient stockholders, and also to myself, to explain its progress and the causes for its delays. And I shall do it in the briefest manner possible, which I trust, with what has before been communicated to you, will be sufficient and clear. The Company was organized in the spring of 1863, the writer having spent the preceding twelve months in the study of Colorado, with unusual advantages, including the manipulating of a Company, which not having the merit on its full acquaintance to command his confidence he withdrew and at some pecuniary sacrifice and experience, and paid the money wholly back to the investers (a rare event among exploiterers), thus losing some months of valuable time and profit earned. Not to digress too much, I will say that two years after, in 1864, the same property in less conscientious, though *worldly speaking*, more competent hands, found ready investers in this city at some $ 200,-000 that the writer declined identifying himself with at $ 50,000 and as the property, to the sorrow of the second exploiterers and their victims was dear at nothing, I think his movements in this Company the more entitled to confidence and consideration. And I am happy to say that it has been manifested and it affords me pleasure to say so publicly in this communication.

The general arrangements having been made and the Excelsior Company organized, as mentioned, early in the spring of 1863, improvements were at once made on the property, in the construction of a forty-stamp mill on its admirable water power. And before the year had far advanced, our general equipments for the same were en route, and means for developing the property already proved to be extensive, abundant and rich ; and early in the spring of 1864, we had a well equipped mill, as could be desired, finished, and all ready for steady and legitimate work in mining our lodes for gold. Then began our disappointments and troubles, and instead of getting the product of gold from the ores we had, that were rich by assay, we proved what had already become to be an established fact, that our mode, as well as every other in use, was inadequate for that purpose. The stamping mills, of which ours was one, was the approved mode superseding many simpler and cruder plans, and up to this time of writing, July 1867, with the exception of what we have done and hereafter to be referred to in detail, they have never been surpassed by any new plan or process of gold saving, when the additional cost of such working is reckoned. I say this deliberately with no prejudice, having full knowledge of the best results of smelting, and of every action in the direction of gold saving in Colorado up to this time. Yet with the stamps by which has been obtained about all the gold that has given Colorado a name, the character or constitution of the Colorado ores is such, that unless superseded by something better, Colorado, as a gold-producing country of any account, would have to be abandoned. By this time, when *we* had proved by experience the refractory character of our ores, there had been considerable attention paid to new plans of saving the gold, and the fact had been and was the fulcrum to encourage investments in the constellation of stock companies that hove in sight during this period. We would have been glad to have seen any merit in these plans, in Colorado, and on paper in the East, but we could not; but thought all the various processes wrong in principle, fundamentally, not only think so now, but know so. It had occurred to us, from careful and studied observation, that the presence of sulphur was the cause of the refractory character of these ores under manipulation, and that the desulphurization of the ore also carried off the gold with it. We were satisfied after many experiments, that the gold was, as a general thing, in chemical combination with sulphur. We make this statement with the knowledge that gold and sulphur will not combine directly, nevertheless we make it as a demonstrated fact, and therefore to save the gold thus combined, the vapors must be manipulated and decomposed; but more in this direction in another place.

When we had found, after a year's toil, that in the ordinary or improved manner of gold mining, there was no value practically to our, or any property as legitimate sources of company profit, what was to be done? Two or three things naturally suggested themselves; one was, to use a common expression, to let it slide; another was, to wait and see what time would develop; it was patent to this writer that nobody was on the right track to develop any thing; another was, to keep the real fact out of sight and lie, as many did, galvanize the stock by false reports and sell it to the unsophisticated; another was, to work at it and see if there was not some cheap way to save this gold, which everybody knew was in the ore. We have acted on this latter plan and I think Excelsior Co. and the territory of Colorado will be institutions, by our having pursued this course. I am aware I shall be liable to the charge of *excessive modesty* for the above expression, but that matters but little to me if it only proves true. The course pursued has been a difficult one, inside and out. I did not feel it to be my duty or for my interest to " *subsidize the press*," and I suppose it has shown its good sense by persistently abusing me or us, and magnifying our mistakes which were many and natural ; but the condition of everything in shape of a process that has had the benefit of press advocacy, is so completely a fizzle practically, that its condemnation of ours or me, is rather an encouraging feature and is unobjectionable.

I felt then, in 1864, and feel now, that my best efforts were due to those individuals, the stockholders of this company, who had invested in this enterprise, and as much from confidence in me, as from its intrinsic value, and those efforts they have had, and I take pleasure in their results.

During the years 1864 and 1865, we worked in the direction already suggested, trying experiments, building and rebuilding, and modifying machines, till we had produced a principle of desulphurizing and made it practical, feeling that when that object was gained, viz., perfect desulphurization of the ore, without loss of gold, it was converting it into surface ore and as was well known, there was no trouble in saving the gold in working what is called top quartz or surface ore. That being established, we had several of these machines made here in the East. At this time, early in the year 1865, many companies which had been organized and were preparing for work, were disposed to see merit in our plan, and the result was, the adoption by some ten or twelve of these companies, of these desulphurizers. I felt sure from what we had done with a crude machine involving the principle, that it was a cheap gold saving process. I attribute my mistake to my having too much faith in the wisdom of scientific men; it has cost me some money to learn how feeble the exponents of chemistry are in new walks or before they have had the experience of new facts; it was they who said, the elimination of the sulphur converted sulphurets into surface ore. The selling of these machines before we ourselves had one of them practically at work, was a great mistake, but a very natural one; we presumed and calculated that the first one would be erected and running on our own property, but by one of those accidents which cannot be helped, we were disappointed. We forwarded the first machine, but instead of its reaching Colorado as it should in the summer of 1865, it was detained on the plains, and Indian troubles disturbing the mails and we communicating via California, we did not learn of the detention, and without making too long a story, it did not reach our locality till December of that year, 1865. The other companies having them, were more fortunate in transportation; several erected them. As a general thing they were badly made, still worse in the manner they were erected; they were, as a matter of course, failures, yet, in every instance, when properly erected, according to instructions, they were a perfect success for all they claimed to do, viz., to desulphurize the ore. But leaving them and coming to our own — which was erected and running on the 20th of January, 1866. It had required much tinkering and adjusting in its mechanism, rather more than we expected or would be required again, but it worked perfectly when finished and always has as a desulphurizer. We felt, as by circular, I had told you, that after so much delay, the end was now reached, and though the remuneration was a year or more behind, it was now near, and the coming spring, would see our efforts blossom into a dividend. I regret that my hopefulness has made me too sanguine, yet that same hopefulness in general has saved the company and created success.

We found great trouble in amalgamating the gold *in* this desulphurized ore; we had not learned the good effects of allowing it to remain for a period hot before attempting it, or the virtue given to it by polishing in a ball scourer, this all came by experience, and we finally amalgamated perfectly in a Hepburn pan. We thought the pan's capacity was as stated, eight to ten tons per day, but to do justice to the ore and save the gold its capacity was only two or less. We had at this time perfectly demonstrated our ability to save all of the gold. For instance, we took eight tons of tailings from which a stamp mill had got about $12 a ton and put these eight tons through our process and the Hepburn pan and obtained $45 a ton from it. These tailings had been carefully assayed, and we saved by this run 90 per cent of the assay. I think such facts as these justified our early hope and promise of remuneration, for eight tons may be considered as on a full working scale.

We then, during spring (1866) put our machinery, such as it was, rather crude, the ultimates of many experiments together for connected action, and got it in shape to run by the latter part of May. At this time I made my second trip to Colorado and proved to entire satisfaction the principle we had of saving gold by saving it. We ran some thirty tons, enough to try it perfectly, and did what no other process had ever done, saving several times as much as stamps would on the same ore. The mechanical part was crude and required the utmost care to do continued work, and we thought as we had proved the principle practicable by actually obtaining in a large way all the gold that by assay was in the ore, that our interests would be furthered by a reconstruction of the inside or machinery of the mill for mechanical perfection, and we decided to do so.

With abundant means that was a three months' job, I returned in July and began, as you are aware, to make the repairs referred to. Owing to the distrust in Colorado matters and the consequent reluctance on the part of stockholders to aid pecuniarily, the work lingered and a job which was of prime necessity to have done, and which ought to have done easily by November, lingered into winter, all winter and a worse spring, till the middle of April, when after this eight months' delay we were ready and started. We took some of the poor quality of ore from the Gold-dirt lode, such as paid by stamp mill $2½ per ton and ran it in our mill; this ore assayed $21.10 per ton and a trifle of silver, making the total assay $22 per ton; after running ten hours we had to stop to repair a defect in the brickwork, and we cleaned up, and obtained from what we had run (some five tons) over $18 a ton which was 85 per cent of the assay, and seven or eight times what the stamp mill got from the same ore.

You will see that basing my calculations on good ore, which we have in abundance, and remembering that the stamps are the staple plan of saving gold, and our experiments proving our plan to be without additional expense, several hundred per cent better, I was justified in giving you assurances of an early dividend, and careful men who have looked into this matter for the purpose, think with me that I was justified, and endorse both my integrity and my judgment.

I should mention that the Hepburn pan as an amalgamator we use only temporarily, the only objections to it being its limited capacity and having to work the ore by batches ; still since we have learned that by letting the desulphurized ore remain hot a few hours before cooling, or using, we decompose the sulphates and deoxidize the gold, which then amalgamates readily, thus overcoming the objection that for a long time annoyed us, by preventing the gold in this desulphurized ore from amalgamating. By this discovery we have increased the capacity of the pan, but we propose using our own plan of amalgamation which is of great capacity, and forming with our pulverizers, desulphurizer and ball scourer, a continuous process without any changing or handling, the work being all done mechanically. I copy from a letter from W. B. Felton who visited our mill the latter part of May. His description of the same, which briefly states how the matter strikes a careful observer who is in no way interested in it, reads as follows :

" The mill struck me as being the most complete of any I have seen. It is so arranged that the ore can be thoroughly manipulated by machinery without handling— requiring but one man to feed, and one to attend to the fire in the furnace—everything has the appearance of economy of labor — in short I was very much pleased with the mill," &c., &c.

As we have got our process practical and have in its perfected arrangement proved it, I do not see anything to prevent us from going right along doing practical work. The frictions necessarily attending new work, especially on new principles, will retard our progress some, these will all be speedily overcome by use, and though at first we shall not do our maximum of work day by day, we shall grow to it and I trust profitably from the start, I expect it will be immensely so, as practice becomes perfect.

GOLD.

——

*Gold has a characteristic yellow color ; its density is
19.5 ; it fuses at a strong white heat,—gives off sensible
vapors at a very high temperature. It is almost always
found in the native or free state; being sometimes pure,
but more generally alloyed with certain proportions of
silver. It occurs in veins, generally quartziferous, which
contain other metallic minerals, as ores of copper, lead,
silver and pyrites—these veins usually traversing primative
rocks ; also in veins scattered through rocks situated at the
separation of the crystalline and stratified rocks, or metamorphic formation ; and also in disaggregated sands,
often extensively seen in alluvial formations, and owing
its presence to the disintegrations of auriferous crystalline
rocks in the vicinity. Gold exists in the drift sands of all
rivers which arise from, or flow over, a large extent of
auriferous rocks.*

*Gold may be so invisibly fine as not to be microscopically
detected, but careful assays will detect it exactly and all ;
there can be no gold which a careful assay will not detect
and approximately measure. — Gold is an element or
primate, — that, intellectually, we may take a grain no
larger than a grain of sand, and suppose it to be divided*

into a thousand parts, and one of those into a thousand
again, and so on, indefinitely, the characteristics of gold
remain unchanged — that in that finely comminuted con-
dition it may go off mechanically by drift and otherwise,
but there is no radical difference between the finest invisible
particle and the nugget that can be weighed.

The foregoing, in italics, is a scientific definition of
gold, as far it goes ; it is as exact as brevity will permit : it is not my definition of gold, but that is of no
consequence ; if I had thought the scientist's knowledge
of gold was absolute or correct, my labors in connection with Colorado would have ended more than two
years ago.

I am not bold enough to criticise *text books*, endorsed
as they are ; yet, I think, a careful observer will find
some slight contradictions between the chemist and the
metallurgist. Possibly when he finds other conditions
for gold than the metallic form. Be that as it may, I
have a few words to say on the subject, and to that
end I quote from standard authority as follows : —

" *Though sulphur will not combine directly with gold,*
by combination of its oxides are produced two sulphides
of gold." (Au$_2$ S$_3$ and Au$_2$ S) And again only for
a point : " *As the substance will not give off its gold to*
mercury, it is evident that gold did not exist in the
metallic state."

I do not here intend to criticise the records of science, but want excuse or authority for saying, that I think the gold in the ores of Colorado does not as a general thing, or in its extent, exist there in a metallic state, or subject to the laws applicable to it as a metal. The chemist, in the text book, with a fascinating modesty, says : " *We know nothing of the cause of chemical force ; its effects appear to be to produce compounds from simple elements, the compounds being radically different from the simples composing them.*" In what I say I will try to be equally modest, if not so fascinating. I wish the living exponents of science were always equally so with their text books ; they often seem unable to look over the walls erected by themselves. As Emerson would say, like the slug on the pear leaf, it sweats out its own house, which afterwards becomes its prison.

It seems to me,— and I apologize for saying it,— with my Colorado experience before me and within me, that I have a duty to perform (modestly of course), if only suggestive to brighter men who are or may be attracted to the subject. I feel sure that this field will yet alter in some respects the school books of metallurgy. No generalizing genius has yet sprung up to filter the floating experience coincident with mine, and analyze it and give us the true expression. The *giants* of science who *have* visited that spot to investigate and report, and also for the laudable purpose of gain, have given us as yet nothing but what was asked for, by interested and anxious parties : they go there or went with educated but traditional ideas, and are consequently incompetent to evolve the latest condition, and state it, or what common observation knows is ready when the right man comes — he certainly has not arrived yet. To facilitate him, if I may hope so much, I contribute my mite.

The fact that science to-day conflicts often with the records of ten or twenty years ago, and that the next decade may and undoubtedly will, on this subject especially, conflict with the light or *lights* of to-day : and while eminent students in several departments, are already treading hard upon and loosening some, the solid platform of even what is considered settled and certain ; for example, though it will be impossible here to more than just hint, Professor Fleury, an eminent rock chemist, right in the line of the knowledge wanted, says " little is known of gold, the epidermis only is penetrated, the field or body unexplored ; " says also his convictions are that it is not *elementary* in its character, intimating that it may be or is the product of chemical action. While other parties that I am not at liberty now to refer to are experimenting and successfully proving every time, that a careful wet assay only shows but a fraction of the gold in an ore (this is not referred to in a practical sense only as of scientific value), and

again the fact with endorsements that command attention, that the learned researches of Dr. Henry Favre
and Mons. M. Franz, a metallurgist of Paris, have demonstrated the possibility of transmuting metals by actually doing it; silver and copper into gold, not for the
profit, there being none, the operation being slow and
expensive, nor for the sake of making gold, its importance lies in demonstrating the instability of *elementary
substances ;* it does not follow, say these savans, *that the
metals are composed of still simpler elementary bodies which
by their intimate union have escaped the means of analysis
— they should rather be considered as simple·in a chemical
sense, but as composite in a dynamic-static sense:* and
much more might be said in this direction which
would be both interesting and instructive, but it would
be foreign to the object of this letter, and I will
only say while this is the condition of scientific knowledge — that competent and cultivated minds are by no
means prepared to endorse but even to refute established
scientific ideas, I thought it might excuse me for reasons
already stated for giving my own thoughts upon the
subject of gold, just for what they are worth — particularly as I am carrying out my thoughts or ideas practically, and it will help elucidate the features of the Crosby
& Thompson's process of saving gold which will be referred to in detail under the head of " Process " and with
that object in view I submit the following definition, or,

REMARKS ON GOLD.

Gold is usually found in the native or free state, but is also found in chemical combination with other metals and metalloids, particularly the latter, more especially with sulphur and notwithstanding its frequency as native gold, most if not all of it is the product of the chemical combinations just referred to, decomposed by natural agencies and forming mechanical combinations in the various rocky ores or metallic veins; sometimes dffiused invisibly, often conspicuous in larger or smaller concentrations, and from these sources is carried by drift and found in the beds and sands of rivers, gulches and alluvial deposits. And in these localities and in the veins referred to the gold is generally free or native.

Whether gold is an element or a product is not positively known, the same may be said however, of anything else, and though rather disposed to doubt its elementary character, yet, not to be too radical will not here dispute its classification in chemistry as an element. There are found veins of sulphurets, iron pyrites and galena ores, with various other earthy or metallic substances, all gold-bearing in their character and as before stated the gold is mostly in chemical combination and but fractionally free, such ores have been called refractory and passed over because unprofitable in working. This is the feature of the ores in Colorado, very much richer by assay than the average of quartz veins, or what is called surface ores; even of those that yield a large profit in working, suggesting the idea that the process of decomposition while it makes the gold free and metallic, reduces also its quantitative value. The usual, or stamp mill process on ores of this class rarely gets more than $\frac{1}{10}$ of an assay, there are exceptions, but the best or least refractory do not yield by ordinary methods, except accidentally, 25 per cent of an assay.

As water always carries some free or uncombined oxygen, so it is probable that some of the gold in this class of ores of which I am now speaking, is uncombined and the little that the stamps get, may be of that character, and it is probable, also, that time is increasing the percentage.

I think careful wet assays may be scientifically and mathematically correct and agree with one another and yet not show the amount of gold that may be in the ore under analysis; that there may be a larger and indefinite amount beyond the assay test, which another mode of analysis may yet detect. I think I am warranted in saying this from my own observation and reliable statements from competent authority. As there is nothing but assumption and convenience for considering elementary matter as particled or atomized, a reference to remarks on page 32 will suggest the rationale of what I refer to in this statement.

By desulphurization, which is a necessity in the process of gold saving, this gold becomes metallic ; the sulphur disengaged by heat uniting with its equivalents of oxygen, forming sulphurous acid, the gold in the vapor becomes free and passes off mechanically in the draft, with the gases formed, hence, must be desulphurized with extreme slowness, almost unprofitably so, or the vapors must be manipulated by condensation before they escape, which is I think the only profitable way of treating the ores of which I am now more particularly referring to.

I think the carefully observed experiments mentioned under another head, in this letter, demonstrate the soundness of this theory.

THE EXCELSIOR'S PROCESS.

Those who have read the preceding pages, particularly under the head of "Gold," will naturally anticipate much that I have to say under this head. Still, if even in some degree a repetition, I feel that a brief account of this process by itself will be worthy a few pages, and worthy also of consideration. It is not my intention to criticise other plans of gold saving, but I cannot present this without, to some extent, referring to them, yet I think in a manner that will be wholly unobjectionable.

I state positively, from unmistaken proven facts, that to save the gold in the ores referred to, viz: the bulk of the ores of Colorado, the vapors must be manipulated and the sulphide of gold decomposed. I have said elsewhere that desulphurization was absolutely necessary, and whoever attempts to desulphurize the ore, without regard to its volatility, will lose a large part that assay proves is in the ore. I know what I am saying, and I am perfectly aware what can be done, apparently in contradiction to my statement, in a chemist's laboratory. I know also some things that chemists generally are reluctant to admit as facts, but they will *after sunrise.* When I speak as positively as I do, I am speaking of the practical working of the ore. I presume no one expects to make money handling ores chemically, or as colossal assays, using tons instead of ounces, because practical working means profitable working; and when I say, which I here repeat, none of the modes of saving gold — (I shall speak of this process farther along) — have proved superior to stamps, nor in my judgment will, I do not mean that more gold has not been obtained from a ton of the same ore — and *that* even is questionable — but that expenses reckoned, the net results favor the stamps as a rule: accidental exceptions are not to, or should not militate against my statement. I am perfectly competent to express an opinion upon the processes before the public, and in reference to the most popular just now, at least in a certain circle, viz., that of "smelting," people who are expecting Colorado salvation through it, are positively certain to be disappointed, not that it has not and will not get out gold, for it certainly will, but that the expense of doing it will not permit it to be generally applicable or profitable. No one will certainly place the expense of working by smelting at less than $35 a ton. I think that low — (I am not losing sight of the value of the copper saved, which is said will pay the expense of smelting;

copper is always very easily saved, when it is wanted, by cheaper processes than smelting)—and no one who wishes to be prudent in statement will place the ores, on the average, as assaying over $ 35 or $ 40 a ton; that is placing them at nearly double the average of the ore of California. I am speaking of working assays; there may be ten or a dozen lodes which go ton after ton higher than that, but I am speaking of the average and of working assays. What is wanted to meet the needs of Colorado is a process that can work at a profit the nineteen out of twenty of the lodes, not the *few*, which are not in number sufficient to be a productive feature in the territory. The people who differ from me in the above, and are competent to judge, will say there are about ten lodes, possibly twelve, that will pay to work, *all* the rest being barren and poor. The process I propose here to speak about is for the thousands of so-called barren ores, which represent the mineral wealth of this territory, to work them at a profit; and it will not be any loss if it should be applied to the few that can afford to pay $ 35 or $ 40 for the expenses of working.

As has been before stated, the reason why the gold was or is not saved, is because it is so combined as not to be reached in the usual ways of working ores, and desulphurization was necessary. The first thing done in this process, after the ore is reduced to about

the fineness of gunpowder, is to desulphurize it. We
do that by feeding it into a pair of iron cylinders revolving over a moderate fire, sufficient in its action to
keep them at a dull red heat. These are revolving on
hollow perforated axes, through which air is forced,
which oxidizes the ore passing through the cylinder;
the sulphur vapor forced out of the heated ore is thus
oxidized, which frees the gold, making it and also what
is in the solid ore metallic. Under the head of " Remarks on Gold," you will see we consider the gold in
the ore as chemically combined with the sulphur, and I
do not consider it in the metallic state. (I make this
statement, being aware that chemical knowledge teaches
that gold will not combine directly with sulphur.) The
oxygen combining with the sulphur (sulphurous acid),
leaves the gold in the burnt ore, and in the vapor *free*
or *metallic*, this vapor consisting of nitrogen and sulphurous acid, and also what may be called a vapor of
gold passes through a spray chamber for condensation,
when all that is condensable, including the gold, takes
substantial form in the vat or tub into which the spray
falls, filling it and flowing off, leaving the substance in
thick deposit at the bottom. By allowing this waste
water from the tub or vat to flow into another one, and
using that to wash down the continuously coming vapor,
thus using the same water over and over, we save all
the gold. None escapes; and by this simple and very

cheap operation we desulphurize the ore without loss of gold. We have found by experience that in many of the ores a further oxidizing is needed to fully decompose the vapor, and we extend the oxidizing surface by a washdown arrangement in the spray column which has proved effectual. By this you will see we not only adhere to our vapor theory, but consider it of more importance than ever. We have found that from 1-5 to 4-5 of the gold follows the vapor, and while the spray chamber is sufficient in its action for many of the refractory ores, many more require the washdown attachment; hence it is wise to use all together, for chemical analysis shows no reason for these differences, which sometimes appear capricious, but it is a proven fact that the sulphur carries the gold chemically, retains it in its vapor condition, requiring for decomposition that the sulphur unite with the oxygen, for the gold to be metalized, and the washdown, as stated, is effectual, and some of the experiments with it, which have proved these statements, would very much astonish some metallurgists who think they have nothing to learn on this point. To continue then with our explanation. We do it *expeditiously*, its capacity being from twelve to sixteen tons per day, or twenty-four hours; we do it *economically*, requiring but little attention and a very small amount of fuel, it generally finding most of its own heat; its *dur-*

ability is demonstrated, competent judges will bear testimony to the fact, and any fears that roasting ores in hot iron cylinders will be injured by sulphur, is entirely groundless ; nothing but the grossest malpractice will cause that result. There are several ready, by actual proof and practice to testify that the above statement is true ; and to testify also that in every case, when the reverse is stated, the fault was not in the least in contradiction to the statement of the question of durability and ability, but was, in every case, owing to faulty construction, faulty erection, abuse, or modifications, from ignorance or otherwise, from the plan or principle of the machine.

This desulphurized ore by remaining heated for a while in the pile, or by polishing in a ball scourer, or both, is ready for amalgamation, the plan of amalgamation is best, that insures perfect and certain contact with the mercury, the Hepburn pan we can recommend is certain to obtain 90 to 100 per cent of the gold ; it is worthless without our desulphurizer, or to express it better, the pan on raw ore, is not a paying contrivance. I ought to say in this connection, that to save the gold at the rate mentioned the ore must be worked in them for a long time, thus reducing their capacity to about two tons per day, but by ourselves and by others it is a proven fact that in this way of amalgamation, about all of an assay is obtained, and we have demonstrated it by doing so in large quantities, measured by tons and on the most refractory ores. I should add here that by the discovery of the ore remaining hot a few hours, we relieve the gold of its oxide coating and the difficulty of amalgamating the desulphurized ore was removed, so that the capacity of the Hepburn pan is more than doubled.

We recommend, however, an amalgamator which forms part of our process, where the finely pulverized desulphurized ore is forced through the mercury by hydraulic pressure insuring perfect contact and complete amalgamation. This differs from the pan in two important points, viz., the ore is not handled in batches as in using the pan, and the capacity of it is very great, while the pan, as I have said, is the reverse, and these two points are so important as of themselves to make a process unprofitable, that would be otherwise with continuous work without handling and ample capacity ; besides this it is very simple, and very economical. — I will not attempt a detailed description here but only say with it our whole process is a continuous one, the ore is not handled except mechanically from the time when in its rough state it is fed into the crusher, passing through the stages of desulphurizing and polishing, till it is *gold* in the mercury, or amalgam.

Thus after the first outlay of equipment and machinery, which is much less than in any other process, the milling expenses will not exceed, even if steam is used and amalgamation with the Hepburn pan, five dollars per ton, with the amalgamator which we as before stated consider a part of our process, the expenses will be at least twenty-five per cent less. Adding then to that the cost of mining, which will be, as every one knows, from $2.50 to $5 per ton according to circumstances, and you have a process as cheap as stamps and which will save 85 per cent and with ordinary care 100 per cent of the gold that assay says is in the ore.

" VAPOR THEORY."

The above heading has no special significance, yet it is appropriate for what I have to say under it; and at the risk of some repetition, I think a few explanatory words on my own account will not be superfluous. Some two or more years ago I was trying with competent assistants, and without much experience to overcome the difficulties encountered in gold mining in Colerado ; finding, as is usual under similar circumstances, the current of action in this field, determined in the line that prescription or custom had taught, and knowing enough of the constitution of these ores, from the phenomena presented by manipulation and from close observation, to feel sure that custom or prescribed rules were radically wrong and that to meet the wants of the case, the whole subject must be started from a new point of view, the above caption I made after due consideration the starting point.

With the highest respect for education and scientific cultivation, and feeling deeply how much the world is their debtor, yet, I have always felt that *common* ᵤₑ *ᵖ*, like the shape of a man's nose or the color of his eyes, was generic irrespective of culture ; and for the practical operations of life, I would like to have both, — culture and common sense — but if but one, common sense without culture is more desirable, than culture without common sense ; — I do not claim in any marked degree common sense, but it did appear to me that people were blind to the phenomena offered ; for instance, finding by correct assay a certain amount of gold in an ore and handling it in a stamp mill and realizing about 12 per cent and not finding the tailings to assay 88 per cent, rarely half of it, it required but a superficial ob-servation to be satisfied that the loss was as a vapor, or in a volatile form and in that direction of gold saving I was willing to spend money. Feeling sure on this point and knowing that the gold was rarely visible in these ores, and certainly was in a more impalpable state than human skill can put it, and feeling sure also that time was acting upon it, making the gold more free and metallic, hence, what is called " surface ore," I used the term *Volatile*, as being more applicable to it than

Metallic; and without much thought I said in my earnest way of talking, "*God never made any metal gold;*" that metal gold was the result of subsequent action; I am not particular to sustain the point, sound or unsound, I have seen no reason from further experience or from light shed by experts to change my opinion; having said it and moving in our manipulations where that led, in my deductions and experiments I feel that I spoke wiser than I knew; at least, following out that thought I or we have suceeded in saving the gold. In all my movements and in all my statements I met much opposition of all qualities, *coarse and fine,* but as long as my experiments sustained me I felt like holding my position; and fortifying it by observation and facts and especially by the thoughts of others in this direction in other departments of science; and tho' the term "*Vapor Wetherbee*" was sometimes applied to me by the *press provincial* and by others, the longer I have lived and studied and practised and proved its truth, I am happy to hear the *vaporous* title, for on it or on the fact that suggested it, hangs much, if not all, that will bless Colorado with a profitable production of gold.

Now my attention has been called by some of my good friends to articles in the papers of late emanating from parties defending their several plans of gold saving, as if I ought to say a word in print also, and hence this chapter, thinking it wiser in this form than in a more extended manner. I wish them all God speed, but feel sure in every case, (I need not mention names or processes,) the cost of working the ores will deprive them of any value for Colorado.

One point which has been prominent in what I refer to I will mention, viz : The emphasized advice to employ cultivated minds in the manipulation and management of mining operations ; this advice is I think unquestionably a bid for scientific approval of plans offered. I have already said, I claim to hold a high estimation of scientific culture and of science in general ; the world is grandly its debtor — but science is not a pioneer, when it attempts to be, it always fails ; it will not risk its prestige ; is afraid of risks — better send out good common sense heads to manage such operations. With the profoundest respect for greatness by culture, I must say, and I shall be endorsed in saying it, if you want to waste money, or build extravagantly, or make *artistic* holes in the ground, or spend ten dollars when one will do, or swell out professionally and fail and see a worker do successfully what the higher talent could not ; employ professionally scientific agents ; all Colorado will endorse this from past experience and I see plainly it will in the future, from what I know is now going on and what in the articles referred to is recommended. I have already said enough under these several heads to plainly convey the idea, that while I respect and give all credit to scientific scholarship, even to idolatry, outside of that sphere and in the development of new and original ideas, it is an expensive hindrance and not a blessing, and its *ipse dixit*, however valuable in ascertained knowledge, should not prevent or embarrass uneducated common sense in any department, from persevering, if their instincts suggest perseverance; this advice has the world's history to back it up; and if what I have in this rough way stated under different heads pointing to one end, proves to be true and valuable, it has met professional and scientific discouragement from the start; aided by the *unwashed*, who are ever so apt to idolize what they do not possess, and echo the voice of prestige, often to the injury of determined men, who may be right after all.

CONCLUSION.

Those who have read the preceding pages will have perceived the *volatile condition* that the gold in the sulphuret ores presents itself; I have made no attempt to elaborate the idea in this letter, only stating enough to make the fact apparent and that I am in earnest in stating it : the field is a wide one for investigation, it suggests that the gold of which I am speaking, as it exists generally, in this ore, is either developed metal but not mineralized, or is developed metal mineralized by sulphur or by some other substance, or it exists, undeveloped, depending upon some force to eliminate it ; — I can hardly believe that gold is made or is the product of chemical action, yet I think there are good grounds for thinking so, but further observation is necessary before the statement can be made with any confidence ; I am inclined to favor the theory, perhaps from a transcendental rather than a positive point of view, that force of some kind has eliminated *it*, and in fact, all the different compounds and primates from a common element, and perhaps there may be a unity of derivation of sulphur and gold from that common element, and perhaps transmutable by nature, and by art, even, if we knew how, conditioned analagously to diamond and charcoal; but as has already been stated this needs further investigation and is not stated as positive, but only possible, or probable.

You will have perceived also that in this letter now about ended, the conclusions have been reached in the two ways that differently constituted minds reach anything, inductively and deductively; *I assumed* the volatility of gold in its *absolute* sense, and in my observations, sought for the facts that would demonstrate it, deductively; I admit *that* not to be the best or safest way of investigation, but, I had associated with me, in more than a business connection, Mr. A. B. Crosby, well known to you, who was more anchored, from study and habit, to the inductive and properly speaking more scientific method : I ran the risk in my course of action of making my facts conform to my theory, but facts once obtained, no matter how, if they be facts, are as valuable as if logically or mathematically obtained, and perhaps but for a transcendental assertion or supposition, we might neither of us, inductively or deductively been sufficiently polarized in the direction of the reality sought for, to have been receptive or perceptive enough to catch the threads that have led each of us to meet on solid ground, or unity of statement.

You will have perceived also in the details of the enterprise that has led to the facts stated, and to the issue of this letter, that we have made very many mistakes in our course of practical action, some that we ought not to have made, and some that could not have been avoided; and in the further practice, we may find ourselves still a great way from perfection, and a year hence, I may wonder that to-day, I dared make such positive statements as I have in this letter, nevertheless I make them, feeling sure I am fundamentally right; *that*, to save the gold in these ores in any considerable per centage it is to be done in the line that we have herein suggested and acted upon no other, for the facts, which would be the same under all circumstances, positively demonstrated, justify me and would any one for being thus emphatic; improvements, as a matter of course, are being and will be made, but they have got to be based on the *vapor* idea and ten times more so than I at first thought; so at the risk of repetition I have again stated it in this conclusion, and if this was the place and desirable, I could state other facts and offer arguments, that I am sure would be considered conclusive.

Our friends, the Stockholders of the Excelsior Company, must be as they have already been, patient, happy in the end to have been right, and if they will take my word for it, they may rest assured that their highest expectations will be reached as we proceed: not however the ultimate at the first start, but I feel that the point of profitably saving the gold has been reached and the mechanical action required to reach it, is in working order ; there will be as a matter of course the frictions to overcome and the adjustments to be made always consequent upon new work and on new plans ; all the mechanical difficulties are apparently after much attention overcome, yet perfection comes only by practice, and it will be a wonder if others do not present themselves that are unforeseen now, but as perfection comes, will come also increase of work and yield, requisite to make our predictions good. I feel more surely than I ever did before that regular work, and remuneration to the shareholders as a matter of course, will be very soon a proven fact.

With the full assurance of faith and hope I submit to you what I have in these few pages written, and remain,

Yours truly,

JOHN WETHERBEE.

STATEMENT

REPORTS AND EXAMINATION

OF THE

ST. LUIS PARK GRANT,

IN COLORADO TERRITORY:

ITS TITLE AND RESOURCES IN

GOLD, SILVER & OTHER MINERAL WEALTH,

By ALBINUS Z. SHELDEN AND OTHERS.

Property Owned, in Fee, by Governor GILPIN.

NEW YORK:

WM. C. BRYANT & CO., PRINTERS, 41 NASSAU STREET, CORNER LIBERTY.

1865.

REPORT

On the San Luis Park, of Colorado Territory, from memoranda of Albinus Z. Shelden, *U. S. Surveyor.*

*   *   In physical features, the " San Luis " Park is very remarkable. The smooth area is 9,400 square miles; the form is a very perfect ellipse; a continuous envelope of mountains encloses it, whose crest everywhere ascends to the line of perpetual snow. It is the bowl of a primeval sea which has been drained. In configuration, this park is the counterpart of the basins of Geneva and Constance, enveloped within the Helvetian Alps. There are four parks within Colorado Territory, of which this is the most southern; they are the *North, Middle, South, and San Luis* Parks. They are of equal size, constituting together a System. They are in close juxta-position, longitudinally arranged. The resemblance, each one to the others, is perfect; yet, in the details, is observable a variety perfectly infinite. The altitude of the San Luis plain, above the sea, is 6,400 feet; of the enveloping peaks 13,000. Between the circumferent rim of the plain (which is prairie,) and the snowy crest, rise undulating mountains of gradually ascending altitude; the flanks of these are gorged by descending streams, thirty-five in number. The northern portion, one-third of all, is called " Rincon." Nineteen streams, descending, converge into the Sawatch Lake of fresh water, but having no outlet. These streams bear the name " Alamosos." The remaining area is bisected by the Rio Bravo del Norte, which enters through the western rim and issues out in the south. The plain is continuous as a water surface, having isolated volcanic buttes resem-. bling islands and an indented rim.

The System of the four parks occupies a parallelogram, cut through the centre of Colorado from north to south, two hundred miles wide and four hundred long. They reach from latitude 36° 30' to 41° 30'. The 106th meridian exactly bisects them all. The mother Cordillera, sweeping in successive and alternate curves east and west, divides them one from another. Each park gives birth to an immense river, departing alternately to the Atlantic and Pacific seas. Here are grouped mountains, parks and rivers of stupendous dimensions and august sublimity. Spurs of the primary Cordillera curve around to embrace those fronts of the parks from which the great rivers debouch by cañons. These parks have the same level as the great "Plateau of America." They form a part of its surface, and assimilate to all its peculiar characteristics. They are parts of it, sunk within the bulk of the primeval Cordillera.

Remarking the identity in physical features of the parks thus closely grouped, but the infinite variety flowing from the juxtaposition of altitudes, depressions, permanent snows, running rivers, and the eccentric courses of the mountains and rivers, the details of the San Luis park offer themselves for specific description.

The plain is a drift soil, abraded from the mountains, and deposited by the currents of water and of the atmosphere. The eastern half partakes of the qualities of the Cordillera, the western half of the qualities of the Sierra Mimbres. The mother Cordillera forms the eastern wall, the Sierra Mimbres the western wall of the San Luis park. The mother Cordillera has a base and flanks of granite slopes inclining inwards, surmounted by stupendous masses of Jurassic limestone, carried up, but not destroyed, by the upheaving volcanic forces. Neither igneous, plutonic rocks, nor erupted lava is anywhere seen or found. The Sierra Mimbres, a mountain chain of the secondary order, has, in a less proportion, the primeval and sedimentary rocks, but presents the throats of ancient volcanoes, streams of lava, once fluid, and immense pedrigals of igneous and plutonic rocks. The calcareous element, therefore, predominates in the alluvial soil, mixed with silicious and plutonic debris. These elements, intermixed by the action of water and of the winds, present to arable and pastoral life a smooth surface for culture, and perfect intrinsic fertility.

Here is recognized an atmosphere and climate purely *conti-nental.* Situated most remote from all the seas; of mountain altitude, and encased all round by snowy Sierras, the atmosphere is intensely tonic, salubrious, and brilliant. Summer and winter divide the year, scarcely interrupted by vernal or autumnal seasons. The meridian sun retains its vitalizing heat around the year; at midnight prevails a corresponding tonic coolness. The formation of light clouds along the crest of the Sierras is incessant. These are wafted away by the steady atmospheric currents coming from the west. They rarely interrupt the sunshine, but, refracting his rays, imbue the canopy with a shining silver light, at once intense and brilliant. The flanks of the great mountains, bathed by the embrace of these irrigating clouds, are clad with dense forests of pine, fir, spruce, and aspen, which protect the sources of springs and the running rivulets. With the forests, alternate mountain meadows of luxuriant and nutritious grasses. The ascending clouds, rarely condensed, furnish little irrigation at the depressed elevation of the plains, which are destitute of timber, but clothed in grass. These grasses, growing rapidly during the annual melting of the snows, cure into hay as the aridity of the atmosphere returns. They form perennial pastures, and supply the winter food of the aboriginal cattle, everywhere indigenous and abundant. The critical conclusion to which a rigid study of nature brings the scrutinizing mind, is the reverse of first impressions. The multitudinous variety of nature adjusts itself with a delicate harmony which brings into concord all the industrial energies ; arable agriculture, pastoral agriculture, and all the kindred pursuits of labor which rest upon this foundation, and accompany its prosperous vigor. These are burnished, as it were, by the perpetual brilliancy and salubrity of the atmosphere and landscape, whose unfailing beauty and tonic taste invite the physical and mental energies to perpetual activity.

In *pastoral agriculture* there is seen the spontaneous production by nature of meat, dairy food, leather, wool, and kindred elements, sustained as fish in the sea. It is here, then, an immense self-sustaining element of this source of food for the human family.

For *arable agriculture* the area is equally ample in proportion, and of equally propitious excellence. The descending mountain streams furnish irrigation to the plain, whose porous soils receive them to saturation. All the cereals and fruits known to the European people acclimate themselves with the same facility as the people themselves and the domestic animals which accompany them. They receive a similar improvement from the tonic purity of the atmosphere and perennial sunshine. Over an area entirely enveloped by mountains, artesian waters may be everywhere procured.

The streams and lakes abound in fish of great variety and excellence. Water fowl and native poultry peculiar to the mountains and plains are everywhere scattered. The swarm of animal life, of the aboriginal kind, and its variety, is astonishing. All domestic animals known to our people, when substituted for them, equal them in adaptability and excellence.

For *manufacturing* in all the departments of food, clothing, and metals, all inducements of facility and economy present themselves. Fuel of wood and coal are accessible. Markets are found in the adjacent active mining regions of Colorado, New Mexico, and Arizona. The present remoteness from navigation and railroads promises present and prospective protection to manufacturing industry.

The Park extends from 36° 30' to 38° 40' in latitude, and is bisected by the 106th meridian. It is an ellipse in form, two hundred miles in longitude and seventy-five of breadth. Roads penetrating the surrounding mountains by easy passes, converge into it from all portions and departments of the external continent. Its whole area is scanned by the eye at one sight from the overhanging mountains. No feature of nature which enters into the composition of scenery rising to the highest standard of sublimity and beauty, is wanting. A vernal temperature; dissolving tints of light and shade; a translucent canopy, intensely blue; a picturesque landscape and fantastic variety of form blend themselves with the milk-white summits of the mountains, to exhibit a panorama forever fresh, graceful, and fascinating,

SANGRE DI CRISTO GRANT.

The boundary on the *east* of the "Sangre di Cristo" grant, for 104½ miles, is the supreme crest of the Rocky Mountain (Sierra Madre). The boundary on the west is the Rio Bravo del Norte, for 42 miles. This area is traversed across by the splendid streams, the Costilla, Culebra, and Trinchera. These rivers, having their sources in the snows of the mountain crest, run across from east to west, parallel and equidistant from one another. The crest and abrupt slope of the Cordillera are a homogeneous mass of the porphyritic quartz. This is the mother rock of gold, containing that metal in permeated form, as the sea holds its salt. This gold bearing formation, occupying the highest elevation, engrosses one full fourth part of the area, or 283,750 acres. The lower slope of the mountain mass, less abrupt, but mountainous, timbered and pastoral, is of homogeneous metamorphic quartz, not permeated through its whole mass with gold, but containing crevices and lodes infused with the rich ores of gold, silver, copper, lead and iron; in short, the whole range of the precious and base metals abound in these two formations. This metamorphic formation is parallel with the gold formation *proper*, includes the foot hills, and occupies less than one-fourth of the area of the grant. The remaining half of the grant, filling out the whole undulating plain to the Del Norte, is of alluvial and diluvial lands, both pastoral and arable. In its natural state, the whole area of the grant is *pastoral*, having been the abode of immense herds of aboriginal cattle, for which domestic stock is now substituted.

In *resources incidental to its natural formation*, as yet unchanged by human labor, the grant abounds in:

1st. *Gold bearing* quartz mountains.
2d. *Gold lodes* of the same.
3d. *Gold and metalliferous mines* of the metamorphic rocks.
4th. *Gold yielding placers* of the streams and drift hills.
5th. *Mines of silver* and the *base metals;* salts; mineral fuel; lime; turf; medicinal waters; rocks and earths.
6th. *Water power:* for mills; for gold washing, and irrigation.

7th. *Forests for lumber:* for fuel; for resin and tar; for tanning leather; for gums and balsams.

8th. *Pastoral lands:* (The whole area of the grant is clad in natural pastures, perennial in character, suitable to the production of meat and dairy food; wool; hides and animals for work and transportation.

9th. *Arable lands*—These lands, occupying the lower levels and easily irrigated from the descending rivers, embrace one half a million of acres. They are of intense fertility, being alluvial and diluvial composts of decayed lava, carboniferous and sulphurous limestoires and humus from the mountain flanks, levelled by the currents of water and of the atmosphere. All crops known to European agriculture, mature in the atmosphere. All animals in use in this country immediately become acclimated and improved in health, size, and flesh. The aboriginal stock is of great variety and value.

10th. *Rivers.*—Four rivers: Del Norte; Costilla; Culebra and Trinchera; having, perhaps, one hundred affluents of all sizes, fed from snows and springs of the Sierra. Here are one thousand mill sites, everywhere scattered, and an abundant flow of water for mills, for the washing of gold, and for irrigation.

11th. *Animals.*—Fur-bearing animals of the streams and forest: Beaver, otter, &c. Foxes and rabbits; mountain sheep; bears; deer; antelopes. Wild poultry and water fowl; turkeys and grouse. Fish.

12th. *Climate.*—The purity, tonic taste, and salubrity of the atmosphere is an immense item in estimating the average results from the systematic employment of paid labor. Losses from sickness and unfavorable seasons may be considered to cease in this region, remote from the ocean, in the middle of the temperate zone, and elevated 6,000 feet.

13th. *Geology.*— This is peculiar and extraordinary The mountain crest elevates itself from the great plains on the east: from the plain of the San Luis Park on the west. Both are overlooked, on either hand, by the naked eye from the dividing summit. The great plains being the bed of the primeval ocean, now the Mississippi Basin, present the whole series of ·calcareous strata, lapping up against the mountain base and exhibiting their edges to the eye, like the leaves of a cabbage. Against the western base of the Sierra appear pedrigals of lava, the overflow of the volcanoes of the Sierra Mimbres, (filling the western horizon of the park,) and arrested and solidified where the lowest level of the park has been reached. Thus, one who looks down from the Culebra peak, to the right and to the left, beholds, assembled within a single field of vision, all the various elements of which geology takes note. These manifest themselves by the tints and structure peculiar to each variety and all the strata; they are all here drawn into juxtaposition, as compact in arrangement and as clear to the vision, as when we look upon the elements of light arranged side by side and condensed into the rainbow.

Such are the elements assembled in this locality, so admirable for its central position and for the abundance of the precious metals, to assist and assure the economy of their production.

Resources Incidental to the Existing Development of the "Sangre di Cristo" Grant, growing out of Human Settlement and Labor. A. D. 1864.

1st. *Population.*—Agriculturists; laborers; shepherds, 5,653.
2d. *Property.*—Personal and real; assessed at gold standard, $336,000.
3d. *Stock.*—Cattle; sheep; horses, &c., 52,000 in number.
4th. *Towns.*—Seven in number.
5th. *Forts of U. S.*, 2; Garland and Massachusetts.
6th. *Mills*, 3: flour-mill; saw-mill; distillery.
7th. *Grey-Back placer gold mines.*
8th. *Use, sale and leases* of gold mines.
9th. *Use, sale and leases* of arable and pastoral lands.
10th. *Use, sale and leases* of sites of towns and town lots.

11th. *Products of Industry.*—Precious metals; lumber; cereals; meat; hides; wool; hay, &c.

12th. *Merchandise.*—Manufactures of the people: blankets; hats; leather; saddlery; shoes, &c.

13th. *Water Aqueducts.*—Revenues of, and of roads; bridges, &c.

14th. *Manufactures and Sales.*—Lumber; hides; wool; food, &c.

15th. *Miscellaneous profits,* incidental to the ownership of the fee; and growing out of the wants and tastes of the population in their religious, social, educational, and other relations.

To these specified elements of value must be added the crowning merit of position occupied by the San Luis Park in the general scheme of our geography and the advance through the continent of the columns of progress. The *column of Mexican progress,* ascending during four hundred years from the city of Mexico, north along the Plateau, is fully established upon the Sangre di Cristo.

The *column of American progress* advancing from the Atlantic, west across the middle region of the Continent, has similarly reached the same point and is pressing through the Sierra into the San Luis Park.

Both these columns bring labor, intelligence, and energy. Both reach the goal where society assumes the form of rest and permanent lodgement. The creation of property and its protection and enjoyment occupy them.

The ,Spanish-American people have been the miners of the world for 450 years, producing chiefly the precious metals of the mountain system extending from Cape Horn to Behring Straits. The history of this, carefully examined, limits the instances of permanent success to localities where rich ores, climate, *the production of food,* water-power, and ease of transportation are locally combined and conveniently blended. It is here, upon the Sangre di Cristo grant, where all these relatively supporting elements bring into harmony all of this mutually combined variety and supporting basis of a complete economy.

WILLIAM GILPIN.

REPORT OF JAMES ABORN

Hon. WILLIAM GILPIN:

As requested by you, I submit the following statement of my trip to the "Sangre di Cristo" grant:

I secured the services of ten of the most experienced and successful prospectors in the territory of Colorado, and with them, in fifty-two working days, discovered twenty-two lodes and two placers. In the time expended in prospecting, many days were expended in opening the lodes to a well defined crevice, the mere location of the lode occupying but a few hours. We never failed to find lodes in abundance, whenever we sunk for them after examining the locality and surface indications.

It is my opinion, and the opinion of every one of the men employed, that the lodes and gulches are fully as rich as any of the mines in Gregory district; the crevices are wider and more strongly defined. Pyrites of iron crop out of the surface frequently in veins eight to nine feet wide. Mines can be worked much cheaper here than in Gregory district, owing to their accessibility, and all the materials requisite being close at hand. Water power is abundant; wood and timber plenty. Farming lands of superior quality are close at hand. Labor is plenty, at about 75c. per day, and the cost of living small, I have no doubt that the mills could be started, and immediately yield handsome returns on any capital invested. I think the tract included in this grant will be found to be unsurpassed as an agricultural, pastoral and mineral country, and that from either of these sources large profits may be obtained, the extent to which they can be developed being almost unlimited.

Respectfully,
JAMES ABORN.

March 16, 1865.

I have examined the public documents and the private deeds upon which Governor Gilpin's title to the "Sangre di Cristo" grant rests, and find the title free from exception. The original Mexican grant, upon the report of the Surveyor-General of New

Mexico in its favor, was confirmed by act of Congress, passed June 21, 1860. This vested a complete title in fee simple, including all mineral rights, in Charles Beaubien, then the holder of the Mexican grant, and the whole estate has been conveyed by his widow and heirs, to Governor Gilpin, by sufficient deeds duly recorded.

WILLIAM M. EVARTS,

New York, April 13, 1865.

ADDITIONAL PARTICULARS.

TITLE.—The " Sangre di Cristo " property lies in the San Luis Park of Colorado; and the title, originally derived from the Mexican Government, was confirmed by a Special Act of the U. S. Congress, approved June 21st, 1860.

ACRES.—The grant contains *more than* 1,100,000 *acres, between its metes and bounds ;* but its superficial area will probably amount to as many as 2,000,000 acres, there being high mountains on it.

FORTS.—ON THIS PROPERTY there are *two United States Forts,* (Forts " *Massachusetts* and *Garland,*") one of which has been handed over to the owner of this property (Governor Gilpin); it contains houses, &c., convenient to accommodate many settlers. These forts cost a large sum of money, and the United States *will continue to have forts or barracks on this Park,* because it is on the line of travel to Santa Fe, New Mexico —(the road to " Santa Fe " is directly across this tract.) This fact will be a constant security to settlers, &c.

RAILROAD.—The *Pacific Railroad* must probably go through the " Sangre di Cristo Pass."

MARKETS.—This " Park " can supply all *North Colorado* (the Gregory District, 80 miles distant), and *all the adjacent active mining regions of New Mexico* and Arizona, with its *farming products* of breadstuffs and meat, and its *domestic manufactures* (besides the settlers and United States garrisons on it), which are now drawn from the East (St. Louis, Mo.,) *over the great plains*, at heavy expense. The return loads for the wagons would be wool, hides, &c.

DISTANCE.—This property is *now nearer to New York* city than any other property of *its kind in the* United States, and it will become nearer as the *Pacific Railroad* extends westward. Distance, by railroad from New York city to *Atchison*, Mo., 1,500 miles, in three days ; from Atchison to *Denver City*, Colorado, *by stage*, 650 miles ; from Denver City to " San Luis" Park, 150 miles ; or, from Atchison, *by wagon*, on the old *Santa Fe route*, about 700 miles to this property. The roads are constantly travelled by Government trains, and there is a weekly mail.

U. S. REPORTS.—There are several elaborate United States official published *Reports* in regard to this " Sangre di Cristo " grant, with many drawings, showing mountains, valleys, forts, &c., &c.

RICHNESS OF MINES.—The *Mines* on this property are richer than those in the celebrated Gregory District, 80 miles north, and can be worked cheaper on account of facilities at hand.

GRIST MILL.—The Grist Mill on this property cost $10,000 ; in 18 months it produced a *nett profit* of $36,000 in gold, and could not grind more than one-fourth of what was offered.

DEVELOPMENT.

It is intended to use and develop this property at once, in something like the following manner, viz. : Employ competent surveyors to run out the Government lines ; locate town sites, &c. ; establish a land-office ; sell and lease land and mines on terms to induce *emigration ;* work mines, &c.; establish stores for merchandizing, &c.

At Denver City, Colorado, the present owner of this property (Governor Gilpin,) is regarded as *intrinsically* the wealthiest man in America, and will be, really, when it is developed.

The *superior advantages and value appertaining to this property, should command* the *attention,* viz. :

First.—Fee-simple title to land and mineral from the United States.

Second.—Its *exceeding richness* in *gold, silver,* &c., &c.

Third—Its large area of *mineral.*

Fourth.—Its large *farming* area.

Fifth.—Its *great extent of acres.*

Sixth.—Its extensive *water-power.*

Seventh.—Its *timber* and other natural productions.

Eighth.—Its location on line of *travel* and *emigration.*

Ninth.—Its *accessibility* and *nearness to markets.*

Tenth.—Its *unsurpassed healthy climate.*

Eleventh.—The number of *bona fide settlers now on it.*

Twelfth.—The number of cattle, sheep, &c., &c.

COLORADO.—The aggregate production of gold in Colorado since its first discovery there, may be estimated at $100,000,000. There are at least ten thousand mines, constituting actual property, now being worked in the Territory. Gold mining is the chief interest of the Territory.

There exists in Colorado ample evidence that the supply of gold in quartz, placers, and in the beds and banks of streams, is absolutely inexhaustible. The amount of transportation between the Missouri River and the Colorado, as the first point of entrance to the great mountain system, is prodigious. The *great plains* represent the Ocean between Liverpool and New York. It is not uncommon to see as many as 5,000 wagon teams in one camp, and it is not setting the figure too high to say that at least half a million of people are more or less interested or engaged in this vast system of intra-continental transportation. New York city is the great Atlantic metropolis from which the bulk of this immense trade flows, and it is to her interest, and to the interest of her merchants and capitalists, that we appeal in the attempt to develop the vast mineral and agricultural wealth hidden in the beautiful valley of the San Luis Park.

BISHOP SIMPSON.

The accomplished and well known BISHOP SIMPSON, of the Methodist Episcopal Church, travelled through Colorado in the year 1862. From one of his letters, published in the *Christian Advocate* of February 28th, 1863, descriptive of that country, we extract as follows : " Even in the mountains very fine vegetables have been produced at an elevation of 9,000 feet above the level of the sea. The pasturage of the plains and mountains is remarkable. The grasses are very nutritious, and they cure standing ; cattle refuse to eat hay in winter when they can have access to the dry grass of the plains. Beef cattle that have not been fed a pound of grain or hay are very frequently brought to market, even in winter. The climate is mild and healthful. For nine months in the year, from October to July, little or no rain falls, and even in summer there are few heavy rains, and none of long duration. The streams are fed by the snows in the mountains. In summer the heat on the plains is at times intense during the day, yet the nights are invariably cool. In the mountains, the temperature is lower, and less liable to extremes. Flourishing villages may be found at an elevation of nine and even eleven thousand feet above the level of the ocean. In the mountains, during the months of July, August, and a portion of September, light showers fall nearly every day, generally in the afternoon, caused probably by the evaporation from the mountains, of snow. Frequently these showers do not reach the plains. On the plains, buffalo, antelope, and hare are abundant. In the mountains are found grizzly and cinnamon bears ; mountain sheep, bison, elk, and other game. Silver, copper, cinnabar, galena, plumbago, antimony, iron, coal, and salt abound, but none of these mines have been extensively worked, in consequence of the want of capital and the general tendency to gold mining. Precious stones have also been found, such as opal, agate, amethyst, emerald, etc. Some beautiful moss agates have been picked up in the middle Park. The streams abound in *trout of delicious flavor.*

* * * * * * * * * * *

Until very recently all the capital used in developing these mines was first obtained from them. The people who emigrated there were generally poor. To carry on lode mining requires capital. Expensive machinery is needed. Supplies of all kinds are high. Although there are, perhaps, no richer mines in America than those of Colorado, no man of limited means should attempt their development. A man or company with fifty thousand dollars *would be almost certain of realizing immense profits.*

SCENERY OF COLORADO.

In a letter to the *Western Christian Advocate*, Bishop Kingsley says:

The scenery in this country is the grandest that can be conceived of. From Denver the view is particularly beautiful. On the southeast, at the distance of seventy miles, and at the northwest, at perhaps the same distance, stand two noted mountains, the former is Pike's Peak and the latter Long's Peak. These mountains lift their snowy heads into the heavens about three miles high, and a circular range of snow-covered mountains reach from one of these vast spurs to the other, the whole forming a tremendous amphitheatre, whose diameter is one hundred and fifty miles. The sight in the morning, as the light of the rising sun falls on these lofty ranges, is most charming. The sunset views, and also the sights by moonlight, are exceedingly beautiful. There never was a finer field for the display of the painter's talent. There is a remarkable fact, to which I do not recollect to have seen attention called, namely, that vegetable and animal life have become acclimated to these mountain temperatures, so that both flourish with a degree of temperature which would prove almost instantly fatal in other parts of the country. I saw strawberries in bloom at an altitude of two miles. Raspberries flourish in great abundance at the same altitude. It often happens, as I was assured again and again in the mountains, that ripe raspberries and strawberries can be taken with one hand and snow with the other. Many of the most delicate and beautiful flowers come right up through the snow.

———

WASHINGTON, D. C., June 1, 1865.

HON. W. GILPIN:

Dear Sir,—Previous to my election as Congressional Delegate from Colorado, and when Associate Justice of the Supreme Court, I visited the county seat of Costilla County (the town of San Louis de Culebra), to hold the semi-annual term of the U. S. Court. I have traversed the Sangre di Cristo grant on each occasion, and can testify to its great value, high state of development, and richness in mines of the precious metals

During the session of the October Term, 1864, I visited the Gold Mines at the base of the Culebra Peak, six miles east of the Culebra, accompanied by Messrs. Stone, Hinsdale and Gaspar, all familiar with the Mines of Colorado Territory. We found numerous veins of gold-bearing quartz, which we examined and found very rich. I learned, in conversation with the resident people, of numerous rich placers having been successfully worked. Information gathered by me in conversation with the people, satisfies me of the existence of gold mines. scattered throughout the mountains, which are high and very precipitous. I remarked the extraordinary ease of access to the summit of the Sierra everywhere upon the grant, and especially at Culebra, which is only thirteen miles from the highest crest. I met, on one occasion, with Capt. James Aborn and the party of miners accompanying him. I fully accord with them in all their statements of the abundance and richness of the mines of precious metals, some of which I have seen and examined.

Of water power and its distribution and convenience, there is the greatest abundance.

The population employs itself exclusively in pastoral and arable agriculture, which is on a very extensive scale and of great excellence.

I learned that stock to the amount of fifty thousand head are owned by the people on the grant.

From the surplus products large supplies have been furnished to the United States Army and the mines of Colorado.

Labor is abundant and cheap, among a population estimated by me at from three to six thousand in the aggregate. The whole area of the grant is very valuable for its pastoral excellence.

The streams are numerous and large in their supply of water. The forests suited for lumber are ample in quantity. The farming lands are of superior quality. The climate is salubrious and very propitious to uninterrupted labor. Besides the abundance and richness of the mines of gold, they are more easy of access and better situated for economical and profitable working than any with which I have been acquainted elsewhere.

(Signed)   ALLEN A. BRADFORD,
Delegate to Thirty-ninth Congress.

BARON EGLOFFSTEIN, an accomplished Engineer, for many years officially connected with the Government, in speaking of this property, remarks:

"My knowledge of the Park of San Luis is based upon critical surveys made by me when officially connected with the explorations of Fremont, Beckwith, Macomb and Ives. All the topographical and other illustrations in the Congressional volumes, embodying the results of their expeditions, have been made by me *upon the ground*, and the publications under my superintendence. When upon the "Sangre di Cristo" grant, in 1855, my explorations extended into the mountains. Here the extraordinary developments of the metals, especially of the gold bearing quartz, due to convenience of access, incidental to the compact structure of the Cordillera, between the Great

Plains (on the east,) and the valley of the San Luis Park (on the west,) especially aroused and concentrated my attention. The richest gold bearing quartz were recognized by me in immense masses, cropping out upon the flanks of the streams near their sources. Dense forests, abundance of rivers, pastoral and arable lands, and wild animals, are all here of extraordinary excellence. Water power is very generally distributed, and the atmosphere and scenery are of the most salubrious and attractive temperature and beauty. Whilst prosecuting my surveys in the Sierra flanking the San Luis Park on the east, I discovered in one locality a very rich gold vein. I was satisfied, at the time, on identifying the gold bearing masses of quartz and the numerous placers on the descending streams, that the mountains abound in gold.

"I have learned that more recent and critical examinations have developed a number of gold mines on the "Sangre di Cristo" grant, which fully accords with my own anticipations and judgments of what would result from the repeated researches following my own preliminary examination."

"New York, June 3d, 1865.

(Signed) " F. W. V. EGLOFFSTEIN."

The following is from the "*Denver Gazette*," under date of July 10th, 1865.

" NEW DISCOVERIES.—Mr. Charles Lascher has just returned from a long prospecting tour down into the southern portion of Colorado, comprising the San Louis Park and adjacent mountains. He reports some of the richest prospects which he has ever seen, and he was one of the old prospectors with Gregory and Russell, in 1858. He says Governor Gilpin is one of the richest men of the United States, made so by his immense mineral lands found in his grant in the San Louis. Mr. Lascher, after collecting some beautiful ruby silver ore from Governor Gilpin's grant, left for New Mexico, where he found some other rich deposits, specimens of which he has with him. The lands

3

are owned by Governor Gilpin and some wealthy Mexicans, who are sole owners of these valuable deposits. We have no doubt that as soon as the Governor arrives in Denver from New York, where he is at present, some arrangements can be made with him to open them for mining purposes; until then, we would advise none to move in the matter."

Hon. Fred. J. Stanton, now a resident of the city of Denver, Colorado, writes to Governor Gilpin a private letter, from which we have been permitted to make the following extracts:

" DENVER, COLORADO, July 10th, '65.
" Hon. W. GILPIN:

" Dear Sir,—Yesterday Mr. Charles Lascher arrived in Denver with big news of mineral discoveries on your grant and in New Mexico. I don't wish to be thought dictatorial, but I must think that your true interests lay *here* just now. Directly you come you will be besieged with parties exceedingly anxious to go in with you in mining speculations. You can have no conception of the excitement Lascher has caused. I have got some specimens which do certainly appear very rich, both of an argentiferous and auriferous character. I have also a very fine specimen of ruby silver ore which was taken from your lands.
" Yours most truly, in haste,
" FRED. J. STANTON."

The following extracts are taken from a letter to WILLIAM K. KETCHEN, Esq., *President of the Park Bank, New York,* by D. A. BUTTERFIELD, Proprietor Butterfield's Overland Despatch, March 1st, 1865.

COMMERCE OF THE PLAINS.

" To WILLIAM K. KITCHEN,
" *President of the Park Bank:*
" SIR,—In answer to your inquiries respecting the business and commerce of the Plains, and the propriety of organizing a

Company with capital sufficient for its present and rapidly increasing demands, I respectfully submit the following facts:

"The territories of Colorado, New Mexico, Idaho, and Montana, contain an aggregate population of 350,000, all depending upon a merchandise interest which for years has and will have to be transported from the Missouri River in freight wagons drawn by oxen and mules.

"In addition to the large merchandise interest of that country, there are now organized in the cities of New York, Boston, Philadelphia and Providence, *two hundred* (200) active companies, designed to open and operate the gold mines of Colorado, Nevada, Idaho, and Montana. Estimating each company's freight at 200 tons, (which is 100,000 pounds less than those shipped last year), there will go forward by this interest eighty million pounds (80,000,000), all of which will have to be transported in wagons. From May to November, A.D. 1864, there were carried from the Missouri River to the territories by cattle and mule trains:

"From Atchison to Kansas,	17,000,000	pounds,
" Nebraska City,	13,337,000	"
" Saint Joseph, Missouri,	5,500,000	"
" Leavenworth, Ks., for Colorado,	5,000,000	"
" Leavenworth, Kansas, for New Mexico,	4,889,400	"
" Omaha, Nebraska	4,300,000	"
" Fort Leavenworth, Government Freight,	13,000,000	"
Making a total in six month,	63,026,400	

"These amounts are taken from the Railroad, Packet Companies, and Forwarding Merchants' books, and are reliable.

"It is stated by the heaviest merchants of Colorado and Utah, that the merchandise shipments to that section the coming year will be two hundred and fifty per cent. larger than the past; but assuming that it remains the same, there cannot be less than one hundred million pounds of freight go over the Plains the coming year. This is based upon an estimate that only 35,000,000 out of the 80,000,000 pounds of mining machinery go forward."

TREASURE.

"It is estimated that Colorado, in its present comparatively undeveloped state, and with existing facilities, will send to the East this year *sixty million dollars* bullion. When the two hundred companies now organized get fairly at work, the amount will be very largely increased. The present rates of taking out currency and bringing in bullion, is *three per cent* each way, and sixty million gold coming East, it is safe to con_ clude that forty million currency will go West, making one hundred million dollars annually to be transported by some company."

NUMBER OF TRAINS.

" There are now over one hundred trains on the Missouri River.

" Butterfield's Overland Despatch is fully organized, with offices in New York, Boston, Philadelphia, Chicago, St. Louis, and Leavenworth, has large and convenient warehouses at Atchison, Kansas, and Denver, Colorado. The details are all settled, and a large and growing business is being done ; so much so, that on the 25th of February, *eleven hundred cases of merchandise* were shipped from the New York office .alone. This Company has now in store at Atchison, for shipment in the Spring, over five million pounds of machinery, a sufficient amount to load forty full trains, and it is safe to say that by May next, a sufficient amount of merchandise for the Territories will have accumulated to load during that month the one hundred trains alluded to in this statement."

One train consists of twenty-six wagons, moving 150,000 pounds.

The undersigned have been entrusted with the formation of a Company for the purchase and development of the celebrated " Sangre di Cristo" Grant, located in the San Luis Park, Colorado, and are happy to announce that they have succeeded in inducing certain well-known capitalists of Boston, Pennsylvania and New York to embark in the enterprise. Comparatively little of the stock for sale remains unsubscribed for. Gentlemen seeking investment of their money can obtain full particulars of this magnificent enterprise on application to

CHAS. H. TODD & CO.,

48 Pine Street,

Rooms 7 *and* 8.

REPORT OF SUPERINTENDENT

AND THE

BY-LAWS

OF THE

TREASURY MINING CO.

OF COLORADO.

BOSTON:
ALFRED MUDGE & SON, PRINTERS, 34 SCHOOL STREET.
1868.

TREASURY MINING COMPANY.

OFFICERS.

PRESIDENT.

ALLEN PUTNAM,

238 Washington Street, Boston.

DIRECTORS.

ALLEN PUTNAM	Boston.
JOSHUA TUCKER	Boston.
F. A. GOULD	Boston.
JOHN WETHERBEE	Boston.
WILLARD B. FELTON	Boston.
L. M. SPRAGUE	Colorado.
ELIAS F. DYER	Colorado.

TREASURER.

F. A. GOULD,

290 Hanover Street, Boston.

SECRETARY.

WILLARD B. FELTON.

REPORT OF THE SUPERINTENDENT.

*To the Stockholders of the Treasury Mining Company of Colo-
rado, Dece nber* 1867.

In May last I went to Colorado to superintend the opening
of mines belonging to the Treasury Mining Company, and to do
whatever else I could for the interest of the Company. The
principal work laid out for me, was the opening of the "Silver
Lode," situated in Lincoln Mining District, County of Lake, and
Territory of Colorado.

In the Fall of 1866, I had brought East some of the ore from
said "Silver Lode," and the result of a pretty careful testing of
it, showed that the average yield, by *assay*, was about one hundred dollars per ton. The yield of seventy pounds, smelted by
Balbach, Diefenbach & Co., in their smelting works, in Newark,
N. J., yielded at the rate of fifty dollars silver, and seven dollars gold, per ton. At a depth of ten feet from the surface, we
had an eighteen inch vein of that kind of ore. My object this
summer, was, if possible, to prove that we had a genuine vein
or lode of such ore, and, if so, to get it into such shape that it
could be worked so as to furnish ore fast enough to keep a furnace busy smelting it.

I was unable to get to the mine with such things as it was
necessary to have to commence operations, until the middle of
July. It being forty miles from any settlement, I had all the
disadvantages to contend against that are met with in all such

enterprises, together with that of having to pack everything we eat, or in any way used, over the snowy range of the Rocky Mountains on the backs of jackasses.

From the middle of July to the last of September, I worked from ten to twelve men. Our first work was to put up buildings for comfort and convenience; next a blacksmith shop, wherein we could sharpen our picks and drills.

As soon as we had a shelter, we commenced work on the mine and worked night and day. We went down first thirty (30) feet in the place where we had made the opening last year, and found there full eighteen inches of ore in every way as good as what we had had tested, if not better. On the north side, we had a solid wall rock; on the south side, we did not have the wall rock, as our shaft (six feet wide) was not as wide as the crevice. The lode pitched at an angle of 45° to the north. In sinking that shaft, we had not timbered it, expecting it would get solid and would not need it; but the water came in so fast, that it softened up the sides, and they began to cave down, and we thought it would be useless to attempt to go down farther without timbering. I immediately sent to Dayton for some cattle to haul the timber and, in the mean time, put the men to taking off the wall rock on the north, so as to straighten the shaft. When we had got the shaft straightened and timbered, we commenced sinking again.

In straightening the shaft, we had moved, so that the windlass was about twelve feet east and about ten feet north of the windlass to the first shaft. In that new shaft, we went down twenty feet deeper than in the other, following down the north wall rock which was still pitching at the same angle, and still we had no signs of the south wall rock. We had but very little *solid* ore in the shaft. At the depth of fifty feet, there was a vein of soft, decomposed material, that I had assayed, and the yield was forty-two dollars per ton. At that depth, the water came in so fast that it was almost impossible for us to accomplish anything in the way of sinking. It came in at the rate of from four to five barrels per hour. Raising that amount of water by a hand windlass fifty feet gave the men but little time for other work; still we were working away, doing the best we could, when, having stopped work over Sunday, on Monday the sides caved down, and filled up the hole so deep that I deemed it useless to try to sink any farther in that shaft. My intention had been to drift in to the south wall rock, and see if that body of ore which had disappeared at the depth of about thirty feet, was running down next to the south wall; but the caving in of the shaft prevented me from doing so. Therefore, I am unable to say positively, what shape the vein is in at that depth. We had in the shaft, all the way down, small veins of ore, but at the depth of fifty feet, there was not enough to be of any value, unless there was more next to the other wall rock.

We then sunk another shaft fifteen feet deep, about twenty feet west of the first shaft. There we found the north wall rock the same; the angle of the vein the same; and vein of mineral about the same, i.e., eighteen inches, and no appearance of the south wall rock. What seemed very singular was, that in this vein of mineral there was no Galena ore. The bulk of the material was decomposed, and the balance apparently a very fine quality of pyritous ore.

My object when commencing that shaft was not to sink it deep, unless it proved much better than the other. But I thought it necessary to prove that we were working on a genuine *lode*, and to do that, ought to open it in different places. Having found by that shaft that the lode was there, I concluded to see what there was *east* of the first and second shafts; and to do that, decided to run a tunnel in on the lode from the west to the east, right on the vein. The ground rose there at the rate of about four inches to the foot; so that going in one hundred feet the end of the tunnel would be at a depth of about thirty feet, from the surface. As we would not be bothered by wate in tunnelling, we could go in one hundred feet as cheap as we could go down thirty, thereby accomplishing in reality the proving of a genuine vein at the same expense, and secure the advantage of always having the tunnel remain open, whereas a shaft would fill up.

We commenced on a level with the little stream that runs close to the opening of the lode, run in on that level and struck the lode a few feet west of the last shaft, went in on the vein, striking Galena ore about three feet east of the east end of the last shaft. From that point to a few feet east of the east end of the second shaft, (about forty feet,) we had from twelve to eighteen inches of argentiferous Galena ore, of first class quality; from that point it began to grow narrower, and at the end of the tunnel, (about twenty-five feet,) it had narrowed down to about three inches. There we had both wall rocks, which were about three feet apart. At that point, I thought it best to suspend operations. I was satisfied that I could not sink shafts there without some other way of hoisting the water than by windlass, and I had not the means or time to rig any other way; neither had I means sufficient to run a tunnel as long as I would be obliged to if I commenced far enough west to be at a depth of fifty or sixty feet, when I should reach the point where I had been shafting. I had not succeeded as I had hoped, for I had not got the mine in such a shape that I could feel confident of being able to supply ore fast enough to warrant putting up a furnace; still I had proved that it was *a genuine lode and a large one.*

I will here state what I omitted to say above, that in caving off from the south side, the fall had disclosed a vein of good ore, about three inches wide, in addition to what we had before had, thus showing the crevice to be over eight feet wide; the ore is first-rate, being rich, and of such character that the silver and gold can be saved with large profits above the expense.

The mine is in an entirely new district, far from other settlements, and therefore the cost of getting in a road and putting up works is necessarily large; consequently it becomes more than usually necessary for us to be sure of the quantity of ore we can command, before putting in a road and constructing reduction works. I should not recommend such an outlay until the mine has been more thoroughly proved up.

We have a great number of lodes in Lincoln District, and also in Red Mountain District, that in a few years will be very valuable; but the ore in them is sulphuret or refractory, and there is no process yet perfected for the treatment of such ore economically, therefore I should not recommend spending any more upon them than what may be necessary to maintain our title until such time as we may wish to develop them for positive working.

In order that you may the more fully understand the distinctive peculiarities of the lodes in Granite District, as compared with those in Colorado with which eastern people are most familiar, it seems to be well to give, as succinctly as may be, an account of the discovery of said District, its location and its claims to a favorable consideration as a quartz mining district.

The first discovery of quartz, in what is now called " Granite Mining District," was made by a negro, from Georgia, in 1862. He showed parties the result of tests made by himself on some of the quartz he had taken from his lode, which indicated it to be exceedingly rich. He tried to interest parties in it, with him to put up a mill, (he had had some experience in quartz mining in Georgia,) but every one in that county at that time was engaged in surface diggings, knew nothing about quartz mining and did not feel like taking any interest in quartz. Not being able to accomplish his object, he covered up the opening to his mine, (the exact location of which was never known by others,) and turned his attention to surface digging, with the intention of putting up a mill as soon as his means would permit. The

2

next year death claimed him, and to others is left the work of carrying out his intentions.

In the spring of 1864 a few lodes were staked, and one was opened to the depth of a few feet; quartz was obtained that prospected well, and there that effort ended. Nothing more was discovered until the fall of 1865, when some quartz was discovered that, by pulverizing in a mortar and washing in a pan, yielded ten cents to the ounce; this created considerable talk, but there was no faith in there being any quantity of such quartz, and so nothing was accomplished that year. The party however who had made the discovery, returned the next season (1866) and made an opening about fifteen feet deep, and took a few hundred pounds of the ore to Black Hawk and had it worked in a Stamp Mill. This yielded at the rate of $160.00 per ton.

The same season, two other lodes were opened to about the same depth, the quartz from each possessed the same general features and was of about the same richness. During the last season, work was entered into with more earnestness, and the lodes were opened enough to prove that the ore was exceedingly rich, and extensive enough to claim the consideration of the mining community in general; then people from all sections came in to prospect, and a great many lodes were discovered.

Said district is situated on the east side of the Arkansas River in Lake County, Colorado Territory, 130 miles from Denver, by road, and 210 miles from Cheyenne, the present terminus of the Union Pacific Railroad. The district is about fifteen miles long, north and south; and from five to eight miles wide, east and west, — is bounded on the west by the Arkansas River, on the east by the summit of the mountains between the Arkansas River and the South Park.

Its claims to a favorable consideration as· a quartz mining district are, that it is exceedingly well situated for advantageously working the mines, for they are situated within one and a half miles of the Arkansas River, which will afford excellent water power the whole year for almost any number of mills. The altitude is less than that of the South Park. There is plenty of timber, the whole district being covered with the exception of a strip half a mile or so wide, bordering the river.

The ground on which the discoveries are made is *very dry;* no water has been found in any shaft yet sunk, and it is the opinion that none will be found until the mines are opened to a considerable depth. There are several mining settlements immediately adjacent, in three of which, there are post-offices; there are two saw mills within three miles. There is a good road to the district, and ordinarily wagons can go in without any difficulty the whole year.

Work can be carried on as well the year round as in any mining district in Colorado; one mill has been taken in there since the 1st of November, and is expected to be in running order before the 1st of January, 1868. There are good farms within twelve miles of the district, on which are raised all kinds of vegetables of the very best quality; grain is also successfully cultivated.

The quartz, which is exceedingly rich, is what is called "free-gold quartz," by which we mean quartz in which the gold is in such a state that, by simply pulverizing and washing, the gold can be saved, whereas in the sulphuret ore, (which is most common in Colorado,) only a very small per cent of the gold in the ore can be saved by that method. Being free-gold quartz the most simple machinery is adapted to working it, and the cost is trifling, compared to the working of any other kind of ore. The veins are not what would be called large veins, but they are of good width; their course is northeast and southwest.

Two arrasters were put up by Capt. Hoyt & Co. this fall to make a working test of some of the quartz; the arrasters were very imperfect affairs worked by horse-power. The quartz worked was out of three different lodes. From between two and three tons of quartz, part of which was selected and part not, they took 6 lbs. 2 oz. of gold — coin value $1,300 — or at the rate of about $500 per ton. I have pounded up specimens, out of a dozen or fifteen lodes, in an iron mortar, and washed in a common miner's pan, and obtained from twenty-five cents to one dollar to the pound of quartz. At some depth or other, the free-gold quartz will probably turn to sulphuret ore; but if the free-gold quartz shall not hold out any deeper than we already know that it extends, and should there be no more discoveries made, even then, we have enough out of which to take several millions of dollars.

Aside from the richness of the quartz, we have additional evidence that Granite District is a rich district, from the fact of there being so many rich gulches in that vicinity.

Within the territory on each side of the Arkansas River, for a distance of twenty-five miles, of which Granite District is nearly the centre, there is California Gulch (the richest ever discovered in Colorado), Colorado Gulch, Iowa, Long, Yuba, Oregon, Gibson, Arkansas, Cache Creek, Lost Cañon, Le Paz, and a host of others, not yet worked for want of water; also the banks and bed of the river for a distance of fifty miles are found rich in gold, several hundred thousand dollars having already been taken from its banks, and companies are now formed for fluming the river so as to work its bed. On the theory that the gold, found mixed with the dirt in gulches, banks and beds of streams and in bars, originally came from quartz lodes (and that *is* the generally accepted theory) we naturally infer that in a section where gold is so universally found in such quantity, there must of necessity be many lodes and some exceeding rich ones. From the tests made of those lodes, already opened in Granite District, we conclude that some of the contributors of gold to the gulches have been found, but it is reasonable to presume only a small number compared to what will be.

The reason why these lodes have not been discovered ere
is because of their being covered with several feet of soil; very
few of them afforded familiar surface indications of their where-
abouts,—such indications as they did give were entirely different from those of other lodes that had been discovered in Lake
County, and prospectors did not know their language. Now
that the signs have been learned, an entirely new impetus will
be given, and prospecting will he carried on with renewed zeal
the coming season.

When I consider the richness of the quartz, the ease with
which the gold can be extracted, the low altitude of the mines,
the splendid water power, the great abundance of timber, the
close proximity to farms and hay ranches, and the fact that saw-
mills and settlements are already surrounding it, I must give as
my opinion that Granite District presents inducements for capitalists superior to any other mining district in Colorado.

Having considered the general characteristics of "Granite
Mining District," we now come to the consideration of the
property in said district belonging to the Treasury Mining Co.

When I had closed up operations in Lincoln District, the last
of September, I immediately, with three men in the employ of
the company, commenced prospecting in Granite District; and
the result of a month's work was the discovery of seven lodes
which were taken up and recorded in the County Clerk and
Recorder's office, Lake Co., according to the laws of Congress,
which allow an association or incorporated company to take up
three thousand (3000) feet, lineal measure, on each discovery,
by fifty (50) feet wide. One of the lodes was discovered
jointly by the Treasury Mining Company and the Brooklyn
Company, therefore we have an undivided one half of that lode
— the Robert Knight.

We have then on the Young America lode . . 3,000 feet.

               Portia   " . . . 3,000 "

               Sucker Boy   " . . . 3,000 "

Massachusetts   lode . . 3,000 feet.

Camille   " . . . 3,000 "

Champ   " . . . 3,000 "

Robert Knight   " . . . 1,500 "

Total, ... 19,500 feet.

On each of the above, enough work was done to prove that we had a vein of ore. We sunk shafts on each from eight to eighteen feet deep. I have brought home ore from several of them; and fourteen pieces, selected with a view to obtain as near as possible, by such process, a fair average, I have had assayed by S. Dana Hayes, State Assayer of Massachusetts — the result was as follows:

$38 58

17 48

122 14

17 99

183 08

520 60

1,374 20

61 79

414 07

24 23

68 98

13 47

155 03

686 35

14)3,697 99

$264 14 average per ton.

The questions that naturally arise are, Can that much gold be saved, and at what expense? I answer that the most of it can be saved by any ordinary stamp mill, and that it can be mined and milled at an expense not exceeding ten dollars per ton. It is generally calculated that one stamp mill will work a ton of ore per day; therefore, with an ordinary twelve stamp mill, we can work twelve tons of ore every twenty-four hours. It will be found by making the calculation, that with ore that will give an average yield of two hundred and sixty-four and $\frac{14}{100}$ (264.14) dollars per ton, a twelve stamp mill would give a clear profit of nearly a million of dollars in a year; but, in order not to raise our expectations too high, let us suppose that the ore will not average that amount, and that delays and hindrances unforeseen may occur. Assuming our average yield at fifty (50) dollars per ton, with a twelve stamp mill in three hundred days we would work three thousand six hundred tons of ore, which at a profit of forty dollars per ton would give us one hundred and forty-four thousand dollars profit per annum.

It would then seem that we could make a very large amount of money, if we have a sufficient quantity of ore; let us then consider that point. In the first place, we have about twenty thousand lineal feet of surface; now supposing this kind of ore only held out to a depth of from thirty to forty feet, (and I know it does hold out to that depth in every shaft sunk that deep while I was there, and I hear the same of several sunk since I left,) and calculating that in taking out a strip thirteen feet long and one foot deep we would obtain one ton of ore; then in twenty thousand feet, forty feet deep, we would obtain sixty-one thousand and five hundred tons, which would keep a twelve stamp mill running seventeen years; this with an annual profit of one hundred and forty-four thousand dollars, would give us in seventeen years the snug little sum of two millions four hundred and forty-eight thousand dollars.

I know the utter impossibility of figuring with any degree of certainty upon the profits of a mine before it has been thoroughly opened and actually worked long enough to give an actual working basis upon which to make a calculation. My object in making the above calculations is to illustrate my points, and to show that it is not necessary to have *very rich* ore to make an immense amount of money, if it is only of a kind from which the gold can be economically extracted, and you have enough of it, and good facilities for working it.

The ore in Granite District is exceedingly rich, and is of such a kind that the gold can be saved by the most simple of all mining machinery, — either stamp mills or arrasters. We have there unusually fine advantages for working the ore, and in no instance yet known in said district, have any lodes deteriorated or capped over in being sunk upon; still, there has not yet been work enough done to actually prove how extensive the ore is; that can only be done by putting up mills and going to work. It is believed that any company, having any considerable amount of ground, runs no risk in putting up a mill; in fact, from six to ten mills, it is already known, are to be put up there in the spring.

But to return to my consideration of the amount of ore we could calculate upon, I have one unexpected and very important point to mention: Up to the time of my having the assaying above mentioned, done by Mr. Hayes, I had supposed that the ore in Granite District would prove the same as the ore in other parts of the Territory had proved, i. e., that at some unknown depth they would change from free-gold ores to sulphuret or refractory ores; but, from the following certificate of Mr. Hayes, which was entirely unlooked for, it will be seen that the ore of this district is entirely different from any other ores yet discovered in Colorado.

OFFICE OF S. DANA HAYES, STATE ASSAYER AND CHEMIST,
20 STATE STREET, BOSTON, 9th Jan. 1868.

W. B. FELTON, ESQ.

Dear Sir : — The samples of gold ores, recently assayed for you, are of a different geological character from those generally brought here from Colorado.

These ores are true hematites, or hematitic iron ores associated with quartz, and as there are very large deposits of these iron ores — without the gold — in different parts of the country, it is a strong indication that the character of your ores will not change : that is, you may expect a large deposit of the same kind of ore, and not a change into sulphuret of iron.

Respectfully,

S. DANA HAYES,

State Assayer, Mass.

If it be true that the ore in Granite District will not turn into sulphuret or refractory ore, it does seem to me that the mines in said district must prove to be far superior to any heretofore discovered or worked in Colorado Territory.

Our lodes are all favorably situated for working; the farthest being not over one and a half mile from the river, where we would want to put up a mill, and the grade down to the river is very gradual, so that there would be no difficulty whatever in getting the ore from the mines to the mill

I believe I am perfectly safe in saying that the Treasury Mining Company owns more mining property than any other company in Colorado. It owns about one thousand lodes, or about two thousand acres of mineral land, upon which is gold and silver. The gold lodes, so far as we know, with the exception of those in Granite District, are sulphuret ores. These may, and doubtless will, be very valuable within a few years, but it does not seem to be expedient to expend much upon them now. The silver mine which I worked upon this last summer is a good lode, and had we no more promising property, I would recommend that it should be thoroughly opened next season; but having those lodes in Granite District so favorably situated for working and promising a great return from a small outlay, I would recommend putting up a stamp mill there as soon as practicable in the spring. After we have got one portion of our property into a paying condition we can turn our attention

3

to the development of other portions. First let us take hold of that which promises a return with the least outlay.

I do not feel like closing this Report without adding a few personal remarks. The property that belongs to the Company was discovered by Elias F. Dyer and myself in 1865; upon my recommendation the company was formed, and to a great extent it is composed of my personal friends; therefore I take the liberty to say that in its conception, formation and operations, up to the present day, there has been no intent to make it a speculative company; the intention has been, and is, to keep steadily at work until we are able to declare dividends from profits from actual working of the mines. I have devoted my whole attention to the affairs of the Company, during the last three years. I have no outside operations, and intend to have none: my interests are inside of the Company, and the Company's interests are my interests, — with it I succeed or I fail; having taken hold of the plow, I do not intend to turn back until the work is a *success*, if success be possible. I believe success is near at hand, and I now congratulate you all, and myself, that I am able to make so good an exhibit to-day.

Yours, truly,

WILLARD B. FELTON,

Superintendent.

BOSTON, Dec. 22, 1867.

APPENDIX BY THE PRESIDENT.

The foregoing Report of the Superintendent, leaves but little that need be added for a fair understanding of the condition and purposes of our Company.

We are not in debt. Our incorporation was effected under the General Laws of Massachusetts, in the early part of 1866. Capital Stock, $140,000 — 14.000 shares at ten dollars each. The matter of increasing the Capital Stock, by from $30,000 to $60,000, is under consideration.

The greater part of our lands was discovered and claimed in 1865 — was examined and partially tested in 1866 — and more fully tested and increased by the "Free-Gold" portion in 1867. Two seasons have now been devoted to preliminary explorations, and we have come to definite knowledge as to *where* to work, and *what* to do.

The arrangement will be to erect a stamp mill on the Arkansas, at once, and go to working the gold ore there. Our Superintendent estimates that with $20,000 he can erect the mill and be ready to work twelve tons of ore per day, by the first of October next. For the last two seasons he has kept within his estimates in both time and cost. Therefore we trust he will do so in future.

The belief is held, in sincerity, that, *considering the extent of our possessions* (about 2,000 acres of mineral land), the *smallness of our capital* (not over $200,000), *the favorableness of location,* in part, (on the banks of the Arkansas, in an inhabited neighborhood), and *the richness of our free gold ore* ($264 per ton), we possess a more valuable property than is often found. We may fairly hope to be realizing satisfactory profits before the close of the present year.

ALLEN PUTNAM,

President.

238 WASHINGTON ST. BOSTON, Jan. 15, 1868.

BY-LAWS.

THERE shall be an Annual Meeting of the Stockholders of the Company on the first Wednesday of February, at such place and hour as the Directors may appoint. Special meetings of the Stockholders may be called by order of the Directors, or by the Clerk, upon the written application of Stockholders holding at least one-fifth of the capital stock.

A notice, stating in general terms the purpose of any meeting of the Company, shall be addressed to each Stockholder, and sent to him by mail, or left at his usual place of residence or business, at least five days before the meeting.

If, from any cause, the Annual Meeting shall not be held on the day above designated, the Directors shall call it as soon thereafter as practicable.

At all meetings, each Stockholder shall be entitled to one vote, in person or by proxy, for each share of stock held by him.

A quorum for the transaction of business shall consist of at least three Stockholders, present in person, holding, either personally or by proxy, not less than one-half of the capital stock.

At the Annual Meeting, there shall be chosen by ballot a Board of seven Directors, to continue in office one year, and until their successors are chosen. A majority of the Directors shall constitute a quorum for the transaction of business. The Directors must be Stockholders ; and if, during the year for which he is chosen, any Director shall die, resign, or cease to be a Stockholder, the Directors may elect some Stockholder to fill his place.

The Directors shall choose by ballot one of their number to President of the Company and of the Board.

The Directors may also employ such other officers and agents as they may deem advisable, fix the compensation of all officérs, assign to them duties, and remove them at pleasure.

It shall be the duty of the Directors to superintend and direct the business of the Company in all its branches ; they shall have power to control all purchases and sales of personal property, and to make purchases, leases and sales of real estate, and to authorize and direct the President to convey the same in the name and under the seal of the Company. Stated meetings of the Board of Directors shall be held on the first Wednesday of February, and quarterly thereafter.

ARTICLE III.

The Clerk shall be chosen by the Stockholders at their Annual Meeting, and shall be sworn to the faithful discharge of the duties of his office. He shall give notice of all meetings of the Company, and of the Board of Directors, and shall call a special meeting of the Board whenever requested so to do by the President, or by any member of the Board. He shall attend all meetings of the Company and of the Board of Directors, and keep a true record of all their proceedings, and perform such other duties as the Directors may assign to him.

ARTICLE IV.

The Treasurer shall be chosen by the Stockholders at their Annual Meeting, and shall give bonds satisfactory to the Directors for the faithful discharge of his duties ; he shall keep the common seal of the Company, and their valuable papers, and collect and disburse all money due to or from the Company. He shall keep or cause to be kept, a regular set of books containing the accounts of the Company, also a stock ledger, and shall keep a separate account as Treasurer in such bank or banks as the Directors shall designate. Said books shall be open at all times to the inspection of the Directors. The Treasurer shall make up a quarterly trial-balance, and an annual account, to be laid before the Company at their Annual Meeting. He shall prepare all returns and certificates required by law. The same person may be chosen to fill the offices both of Treasurer and Clerk.

ARTICLE V.

The Company shall have a common seal, bearing the words " Treasury Mining Company, Mass., 1866."

ARTICLE VI.

Certificates of stock shall be signed by the President and Treasurer, and be in such form as shall be approved by the Board of Directors. No new certificate shall be issued until the old certificate for the same shares be cancelled, or until a memorandum of the number of shares transferred from such old certificate is made thereon by the Treasurer, except in case of the loss of a certificate, in which case a new one may be issued by vote of the Directors on proof to their satisfaction of the loss, and on receiving security satisfactory to them to indemnify the Company against loss by reason of the issue of the duplicate certificate.

ARTICLE VII.

No By-laws shall be repealed, amended, or suspended, except at the Annual Meeting of the Stockholders, duly called for that purpose, and upon a vote of a majority of the Stockholders present.

THE

Poorman Gold and Silver Mining Co.

OF

IDAHO.

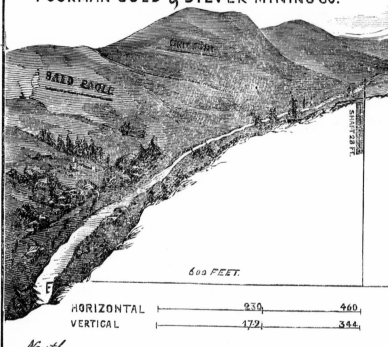

FIRST NORTH EXTENSION

POORMAN GOLD & SILVER MINING CO.

600 FEET.

HORIZONTAL 230 460

VERTICAL 17.2 344

SHAFT 28 FT.

SHAFT

North.

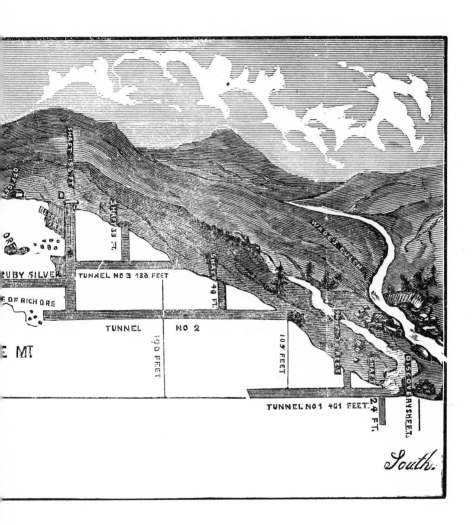

South.

THE

Poorman Gold and Silver Mining Co.

OF

IDAHO.

———◆———

CAPITAL STOCK 100,000. SHARES OF THE NOMINAL PAR VALUE OF $10
EACH OF WHICH 12,500 SHARES HAS BEEN PLACED
IN THE TREASURY FOR WORKING
CAPITAL.

NAMES OF TRUSTEES:

OFFICE OF THE COMPANY, NO. 21 BROAD-STREET, NEW YORK.

NEW YORK:
AMERICAN MINING INDEX ENGRAVING, JOB PRINTING AND LITHOGRAPHING
ESTABLISHMENT, 151 FULTON STREET.

T H E

Poorman Gold and Silver Mining Co.

OF IDAHO.

The Poorman Gold and Silver Mining Company was organized under the general incorporating laws of the State of New York in the year 1866 with a capital stock of one million dollars divided into 100,000 shares of the nominal par value of $10 each.

The stock was issued for the purchase of mines, and is full paid and unassessable. The property of the company consists of six hundred lineal feet on the Poorman Lode, known as the first north extension, situated in Carson Mining District, County of Owyhee, Territory of Idaho.

There are several shafts or experimental openings on the mine varying in depth from nine to twenty-eight feet, attesting the presence of the vein and affording strong proof that this mine on further exploration, will be found to possess all the remarkable characteristics of the adjoining claim.

Great care has been exercised since the inception of this enterprize to fully understand the character and condition of this property, and we confidently assert that no mining estate gives promise of surer or larger returns. The company has sufficient money in its treasury to meet the present demand and has reserved one-eighth of its stock to be sold as needed for future cash capital.

It is the settled policy of the company to attend strictly to the development of its mine, avoiding ruinous expenditures for large expensive mills in advance of the requirements of the company.

Smelting we believe to be the most economical and approved system for the reduction of Poorman ores, yet fabulous returns are obtained by the ordinary milling process—the selected ores are so rich that they will bear transportation to Swansea, or to this seaboard for treatment, but for permanent operations we contemplate the erection of reduction works at the mines.

The foregoing map indicating the route of the Pacific Railroad and various wagon roads leading to and from the Owyhee silver region will be perused with interest.

It will be observed that the road will pass within 90 miles of the mines, and it is estimated that within the year 1869 the traveller can pass from ocean to ocean by continuous rail. The completion of this road will add immeasurable value to all mining interests located in that region, cheapen both labor and supplies, and afford safe, rapid and cheap transit for bullion and other commodities pertaining to the developmhnt of the country.

The longitudinal section of the mine was made by Prof. Ford from actual survey. It shows the discovery claim, owned and worked by the New York and Owyhee Company, and the extent of its development. The first north extension is most admirably adapted to the tunnelling or adit system, which will greatly facilitate its rapid development. This portion of the vein is accessible to mills by easy down grade through Webfoot Gulch. The Poorman Lode has no parallel for richness in the history of American mines—it has given the most astonishing yields from the very surface to the greatest depth attained, a little more than five months work on the discovery, using only the rude appliances of mining incident to every new country, has returned to the proprietors a yield exceeding $800,000 in bullion ; this is only an indication of what may be done when this extradinary lode is fully developed.

General E. M. Barnum, an old resident of the Pacific slope, writing of the gold and silver fields of Oregon and Idaho says.

The disclosures of the past year, show that Idaho embraces within her borders some of the richest silver mines in our country ; and that with an increased population and judicious expenditure of capital, she will shortly rival Nevada in her yield of that metal.

Previous to the opening of the Comstock lode, in 1849, there were no proper silver mines known within the territory of the United States, and although there are several localities where a small amount of this metal had been obtained from lead ores, the silver furnished by this country had chiefly come from being parted from native gold.

Upon the marvelous yield of treasure produced from the Comstock and other silver lodes, which lie on the eastern slope of the Sierra Nevadas, prospecting and discovery was stimulated throughout all that vast region of metalliferous ranges lying between the Cascade and the Rocky Mountains, and extending northward into the Great Columbia River Basin.

In the summer of 1863, the mining district of Owyhee, in south-western Idaho, was discovered and occupied by the pioneer miners, and in the fall of 1864, and spring of 1865, many of the richer ledges were located and opened. Within this brief period, there have been erected ten quartz mills, with an aggregate of 102 stamps ; and there has sprung up a thriving mining town, and a county seat of over 2,000 inhabitants.

Of all silver lodes yet discovered within the United States, and probably in either Mexico or Peru, the "Poorman," (so called), in Owyhee, may easily bear off the palm. Located in the midst of a perfect net-work of auriferous and argentiferous lodes, which thread a range of mountains, that rise from 1,000 to 2,000 feet above the valley on either side. This ledge was not discovered until September, 1865.

By reason of a conflict of claims among miners, work upon the lode work was not continued later than November of the same year, and not until the latter part of July, 1866, when a compromise was effected, was it again resumed and continued without interruption up to the first of November, when by agreement, the further crushing and reduction of ores was again suspended for the winter, to admit of the proper adjustment of rights, and a more through exploration of the mine.

This vein has therefore only been worked about two months in 1865, and three months in 1866. The amount of ore raised and treasure extracted in 1865, can only be approximately stated at 200 tons, producing $84,000 af bullion.

In the three months working of 1866, the lode was mined to a depth of 156 feet, and 450 feet in length, with a result of 2,388 tons of ore reduced, yielding of silver bars, duly assayed and reported under the Internal Revenue law, $546,000 ; the ores were treated so imperfectly, that more than $100,000 of treasure still remain in the "*tailings*," to be hereafter extracted.

At the same time there was selected and sent to New York over 14 tons of the richer ore, exhibiting of ruby silver, horn silver, silver glance, and other varieties of the sulphurets and chlorides of this metal, solid masses of from 100 to 300 lbs. each ; the value of this shipment of ore has been by competent judges, estimated at an average of over $5,000 per ton ; making the entire product of the "*Poorman*" Lode, in five months' work ing, over $800,000.

The ores of silver, which have been found along this vein for a distance of a thousand feet, comprise almost all the forms of that metal known to mineralogists, and the value of the lode is beyond all ordinary calculation.

Subjoined will be found certificates of various assays made from Poorman ores, and the report of Prof. D. R. Ford :

Office of Levison, Metallurgical Laboratory, 19 Broad street, New York.

30th January, 1867.

A sample of ore submitted by the Poorman Gold and Silver Mining Co. for my examination had an average specific gravity of 4.70, and consisted of black sulphide of silver with an admixture of lamellar horn silver sufficient to render it in character sectile. Hardness = 1.3.

By carefully conducted fire assay, I determined it to contain a trace of gold and fifty per cent of metallic silver which gives the subjoined :

Yield per ton of 2,000 pounds—

1,000 pounds fine silver at $15.48 = $15.480.00.

W. GOOLD LEVISON.

New York, March 17, 1866.

No. 139.

Statement of bar assayed

for

Mr. H. S. Jacobs.

	021. thousands 21 "	979 thousand.
Weight 797 dws. 2 carats gold, 23½ carats silver.		
26½ lbs. of } Contains	dws. fine gold at $17 13	
Ore. }	oz. fine silver 50 45	

$67 58

Less per cent for assaying, refining, &c.

GEO. W. PLATT, late

PLATT & BROTHER.

Assayers, No. 4, Liberty Place,

Per WM. D. CUHSEE.

The above mentioned 26½ lbs. of ore was mined from the 1st North Extension.

New York, Feb. 26th, 1866.

HIRAM A. JOHNSON,

Dear Sir :—I hereby certify that the Silver Brick this day sold and de-livered to you was extracted by me at my laboratory in Ruby City, Idaho Territory, from ten pounds of ore mined from the Poorman Lode.

That the brick contains an admixture of gold with the silver, making the cempound worth $1.76 per oz. the entire brick is worth $35.00 gold valuation. Yours, &c.

T. H. WILLEY.

Assayer, Ruby City, I. T.

Statement of sample of Ore assayed for
Mr. H. S. Jacobs.

Contents per lb. avdps.	708 grs.	16 grs.
" " ton 2,000 lbs.	2,950 oz.	1,333⅓ dwts.
Valur per ton 2,000 lbs. $3.814.05		$1,377.73

Total.................................... $5,191.78

Charge $ gold coin.

G. W. PLATT, Assayer.

Per M. WATERS.

To the President and Directors of " The Poorman Gold and Silver Mining Company of Idaho :"

Please find accompanying, and herewith submitted, my report of journey and exploration of the *Poorman Lode*, Territory of Idaho, made by me, at your direction, in Sept. 1866.

Respectfully,

D. R. FORD,

Professor of Chemistry and Mathematics in Elmira College, N. Y.

LOCATION AND ACCESS.

The property examined, was formerly known as the 1st North Exten-sion of the Poorman Lode, discovered in Sept. 1865. It is situated in

Carson Mining District, Owyhee Co. Idaho. It is accessible in five days travel from San Francisco, Cal. by boat and rail to Chico and thence by stage to Silver City, near which this silver vein is situated. It is accessible also by Holaday's Overland stages from the Atlantic States, being about 464 miles northwest of Salt Lake City. It is eighteen days coaching from St. Louis. There is also direct and easy communication by stage 376 miles with Umatilla and Steam navigation on the Columbia. There is a steamboat landing on the south fork of the Columbia only thirty miles from the mines, though for want of coal, the boat lies idle for the present. The Pacific Railroad as now projected, is a short hundred miles south of this mining district. A map of location and routes accompany this Report. The Chico route can be made in five days from San Francisco.

Structure of the Lode.

There can be no doubt but that the Poorman is a true fissure vein of the very richest quality of silver ores. As yet it has been worked only upon one claim, that of the New York and Owyhee Co. The marvelous success of their operations through about three months the past summer, upon 146 feet in length, by 110 feet in depth, leads unmistakably to the richest promise for the undeveloped lode. The general run of the vein is northeast and southwest through a granite rock, cutting the strata ; it is almost vertical, the dip being only 3° to the east. A longitudinal section of the lode, and also of the mountain, is furnished in the accompanying sketch.

The vein at the surface is on the average two inches wide, with a gradual increase downward till it is an average of three feet wide at the depth of 110 feet. One wall of the vein seems, in some convulsion of nature, to have slipped forward a little, so that the two halves of the crevice do not stand parallel, thus forming alternate contraction and enlargements of the vein. The structure is somewhat thus :

The discovery, or that part of the vein worked by the New York and Owyhee Co., is about 600 feet by a horizontal line south of the experimental shaft opened on your property. The vein at this point presents the same magnetic direction. It has the same peculiar dip and angle to the west. It also has the same identical width at the surface, and like the discovery claim, it gradually and surely widens in going downward. At the depth of 30 feet it is 13 inches wide and clearly defined.

The following diagram is very nearly accurate, representing the dip or underlay of the vein :

East   Surface.   West.

The line A B is a vertical line into the earth, from the surface of the mine. A C is the east wall of the vein, forming an angle of about 3° with the vertical. A D is the west wall of the vein.

This lode being so very nearly a vertical one, renders a perpendicular shaft possible, and thus the ores are elevated simply and easily.

A reference to the longitudinal section marked 1°, show as a cut of War Eagle Mountain, as if riven down through directly on the length of the Poorman vein. From A to E is situated your property, with a shaft and tunnel, suggested as a convenient method perhaps of a future opening on the vein. A K is the property of the New York and Owyhee Co. B D is their present mining works, with two shafts, 146 feet apart or thereabouts. From

B the shaft where the richest ores have been lifted out, to A is, on a horizontal line, very little over 600 feet, and on the slope it is less than 700 feet. The vein was seen by cross-cuts about 60 feet apart, from B to A, where is situated an experimental shaft about or nearly 30 feet deep, and in one corner of the opening, going a trifle deeper to avoid a granite "horse" at that point. H is a beautiful spring, and W, W, W is the depression called Webfoot Gulch. Silver City is down to the left about $1\frac{1}{2}$ miles. The vein had the appearance of cropping out again at a little spring at O.

It is reported to have been struck again by other parties, since I left, about 10 feet north of your property, at F in the section

Minerals in this Lode.

The gangue, or vein matter, unlike all others in Idaho, is a sort of white soft chalk, or calcareous substance, never requiring any blasting. Its smell and feel is characteristic of chalk. In portions there is talc. The chief forms of silver ore diffused through this vein stone are the following, viz. :

1. *Kerargyrite ;* or horn silver.
2. *Silver Glance ;* or a dense black sulphuret of silver.
3. *Ruby Silver ;* or arsenical silver ore.
4. *Embolite ;* in minute quantities, a bromide of silver.
5. *Auriferous Silver Ore* ; mainly a silver sulphuret with small gold nuggets, scattered upon its surface.

The 1st or *Horn Silver*, ought to yield 108 pounds of bullion to every 143 pounds of the ore. It is pure chloride of silver, and is found in small scales in the vein everywhere, and also adhering to the walls from B to D even in sheets several inches square. It also shows itself sparsely in the vein stone at A, and it is confidently expected to increase with a corresponding depth.

The 2nd or *Silver Glance*, presents a black or bluish black appearance, and is very generally diffused through the white chalky cement, and often accumulated in lumps of considerable size. It is the main ore of the vein, and is perhaps the richest form of silver ore that is known. It yields 108 pounds of bullion to every 124 pounds of the pure ore.

The 3d or *Ruby Silver*, is the rarest of ores in silver countries. It yields about 68 per cent of silver. It is found as yet only in the deepest part of the vein hitherto worked. The largest mass of Ruby Silver in the world, by all accounts, was raised from this vein in September, weighing 525 lbs. ; worth by estimate $7,162.08.

4th. *Embolite* is found only in minute specks upon the black sulphret.

5th. The *Auriferous Silver ore* has only been found hitherto in the deepest part of the vein, and near the shaft B in the New York and Owyhee Company's works. It is marvelously rich, and is of itself a first class gold ore, to say nothing of the silver.

The gold is apparent in a multitude of little lumps. Although gold is found in connection with silver everywhere in the vein-matter, yet the metal does not appear in the form of little nuggets until a considerable distance under ground. Here it is found in quantities.

Interspersed occasionally in the vein are chunks and masses of rotten granite called "horses" by the miners. A large one was found at A in the diagram. Other veins in this district are hard quartz with silver sulphurets alone. The Poorman vein is so peculiar and distinct in its ores, richness and softness that even a stranger will distinguish them from all others at first sight.

The soft granite walls of this vein are so much impregnated with Horn Silver, at points, as to make it very profitable to mill this wall-rock or country rock, back to the depth of many inches from the vein. The walls are smooth and well defined with a good show of flucan lying

between them and the mineral. This is a grand characteristic of true
fissure veins, and is so held by old miners.

MINING, MILLING, AND VALUE OF THE ORES.

The facilities for working your property are very good. Five good quartz
mills are within two miles. Silver and Ruby cities are about the same
distance, and there is a good worked road from the discovery claim to both
towns and mills. A quarter of a mile of additional road (very easily
built) would shorten the distance very much, if built from E, down Webfoot Gulch to the main road. Good spruce timber grows within a mile
of the property, abundant enough for all present wants.

The vein is remarkably easy to work. No hard tough rock is found in
it. No blasting is required.

The ore is singularly free from base metals. The almost imperceptible
quantity of arsenic does not affect its milling in the least.

A great advantage in developing a vein into a valuable mine is gained
by its situation upon a slope of the mountain. An adit level or tunnel,
connecting with a shaft, at once drains the mine cheaply, ventilates it
thoroughly, and releases the miner from hoisting out his ore at great
expense.

As to the value of the ores found in this lode, no man can hardly over-
estimate them. Nowhere in the number of mines I have visited in Colorado, Idaho, or California, have I ever seen nuggets of gold and sheets of
silver in such profusion.

I can truthfully endorse the following extract from the recent book of
a European traveller through Idaho. " Of all silver lodes, ever yet discovered, the Poorman of Owyhee, challenges the world for an equal; neither Mexico nor Peru furnishes anything that can be successfully compared with it. This ore contains from 30 to 60, and even 85 per cent of
pure metal. The ledge was discovered in August, 1865—and work was

suspended in December by reason of a conflict of claims—yet in less than six weeks the amount of gold and silver bullion taken out of the ledge exceeded half a million of dollars ; the exact amount cannot be known, but enough to show that 217 tons exceeded $2,200 per ton ; and 16 tons selected ore ran from $5,000 to $10,000 per ton." Thus he says, and I myself took out of the vein a single three pound lump, which yielded at the rate of $35,954.88 per ton. Surely this is good enough for silver ore. Consider with this also the great mass of Ruby Silver worth, according to analysis, over seven thousand dollars, as before mentioned. The common or second class ore, I was informed at the mills, turns out an average of $2,000 per ton by common mill process.

I am no prophet, but unless all miners' signs fail, your property is destined, like its neighbor on the same vein, to make its contented stockholders happy with frequent and fat dividends. This prediction is of course based upon the array of proof that it is truly located upon the famous Poorman Lode.

That it is, appears to me incontrovertible, from the IDENTITY and EXCLUSIVE PECULIARITY *of magnetic bearing ; of the dip or underlay ; of the sameness of peculiar veinstone ; of the identical width and rate of widening in both ; of the sameness of wall rock, and selvage of cement adhering ; from close proximity; from its having been traced by crosscuts between both properties ;* and from the uniform judgment of all the miners, that it is the same one continuous marvelous Poorman Lode.

The ore of the Owyhee Silver mines, on an average costs $30 per ton for reduction to bullion at the Custom Mills. When the present inflated prices for labor, machinery and supplies, have been brought down, as they soon must be, the *profits* of a good mine must be still greater. A list of present prices of lumber, labor, freight, and supplies mainly required in developing a mine, will accompany the financial report to the Treasurer.

Origin of the Poorman Lode.

War Eagle Mountain is one vast network of quartz lodes. All except the Poorman appear by their parallelism and similarity to have been formed at the same time, and filled with about the same hard vein matter. Query :—Were they once volcanic fissures, and filled by igneous action? At all events, it seems to me that the Poorman fissure was formed much later, and that its soft veinstone has been extensively acted upon by steaming vapors and ebullitions of hot water. Probably it might have been the vent of some ancient water vólcano. The boiled, rotton and sodden character of its wall rock, looks like this. We also know that horn silver is a compound of silver and salt. If this crevice had been for ages a boiling salt solfatora or mud volcano, whose walls were often slipping and grinding upon each other, and whose rocks were softening, and the rich sulphurets and ruby ores, were slowly changing to chlorides till all at last became quiet and full, we have, in my opinion, a fair theory for this celebrated vein.

BY-LAWS

OF THE

POORMAN GOLD AND SILVER MINING CO'Y.

ARTICLE I.

MEETING OF STOCKHOLDERS.

1. All meetings of Stockholders shall be held at the office of the Company in the City of New York; and the annual meeting for the election of Trustees shall be held on the second Monday in January, at 2 o'clock P. M. If for any cause an election of Trustees shall not be had on the day above designated, it may be had on any subsequent day to be fixed by the Board of Trustees.

2. Notice of all meetings of Stockholders shall be given at least ten days prior to such meeting, by advertising the same in at least one daily newspaper published in the city of New York, and by mailing notices thereof to each of the Stockholders.

3. All elections of the Stockholders shall be by ballot: Stockholders may vote in person or by proxy, and each Stockholder shall be entitled to as many votes as he represents shares of stock; and the persons receiving

the greatest number of votes shall be Trustees for one year, and until their successors shall have been elected.

ARTICLE II.

THE BOARD OF TRUSTEES.

1. The Board of Trustees shall consist of seven members, four of whom shall constitute a quorum for the transaction of business.

2. All meetings of the Board of Trustees shall be held at the office of the Company in the city of New York.

3. Special meetings may be held upon the call of the President or any two Trustees: due notice being given by the Secretary to all the Trustees.

4. The order of business of the meetings of the Board of Trustees shall be conducted according to Parliamentary usage.

5. The officers of the Company shall be a President, Vice-President, Secretary and Treasurer.

6. The Board of Trustees, as soon as may be after their election, shall hold a meeting and elect, by ballot, a President, Vice-President, Secretary, and Treasurer, who shall hold their office for the ensuing year, and until their successors have been elected and duly qualified to enter upon their respective duties; they shall also appoint an Executive Committee, to consist of two members with the President.

7. The Board of Trustees shall appoint a Superintendent and such agents to manage the affairs of the Company as may appear to them to be necessary; they shall also direct the prosecution of such works, and generally do all such acts and adopt all such measures not inconsistent with the Charter or By-Laws of the Company as they shall deem best calculated to promote to the fullest extent the interests of the Stockholders; they shall also fix the compensation, and define the duties not fixed by the By-Laws,

of the President, Vice-President, Secretary, Treasurer, Superintendent, and Agents ; they shall declare such dividends from the net earnings or profits of the Company, when and as often as the state of the funds will warrant ; they shall for cause remove any officer of the Company ; but no officer shall be removed until after investigation and concurrence of a majority of the Board of Trustees ; and they may buy and sell such real estate as they shall think best for the interests of the Company.

8. They shall select a bank or depository in which all moneys shall be deposited by the Treasurer to the credit of the Company, subject to the Company's check, drawn by the President and Treasurer.

9. They shall make a report and render an account to the Annual Meeting of the Stockholders, showing in detail the situation of the property and financial affairs of the Company.

10. They shall have power to fill any vacancies which may occur by death, resignation, or otherwise, in the interval between the Annual Meetings of Stockholders in the Board of Trustees and Executive Committee, and in the offices of President, Vice-President, Secretary and Treasurer.

11. They shall appoint three Inspectors of Election, to receive the ballot from Stockholders for Trustees prior to their annual meeting.

ARTICLE III.

PRESIDENT AND VICE-PRESIDENT.

1. It shall be the duty of the President to attend to the business of the Company daily, Sundays and Holidays excepted ; to preside at all meetings of Stockholders and Trustees, except those convened to remove him or inquire into his official conduct; to sign all documents and contracts authorized by the Board of Trustees ; to sign all checks and certificates of Stock, and to perform all such duties usually incidental to such office

and required by the provisions of the Act of Incorporation and their By-Laws.

2. In case of sickness or absence of the Secretary or Treasurer, he shall appoint some person to perform the duties of Secretary or Treasurer until the Board of Trustees shall be convened.

3. In case of sickness or absence of the President, the Vice-President shall perform all the duties required of the President; and he shall countersign all Stock issued by the Company.

ARTICLE IV.

SECRETARY.

1. It shall be the duty of the Secretary to be in attendance attendance at the office of the Company during business hours, to give the necessary notice of all meetings of Stockholders and Board of Trustees ; he shall record the same in a book to be kept for that purpose ; shall keep all proper books of accounts for the business of the Company with Stock Ledger, Transfer Book, and such other books or papers as the Trustees may direct ; shall present at each regular meeting a statement of the affairs of the Company ; keep the seal of the Company; register and sign all Certificates of Stock ; and generally shall perform such services and duties as usually appertain to his office in a corporate body, and are required by the provisions of the Act of Incorporation.

5. All the books, papers, and correspondence, except the Treasurer's cash-book, shall be kept in the office of the Company, and considered in the possession of the Secretary and under his charge, but open at all reasonable times during business hours to the inspection of the Trustees.

ARTICLE V.

TREASURER.

1. It shall be the duty of the Treasurer to receive all moneys of the Company, give receipts therefor, and place the same in the depository of the Company under the direction of the Trustees, keeping a true record thereof.

2. He shall receive all ore, gold dust, or bullion transmitted from the mines, and dispose of the same with the concurrence of the President, placing the proceeds to the credit of the Company, reporting the same to the Secretary.

3. He shall, with the President, sign all checks of the Company.

ARTICLE VI.

CERTIFICATES OF STOCK.

1. The Certificates of Stock shall be numbered and registered as they are issued; they shall exhibit the holder's name and number of shares, and shall be signed by the President and Secretary, and countersigned by the Vice-President, and have the seal of the Company affixed thereto.

2. Transfers of stock shall be made on the books of the Company by the President or Secretary, upon the surrender of the Certificate either by the holder in person or by Attorney ; and the surrendered certificate shall be pasted on the margin in the book from whence it was taken when issued.

3· The Transfer Book shall be closed at least five days previous to an election or the payment of dividends; and the dividends shall be paid to the Stockholders standing on record at the closing of the books.

4. If any person claim a certificate of the stock of the Company in lieu

of one lost or destroyed, he shall make an affidavit of the fact, and state the circumstances of the loss or destruction; and he shall advertise in one or more of the daily newspapers to be designated by the President, for the period of one week, an account of the loss or destruction, describing the Certificate, and calling upon all persons to show cause why a new Certificate shall not be issued in lieu of that lost or destroyed; and he shall transmit to the Company his affidavit and the advertisement above mentioned, with proof of its due publication, and shall give to the Company a satisfactory bond of indemnity against any damage that may arise from issuing a new Certificate; whereupon a new Certificate may be issued to him of the same tenor and amount with that said to be lost or destroyed, and specifying on its face that it is in lieu thereof.

ARTICLE VII.

SUPERINTENDENTS AND AGENTS.

The Superintendents and Agents of the mining operations shall reside at or near the mines, and transmit to the Secretary monthly reports of their operations, with vouchers; and in the performance of their duties be at all times subject to the direction of the President; and make all shipments of gold dust or bullion to the Treasurer, giving due notice thereof to the Secretary of the Company and to the Treasurer.

ARTICLE VIII.

BY-LAWS.

These By-Laws shall not be altered except by the consent of two-thirds of the whole Board of Trustees; and all proposed amendments or alterations shall be submitted to the Board, in writing, at a previous regular meeting to that at which the action of the Board shall be had thereon; and previous notice in writing shall be given by the Secretary to each Trustee of the Company of the contemplated amendment, and the time when they will be passed upon.

Adopted August 7, 1866.

HIRAM A. JOHNSON, *President.*

JOHN I. NICKS, *Vice-President.*

F. M. HIBBARD, *Secretary.*

UTAH

Gold,
Silver
and Lead

MINES.

LEAD MILL AND COMPANY BUILDINGS, BINGHAM CANYON.

DALTON AND LARK

GOLD, SILVER AND LEAD

MINING AND MILLING

COMPANY.

Capital $2,500,000, fully paid.   Shares $1 each, non-assessable.

SALT LAKE CITY:
The Utah Lithographing Co.
1896.

ERRATA.

Second and third paragraphs on page 5 should read as follows:
The engraving opposite page 5 shows the other mill of the company located on the Dalton and Lark claims at the mines of the company.
The engraving opposite page 3 gives a general view of the mill, hoists, etc., also part of the mountains upon which the mining claims of the company are situated.

PROSPECTUS.

~~~~~~

~~~~~~

THE West Mountain Mining District, commonly known as Bingham, is one of the largest producers and best mining camps of Utah—in fact of the intermountain country. It is about 2200 feet above Salt Lake City, and about 6500 feet above sea level.

It was the first mining district located in Utah, and has furnished a large percentage of the gold, silver and lead ores produced in Utah, as will be seen by the following table:

3

COMPARISON OF PRODUCTION OF METALS

Between West Mountain or Bingham District and the District West of Missouri River.

LEAD.

Year.	Lead Tons West of Missouri River.	Lead Tons from Utah Ores.	Per cent. Utah to West of Missouri.	Lead Tons from Bingham.	Per Cent. Bingham to West of Missouri.	Per Cent. Bingham to Utah.
1889	192 012	30 391	15 8	13 400	7.0	44.0
1890	133,832	34 132	25.4	13 090	9 8	38.3
1891	144.021	43.263	30.0	18 594	12 9	43.0
1892	139,438	45 559	32 6	15,053	10.8	33.0
1893	110,800	35 049	31.6	17,552	17.6	50.0
1894	132,211	27,877	21.0	9,816	7 4	35.2

SILVER.

Year.	Ounces Silver Produced West of Missouri River.	Ounces Silver from Utah Ores.	Per Cent. Utah to West of Missouri.	Ounces Silver from Bingham.	Per Cent. Bingham to West of Missouri.	Per Cent. Bingham to Utah.
1889	68 421,391	7 147,651	10 4	561 280	.82	7.8
1890	60 510 414	8 165 586	13 5	450,990	74	5.5
1891	61 851 229	8 915 223	14 4	750 500	1.2	8.4
1892	58 169.656	8 969 656	15 4	605,896	1 0	6.7
1893	52 015 569	7,107,503	13.6	686 618	1.3	9.6
1894	45.588 911	6,659,798	14 6	715,708	1 5	10.7

GOLD.

Year.	Produced West of Missouri River.	Gold from Utah Ores.	Per Cent. Utah to West of Missouri.	Gold from Bingham.	Per Cent. Bingham to West of Missouri.	Per Cent. Bingham to Utah.
1889	$32 527,661	$ 499,500	1 7	$ 94 100	.289	17
1890	31,795 361	677 020	2.1	80.740	.252	12
1891	31.685,118	723,200	2 4	131,280	.432	18
1892	29,847,444	763 640	2 6	92,880	.312	12
1893	33,948,723	1 081,440	3 2	178 020	.512	16
1894	45,623,291	1,128 540	2 5	241,540	.525	21

It is estimated that the production of Bingham for 1895 as compared to 1894, was, gold 15 per cent. increase, lead and silver about the same as 1894, though exact figures cannot yet be obtained.

4

DALTON AND LARK MILL.

Property of the Company.

The engraving opposite title page represents one of the concentrating mills and other buildings of the company situated upon the Rio Grande Western Railroad.

The engraving opposite page 3 shows the other mill of the company, located on the Dalton and Lark claims at the mines of the company.

The engraving opposite page 5 gives a general view of the mill, hoists, etc., also part of the mountains upon which the mining claims of the company are situated.

The engraving opposite page 10 gives the hoists and mountains upon which the Brooklyn mine is located.

The engraving opposite page 12 shows the Lead Mine buildings and the mountain upon which it is located.

The engravings above referred to were copied from photographs of the company's property.

The map opposite page 6 is a cross section of the mountains upon which all of the company's mining claims are situated and shows the location and dip of the veins as mentioned in Mr. Palmer's report. It also shows the level at which the tunnel now being constructed by the Bingham Tunnel Co. will intersect these properties. This tunnel will completely drain these mines, and save the expense of pumping the water to the surface. The Tunnel Company contemplates using this water for irrigation upon its lands in Salt Lake Valley.

The surface map opposite page 14 shows the location of the mining claims of the company, and the location of the veins as to the surface longitudinally as they crop out at the surface.

The map opposite page 8 gives the location of the lead mill, tramway and mines as to the railroads, smelters and Salt Lake City.

Mr. O. A. Palmer, Mining Engineer, whose report we publish herewith, has followed his profession for the last thirty-three years, in Utah, Idaho, Montana and Nevada. Probably no one is better qualified to make a reliable report upon this company's property than Mr. Palmer, with his long experience in the mines of the West Mountain Mining District. He is now, and has been or twenty-two years the mining engineer of the great Ontario Mining Company, of Park City, Utah, and is also now the mining engineer of the celebrated Silver King and Daly Mining Companies, of Park City, Utah, also of the Centennial Eureka Mining Company, of Eureka, Utah. As to Mr. Palmer's ability and integrity, we refer to said companies and the following letter:

SALT LAKE CITY, UTAH, Feb. 1, 1896.

Dalton and Lark Gold, Silver and Lead Mining
and Milling Company, City:

DEAR SIRS:—We have known Mr. O. A. Palmer, Mining Engineer and U. S. Mineral Surveyor, for many years last past.

Mr. Palmer is most thoroughly posted in his profession, and a first class Mineralogist and Engineer.

He is perfecty honest and reliable, and we most cheerfully and fully recommend him.

Yours truly,

J. E. DOOLY,
Cashier of Wells, Fargo & Co's Bank.
W. S. McCORNICK,
Of McCornick & Co., Bankers.

There has been but little ore taken out of the original Dalton and Lark property. Most of the ore shipped from that property has been taken out in doing development work, and, as shown by Mr. Palmer's report, there is enough ore now in sight, to give the com-

Cross Section of Mountains sho␣

SCALE ␣

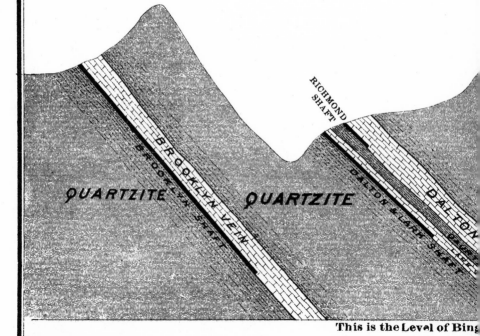

This is the Level of Bin␣

cation and Dip of the Ore Veins.

TO AN INCH.

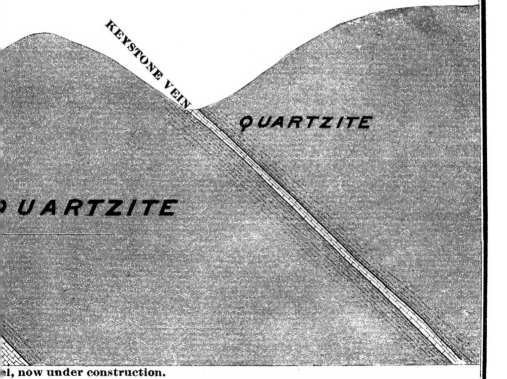

l, now under construction.

pany, after paying all mining, treating and other expenses, the sum
of $2,160,000.00. The indications are that many times that amount
of ore is in the combined properties, below their present workings.
After visiting these mines as now consolidated by this company, all
experienced mining men pronounce it to be one of the largest and
best properties in Utah.

Mr. Palmer states that the three great mines, namely: the "Old
Jordan," the "Spanish" and the "Old Telegraph" mines are all
located upon the famous "Brooklyn Lode" and he also states that
this same "Brooklyn Lode" extends through the Dalton and Lark
properties.

From this fact, one can get some idea of the future prospects
of this company, when they learn of the vast output of these three
great mines.   It is stated, upon the best of authority, that the gross
value of the ores taken out of these mines to date is about as
follows:

<pre>
Old Jordan $15,000,000.00
Spanish 6,000,000.00
Old Telegraph 10,000,000.00
</pre>

Considering the immense amount of ore our company already
has in sight, the valuable mills and other machinery, the Tramway
and equipment, and the very important fact that the "Brooklyn
Lode" extends through its property, also the large amount of its
well located, undeveloped ground, and unexplored veins, there can
be no doubt but that it is capitalized for less than the real intrinsic
value of its property.

This company was incorporated February 24, 1896, and will,
on March 1, 1896, and monthly thereafter, declare a dividend.
To our knowledge, there never has been a corporation organized
prior to this one, that was able to pay a dividend six days after it
was incorporated.

7

Report of O. A. Palmer, M. E.

To the Dalton and Lark Gold, Silver and Lead Mining
and Milling Company, Salt Lake City, Utah:

DEAR SIRS:—As requested, I have personally visited, and made a thorough and careful examination of all of your property, and submit the following as my report upon the same:

LOCATION AND GENERAL DESCRIPTION OF PROPERTY.

The property of the DALTON AND LARK GOLD, SILVER AND LEAD MINING AND MILLING COMPANY, consisting of mines, mills and tramway, commences about twenty-two miles from Salt Lake City, Utah, on the Rio Grande Western Railway, and extends about five miles southwesterly, consisting of two concentrating mills of 200 tons capacity per day, five steam hoists, about eight miles of tramway and equipment, and thirty-one mining claims, covering about 155 acres. These properties are in the very heart of the West Mountain (Bingham) Mining District, and are now, and will be for many years to come, among the greatest combined gold, silver and lead producers of the State of Utah.

MILLS.

The "Lead Mill" is situated in the Bingham Cañon, on a side track of the Rio Grande Western Railroad. It is one of the best concentrating mills in Utah and is now being enlarged and thoroughly

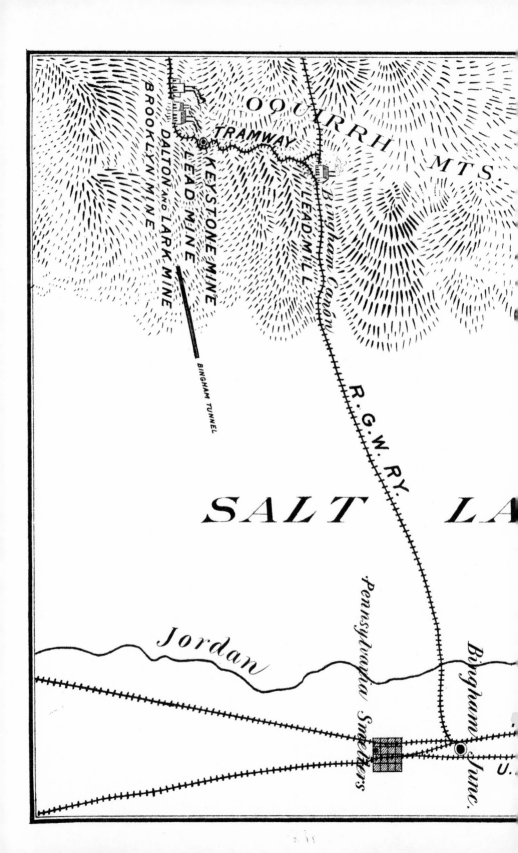

E VALLEY

SALT LAKE CITY

River

Germania Smelters

Hanauer Smelters

RAILWAY

BRANCH OF U. P. RY.

.S.L.

overhauled and repaired and will be ready to run again by March 1st. When completed, it will be in splendid condition and have a capacity to treat 150 tons of crude ore daily, thereby reducing three tons of ore into one ton of concentrates.

The "Dalton and Lark Mill" is on the Dalton and Lark claims about four miles from the "Lead Mill." It is a first class concentrating mill of fifty tons capacity daily. This mill, also a complete pumping and hoisting plant, has only been completed about three months, and is all new and in excellent condition.

The ore from the Dalton and Lark mill passes direct from the hoist to the mill where it is concentrated. The concentrates are carried by gravity from the mill in the tramway cars to the railroad. The balance of the ores from the company's mines is carried by gravity in the tramway cars to the "Lead Mill" and the railroad. The cost of treating and handling the ores is reduced to the minimum by your plants. There is ample machinery on the premises for all pumping and hoisting purposes for many years.

TRAMWAY.

The company owns and is operating a tramway extending from the "Lead Mill" and Rio Grande Western Railroad side-track to the "Keystone" mine, the "Dalton and Lark," the "Lead Mine" and the "Brooklyn" mine, all of which are owned by the company, and to the "Antelope," the "Sampson," the "Yosemite No. 1" and the "Yosemite No. 2" mines, all of which are producers, and employ this company to haul their ores to the railroad and their supplies from the railroad to their respective mines. The tramway is operated by gravity for its entire length for the "down" freight, which is the ores.

The "up freight," consisting of coal, timbers, supplies, etc., for the mines, is hauled over the tram by horses and mules.

9

The tram and equipment is in first-class condition and capable of handling the entire output of all of the mines.

The company's mines consist of four groups of patented claims, situated upon as many distinct and separate ore-producing lodes, more fully described in detail as follows:

BROOKLYN GROUP.

This group comprises the following claims: Revere Lot 120; Telegraph Lot 115; 1st West Ext. Telegraph Lot 167; Banner Lot 343; Trinity Lot 124; Trinity Mill Site Lot 148; Spring Lot 337, and Summit Lot.

This gives a length of 4,500 feet on what is here known as the "Brooklyn lode." This is the same lode upon which the Old Telegraph, Spanish and Jordan are located at the southwest end of the district. These have been constant ore-producers for the past twenty years. The Brooklyn has been developed by an incline shaft to the depth of 1,500 feet. Levels have been run on the strike, something over 2,500 feet. At the present depth of 1,500 feet, an ore body is encountered on the foot wall, about thirteen feet wide. This has been followed but a short distance, and little or no stoping done on it. Development work has been suspended, pending the negotiations which have now resulted in the purchase of the property by the Dalton and Lark Company. It is the intention of the company to run a crosscut from the face of the 800-foot level of the Lark Shaft No. 2, to a point below the bottom of the present shaft on the Brooklyn lode, through which the ores mined from this lode will be taken to the Lark Shaft, and there raised to the surface. It will also give good drainage, as at the Lark Shaft there is ample pumping power to free the entire property of water for several hundred feet below the present workings.

Upon the completion of this crosscut, the Brooklyn may be de-

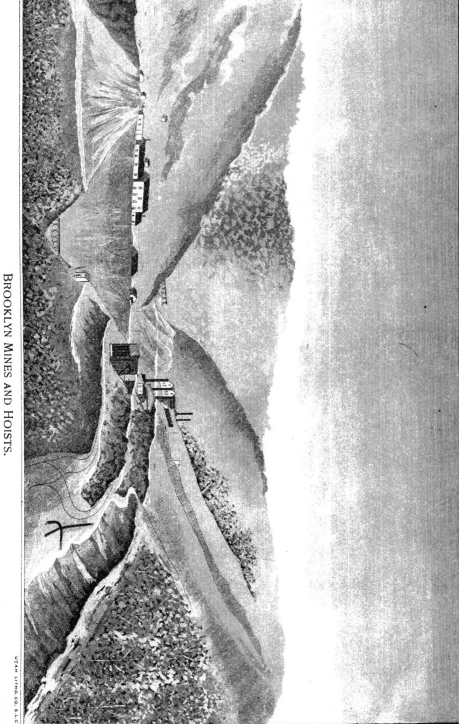

BROOKLYN MINES AND HOISTS.

pended upon for a large and constant supply of ore. The history of the production of this lode for the last twenty years is a good guarantee for the future, both as to quantity and quality of ore which, from its past record, is first-class, and as follows:

AVERAGE VALUE OF THE ORES.

First class: lead 45 to 50 per cent; silver 10 ounces, gold $1.50.

Second class: Lead 16 to 25 per cent; silver 6 ounces, gold $1.50.

LARK GROUP.

This group comprises the Lark lot 349; Dump lot 370; June Blossom lot 346. This gives a length of 2300 feet on the Lark lode. Lark Shaft No. 1 is down 680 feet. It has a thirty-five horse-power hoist. Shaft No. 2 is down 840 feet and has three eighty horse-power boilers, electric light plant, and sixty-five horse-power engine. Shaft No. 4 is down 150 feet and has a ten horse-power engine.

The ore chute now being worked upon Lark vein is one continuous body of ore 1500 feet long with an average width of five feet, and extends from the 560 foot level down to the 800 foot level. But little stoping has been done on it. This one body of ore then gives stoping ground 1500 feet by 240 feet by 5 feet, which should produce 180,000 tons of ore. This ore makes a net average profit of $10.00 per ton, as shown by the shipments already made. So far the estimate is only for what is in sight. Judging from the Brooklyn and Lead mine and others in the district, there is every reason to believe that the last body of ore will increase its present size and richness for at least 800 feet below its present workings. At the 800 foot level the ore is thirteen feet thick, as it is in the Brooklyn at the 1500 foot level, and it is fair to presume this continues.

DALTON OR LEAD MINE GROUP.

This group contains the following claims: Clara lot 347 A; Fraction lot 338; Murray lot 339; Carlile lot 340; Penrith lot 341; Louise lot 342; Lead Mine lot 343; Carbonate lot 329; Rustin lot 330; Nash, Richard, Richmond, Dalton lot 348.

This gives a run of 4500 feet in length on what is known as the "Lead mine" lode or "Dalton" lode.

The ore here as in the Brooklyn occurs in irregular chutes or chimneys, appearing sometimes upon the foot wall sometimes the hanging wall and in a few instances showing a pronounced mineralization, and even workable ore bodies the entire width from wall to wall.

The lead mine at the southwest end of this group has been developed to the 1000 foot level. Upon this level some drifting has been done. At this point the ore body is three feet wide. On the Dalton claim at the northeast end of this group, a shaft has been sunk 200 feet. At this level a foot wall ore body was found twenty feet wide, while on the hanging wall was one four feet wide. That on the foot wall has been followed 100 feet on the strike. That on the hanging wall about the same distance. In each place the ore still continues without any indication of quitting. This ore samples $3.00 in gold, ten ounces in silver and forty-six per cent. lead. This ore body now has in sight 20,000 tons of ore, of an average net value of $18.00 per ton, making $360,000 net profit.

KEYSTONE GROUP.

This group contains the Keystone lot 357; Keystone No. 2 lot 358; Freedom lot 360; Blaine lot 359. On this lode the company has a length on the vein of about 2000 feet. This is a constant producer and regular shipments are being made. In grade, the ore is about the same as that from the Lark vein.

LEAD MINE PROPERTY.

CHARACTER OF THE LODES.

These four lodes are simply four zones or belts of limestone beds, or strata, more or less mineralized and ore-producing. The Brooklyn and Dalton belts are each 150 feet thick. The Lark and Keystone are each twenty-five feet thick. They alternate with bands of quartzite strata of varying thickness. The quartzite is always barren. The lime belts are now being successfully worked on their strike, in a northeast and southwest direction, for a distance of some three miles. Upon them are located at least three-fourths of all the productive mines of the West Mountain (Bingham) Mining District. They are essentially gold, silver and lead ores. The principal mines on these belts have been producing continually for the last twenty years, and only in two or three instances have they attained a depth of over one thousand feet. As the lime strata constitutes the lode, it may be depended upon to continue to an indefinite depth, or at least until it bottoms on the final granite.

Three maps accompany this report. One is a plan or horizontal map, showing the various mining claims owned by the company, and their exact relative position. Another, is a section at right angles to the strike of the lodes, showing their dip, width and manner of occurrence of the ore bodies. Also a general map showing the relative position of Salt Lake City, the smelters along the Jordan River and the company's mines, mills and tramway in West Mountain Mining District.

One of said maps shows the level at which the tunnel now being constructed by the Bingham Tunnel Company will pass through your property. By an examination of said map you will see that the tunnel will cut your ore veins over 600 feet below any of the present workings.

This tunnel will be of very great benefit to your mines, because it will drain all the water from the mines without pumping and give you dry mines to work in down to the tunnel level. It will be an additional guaranty of the mines being great producers for many years to come.

O. A. PALMER, M. E.

Board of Trade Building,

Salt Lake City, Utah.

Feb. 21, 1896.

GOLD

HISTORICAL AND ECONOMIC ASPECTS

An Arno Press Collection

[Bonus, Petrus of Ferrara]. The New Pearl of Great Price. 1894

Emmons, William Harvey. Gold Deposits of the World: With a Section on Prospecting. 1937

Father Coughlin on Money and Gold: Three Pamphlets. 1974

Gold and Silver in the Presidential Campaign of 1896. 1974

Gold Mining Company Prospectuses. 1974

Hammond, John Hays. The Autobiography of John Hays Hammond. 1935. 2 volumes in one

Johnson, Obed Simon. A Study of Chinese Alchemy. 1928

Letcher, Owen. The Gold Mines of Southern Africa. 1936

Nesbitt, L[ewis] M[ariano]. Gold Fever. 1936

Ogilvie, William. Early Days on the Yukon and the Story of its Gold Finds. 1913

[Preshaw, G. O.]. Banking Under Difficulties or Life on the Goldfields of Victoria, New South Wales & New Zealand. By a Bank Official. 1888

Rickard, T[homas] A[rthur]. Man and Metals. 1932. 2 volumes in one

Russell, Henry B. International Monetary Conferences. 1898

Seyd, Ernest. **Bullion and Foreign Exchanges Theoretically and Practically Considered.** 1868

Speculation in Gold and Silver Mining Stocks. 1974

Taylor, F. Sherwood. **The Alchemists:** Founders of Modern Chemistry. 1949

United States Congress. House of Representatives. Committee on Banking and Currency. **Gold Panic Investigation.** 41st Congress, 2d Session, House Report No. 31. 1870

Weaver, James B. **A Call to Action.** 1892